DAMP BUILDINGS, OLD AND NEW

DAMP BUILDINGS, OLD AND NEW

Giovanni and Ippolito Massari

Translated by Cynthia Rockwell

Rome, 1993

ISBN 92-9077-111-9

Originally published in Italy under the title
Risanamento Igienico dei Locali Umidi
© Ulrico Hoepli Editore S.p.A., Milano 1985

English translation © 1993 ICCROM

ICCROM – International Centre for the Study of the
Preservation and Restoration of Cultural Property
Via di San Michele 13
I-00153 Rome RM, Italy

Printed in Italy
by Sintesi Grafica s.r.l.

Layout: Cynthia Rockwell

Cover design by Studio *PAGE*

CONTENTS

Chapter Nine – WHEN CONDENSATION IS DUE TO THE IGNORANCE OF VARIOUS SPECIALISTS

Chapter Ten – OUTER WALLS WITH HOLLOW BRICK OR CAVITIES BENEFIT THE BUILDER, NOT THE TENANT

Chapter Eleven – DRIVING RAIN NEVER PASSES THROUGH A WELL-CONSTRUCTED WALL

Chapter Twelve – ARE HEATING AND VENTILATION USEFUL AGAINST HUMIDITY?

Chapter Thirteen – PROTECTION OF ART WORKS AND HISTORIC CENTERS

PREFACE TO THE ENGLISH EDITION

I made many discoveries during the year that I spent as an ICCROM student in 1982. Many of these discoveries came from a practice which may have confounded ICCROM's administrators but which seemed to suit my eclectic interests – the practice of attending only those lectures in the institution which interested me, without any particular regard for offerings within the course in which I was enrolled.

The most significant discovery came when I opted out of a week on biological decay in my Scientific Principles of Conservation course in favour of a series of talks offered within the Mural Paintings course by Ippolito Massari on humidity in buildings.

I was introduced to a critical conservation subject which, as an architect, I had never properly understood – the sources and means of moisture movement in structures, and approaches to alleviating associated distress – and more intriguingly, to a father and son team, Giovanni and Ippolito Massari, both of whom had dedicated their careers to this particular subject.

I wrestled with Ippolito's Italian during his presentation – not too difficult given his ability to walk his way through the subject with ample illustrations – but not entirely satisfactory. The ICCROM Library disclosed a Massari text on the subject *Risanamento Igienico dei Locali Umidi,* pioneered in Italian by father Giovanni but now a father-and-son effort, after a series of updates and subsequent revisions; to my great pleasure, the Library also contained translations in Spanish and French, the latter of which brought the material within range of my limited language skills.

I soon learned from Cynthia Rockwell, ICCROM's Head of Publications, that in fact an English language version existed. Cynthia herself had translated the material and was looking for an interested publisher. I prompted APT (The Association of Preservation Technology), a North-American based professional membership organization, into publishing two chapters (six and seven) in its quarterly Scientific Journal (*The Bulletin* – APT XVII, No. 31, 1985), hoping that readership response would spark a rush of interested publishers. Readership response was in fact very good, but all too obviously, APT members were practising professionals and not publishers!

But the long overdue appearance in 1993 of *Damp Buildings, Old and New* by Giovanni and Ippolito Massari, within ICCROM's publishing programme, meets a genuine need in the field and assures wide distribution and long-term accessibility of this important material.

There are a number of other significant English language texts in the field (notably Baird Smith *Moisture Problems in Historic Masonry Walls. Diagnosis and Treatment,* and T. A. Oxley *Dampness in Buildings: Diagnosis, Treatment and Instruments*), but none do the job with the same sense of style, humour and care as the Massari opus. Their approach to the subject is down-to-earth, pragmatic, filled with the anecdotal support drawn from thousands of consulting experiences and focused on the how-to. This is where the book shines, in its appreciation of methodology and in leading the reader to understand how to analyse and diagnose moisture problems, to differentiate between symptoms and cause on the basis of both observation and testing, and how to arrive at solutions which respond both to needs and to circumstances. The tone of this book is a wonderful accompaniment to its content: a slightly acerbic, no-nonsense approach, admitting of no patience for the field's quacks or those not prepared to bring the same serious and rigorous analysis to their technical problems as the Massaris do.

No serious conservation architect can afford to be without this guide, built on over 40 years of experience working with Italian and indeed European buildings of great cultural significance.

Herb Stovel
Secretary-General, ICOMOS

Chapter One

ORIENTATION TOUR

¶1.   Do not rely on common sense; dampness can and should be measured.

— The ailment of dampness in buildings, whether they be simple dwellings or monumental structures, is found all over the world – even in desert areas. It is as old as human civilization. The Bible (Leviticus XIV:34-57) gives prescriptions ranging from common sense to pedantry for the treatment of a condition called '*leprosy of houses.*' In those days, a priest, after supervising a mason's work of scraping, replastering or replacing stones, would conclude with a complicated exorcism and bless the newly restored house seven times. Perhaps at heart he was not too confident of the outcome and appealed to God to keep the 'leprosy' from returning.

The phenomenon of moisture in walls can be misleading and, for people living in an age of scientific research, it is dangerous to rely on common sense as did the priests of biblical times. Often the true remedies, capable of eliminating the cause of dampness, are *counter-intuitive* – hidden from our instinct and especially from our common sense. The truth slowly emerges only when we examine the ailment and study its various symptoms, using suitable instruments and following a scientific approach. What would we think of a physician who says a patient has a burning fever but does not bother to measure it with a thermometer?

The adjective *damp* is often used without a frame of reference, and thus is equally applicable to any environment or wall, no matter how damp. A quantitative appreciation of the phenomenon (i.e., the gravity of the ailment) is left up to the observer's impressions and not translated into hard figures. This is contrary to good working procedure for any technically defined problem.

Measurements quantify the term *damp*; otherwise, it is vague and sometimes controversial. Although such measurements are easy to take, as we shall see later, they are not interchangeable because each represents only one aspect of the dampness phenomenon. It is most important to measure the amount of water inside the walls. With a certain number of evenly spaced recordings, one can deduce the topographical distribution of the water and its point of entry, information that is indispensable for any restoration work.

Plaster stains are not reliable indicators of dampness. Indeed, in old walls they might simply be scars left over from previous events rather than signs of active infiltration. The presence of surface deterioration is usually linked to alternate states of dryness and wetness (fig. 1). This condition can be found in exterior walls that are exposed to inconstant heat and cold or to random air currents (entryways, property walls, pillars,

Fig. 1.

Exterior deterioration depends less on moisture penetration than exposure to weather changes: wind and calm, sun and shade.

etc.); at the same time, interior walls in cool and unventilated environments with high relative humidity usually show no surface deterioration. Thus, it can happen that *in the worst cases of dampness the plaster shows no change*.

The presence or absence of efflorescence or 'saltpeter' – another impressive symptom – is closely related to another factor: the availability of migrating salts. One wall is not necessarily damper than another simply because it shows more salt crystallization.

Mold itself is often restricted to the insides of drawers, the backs of furniture or spaces between crates, and is not found in other parts of the room; it requires only a minimum of moisture when the air is still, the light level is low and an organic food supply is available. These three factors are almost more important than moisture. *Thus, the mere presence of mold should not be used to judge either the extent or the origin of dampness*.

When the water source and the degree of dampness of a room have been precisely ascertained through proper measurements, the health officer can make a responsible judgment concerning borderline cases of habitability, or the art conservator can decide whether action need be taken. Finally, the most effective treatment can be selected from a range of traditional and present-day restoration techniques. Each of these techniques will be critically discussed in the following pages, and precise instructions for its application will be given.

¶2. The water source. Difference between old and new constructions.

— In old buildings, dampness stems from *moisture penetration* which is chronic by nature; in new buildings it is usually due to poor *construction*, and is acute but transitory by nature. The difference in behavior between the two is substantial, although the damage to goods and inhabitants is the same. In a new wall, the water is usually carried and distributed by the mortar (and, therefore, the central nuclei of the bricks or stones remain dry), whereas in an old wall, the water is often evenly spread throughout the building material (fig. 2).

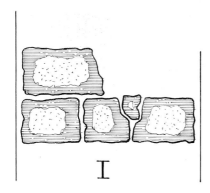 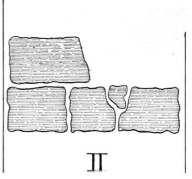

Fig. 2.

Distribution of moisture in the stones of a new wall (I) and an old wall (II).

Construction humidity:

is uniformly diffused throughout the new building

exhausts itself in time.

Invading humidity, however:

is irregularly distributed and found only in parts of an old building

is either stationary or increases progressively in time.

In both cases, an evaluation based on quantitative measurement of moisture within the walls is easily made, bearing local climate and construction factors in mind, as we will see later. In buildings of a certain age, dampness can be caused by moisture penetration from:

- the subsoil, by means of rising capillary action
- the air, by means of condensation

Figure 3 illustrates that the distribution of moisture in a brick wall varies according to whether it rises from the subsoil (rising damp) or comes from the air (water-vapor condensation). In the first vertical wall section on the left, the moisture rises from the foundation in successive stages, with a greater quantity in the core than in the sides. The second, third and fourth vertical wall sections show the three most common types of condensation humidity, which are airborne and deposited in liquid form on the inner face of the wall. The second section is a *homogeneous* wall (made, for example, entirely of similar bricks) and equally cold from floor to ceiling; the condensation is deposited uniformly on the wall from top to bottom. In the third section, the wall is *heterogeneous* (perhaps it contains old bricks or stone blocks that have been recycled from old buildings

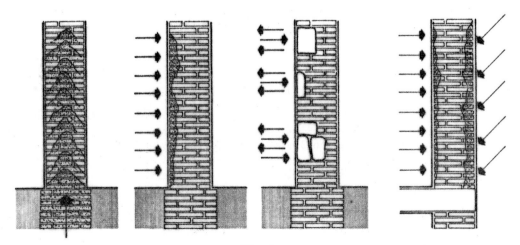

Fig. 3.

The distribution of moisture in a brick wall depends on whether it rises from the subsoil (rising damp, first on left) or comes from the air as water vapor condensation (second, third and fourth wall sections).

and are full of hygroscopic salts), and the dampness appears *in spots*. These come and go, depending on the temperature and relative humidity of the environment, but always where the heavier material is located. These are the so-called *variable stains* that can frustrate an inexperienced fresco restorer, as they disappear and reappear in the same place.

Finally, the last wall section on the right of figure 3 reveals the mechanism of moisture from driving rain. There are construction workers, restorers, architects, landlords, tenants, monument or church curators all over the world who, guided by common sense, mistake this for rainwater entering the wall. The idea that rainwater passes through walls is one of the most common errors; normally it does not, barring serious construction defects. To be convinced of this, one need only chisel 15 cm into the wall and measure the moisture content: it is dry. The truth is that driving rain cools a wall, and cools it more quickly when bursts of slanting rain alternate with dry wind (in Europe this wind comes from the northeast and the Russian steppes).

The cooling does extend to the inner face of the wall, causing deposition of water vapor from the air in the room itself. This is what happens in winter when we find our bedroom windows steamed up. Dew on windows doesn't surprise us; why then should we be surprised when it forms on walls? Yet, wherever one goes, some people in the construction industry believe that driving rain passes through walls. As stated above, when wall dampness is in question, common sense is useless; measurement is the only valid approach. Details of effective remedies against the four types of humidity invasion shown in figure 3 are given in the chapters that follow.

The chart below is intended to help the reader to exercise critical sense instead of common sense, and to distinguish quickly between rising damp and condensation.

CHART I.   DIFFERENCES BETWEEN RISING DAMP AND CONDENSATION

The five characteristics of moisture when it comes *from the ground* (**rising damp**)		The five characteristics of moisture when it comes *from the air* (**condensation of water vapor**)	
I	Independent of the season.	I	Appears every year during *the same season.*
II	*Does not rise far* up the wall: 2 or 3 meters.	II	Found *at any height* in the building.
III	Impregnates the *entire thickness* of the wall, from one side to the other.	III	Wets *only the wall surface,* but with liquid water which contains air pollutants.
IV	Takes water from the ground: either *superficially* (seepage from sewers, pipes) or *deeply* (from water table).	IV	Precipitates water by *cooling the vapor* in the air.
V	Eliminated *in a few years* after drainage of all dispersed water or cutting the wall (if drainage is not possible). Does not return.	V	Eliminated *quickly* by heat and ventilation but, naturally, returns. Extremely capricious.

Chapter Two

DETAILS OF THE MOST COMMON PROBLEMS

¶3.   Why moisture rises in walls. Capillary action.

— Moisture enters and spreads in walls exclusively because of capillary action – a curious physical phenomenon that might be considered to defy the basic law of gravity. Capillary action is illustrated by the fact that the liquid in two communicating containers ought to settle at the same level, but sometimes one of the two breaks the law of gravity (fig. 4). This happens when the container acts as a capillary, i.e., when its diameter is as fine as a hair. Here, the liquid does not remain at the proper level, but rises; the finer the tube, the higher the liquid can rise. Water can rise 31 mm in a tube one mm in diameter; it can rise 154 mm if the diameter is reduced to 0.2 mm. The case of a single tube is the most elementary. Lamp wicks, which draw up oil, or plant systems, which draw up lymph, function like bundles of capillary tubes.

In a damp brick wall, the weight of the moisture (which is expressed as a percentage of the weight by volume) provides an indication of the capillary force that sustains it; in the walls of many old buildings one finds a moisture content that reaches and often exceeds 30%. This means that every cubic meter of wall holds up 300 kg of water against the force of gravity.

In the Palazzo Corsini in Rome, we have calculated that the mass of water held in suspension above street level is about 300 tons.

Although the force of gravity is easily overcome by capillary suction force, this force is counteracted by the evaporation of water from the wet surfaces. Actually, capillary rise in a wall will stop when the amount of water that enters from its base is equal to the amount that evaporates from its surfaces.

Capillary action is also affected by temperature:

- Capillary rise increases slightly when the temperature is reduced.
- Surface evaporation decreases when the temperature is reduced.

(The latter factor has a much greater influence than the former.)

Capillary rise also increases considerably when salts are present in walls, due to the attraction of water molecules to concentrated salt solutions (osmosis). This principle can be illustrated by the walls of vessels containing salt solutions (such as the old Leclanché electric batteries), where the salts conducted by a combination of capillary action and osmosis often seem literally to climb upwards. Capillary water coming from the earth is often loaded with salts, and sometimes it draws salts from the wall material itself.

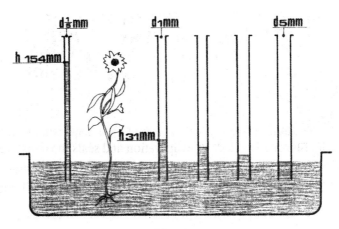

Fig. 4.

Capillary action is a curious physical phenomenon which makes water rise upwards, against the force of gravity, inside pores as thin as a hair, or thinner.

These two causes of increased capillary action (low temperature and the salt concentration in the solution) are helpful in explaining differences between the moisture penetration in walls that are built in the same way and with the same materials, but situated differently with respect to the ground and the sun. For instance, where water has the opportunity to take on soluble substances, it can rise a great deal, and where water remains pure, it rises less. A northern exposure will cause an increase in the level of absorption due to the lack of heating by the sun and the consequent reduction in surface evaporation.

In addition to the health hazards caused by moisture penetration, capillary action incites a demolition process in some of the wall components. In addition, it can cause disfigurement and spoil the decorative quality of the wall.

The most typical signs of capillary action in a wall include:

- destruction of plaster surfaces and binding mortar due to transmission of salts from the inside to the outside of the wall, causing subflorescence (crystals of salt inside pores) and efflorescence
- surface spalling and flaking, in some stone and brick, due to pressure from crystallizing salts
- chemical substitution of resistant components by others that are inconsistent or weak – in some types of stone
- shattering after frost

What is capillary action? Let us not be misled by the word 'capillary.' The mysterious force that sucks water in fine tubes with a diameter of a hair or less also sucks water between two parallel surfaces that are a hair apart or less. For instance, when a crack 0.2 mm wide (the same diameter as the capillary tube in fig. 4) forms on the face of a block of marble or in the joint between two facing slabs on a building exposed to driving rain, rainwater is quickly drawn into the crack; it rises some 154 mm, just as it would in a narrow tube. It not only advances upwards against the force of gravity, but can also follow the crack horizontally or even downwards.

When buildings or monuments are beaten by driving rain, it is a grave error to cover them with renderings of impermeable cement. After a period of exposure to the elements, cement facings develop numerous fine cracks but remain firmly attached to the wall fabric. These fissures are difficult to see, especially when they are high up on the wall. After two or three years, the intact cement rendering acts, in reality, like a pump that sucks up rainwater (fig. 5). At this point a curious physical complication sets in: the moisture that has risen within the wall by means of capillary action has reached and impregnated the wall core, but it cannot escape by evaporation. The rendering – still durable and adherent despite its fine cracks – blocks evaporation and seals the moisture inside in the wall. Year by year the wall becomes damper on account of the rendering.

Some architects set up geometrical capillary networks while a building is still under construction. They do so by facing their exterior walls with decorative stoneware tiles, which are economical, robust and easy to install (fig. 5). An example is a recent thirteen-story high-rise in Trieste, which presented grave defects from humidity. The problem, which affected the entire height of the building, was limited to the northeast exposure which was beaten by the rainy 'bora' wind. In the rooms on that side, the occupants would wake up in the morning and find the floor covered with a film of water. Precise measurements demonstrated that the origin of the problem was condensation from the cooling of the entire structure. The outer wall was cooled by rainwater drawn in by the geometrical capillary network formed by the fine, open joints of the impermeable, stoneware cladding. Every square meter of facing presented a complex development of 19 linear meters of capillary suction cracks. The floors were also cooled because the floor beams extended to the outside of the building. These beams were beaten by rain on the outside balconies and acted as heat dispersal fins.

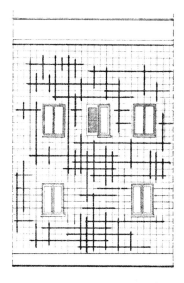 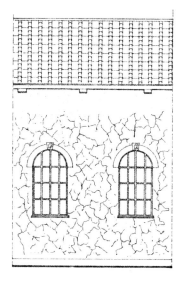

Fig. 5.

Two types of capillary networks that absorb driving rain: at left, a natural network in cement rendering; at right, an artificial network created by the open joints of flat, decorative facing tiles.

External work, which would have involved expensive scaffolding costs, was ruled out and it was recommended that two measures be taken on the inside:

- installation of inexpensive polystyrene insulation on the damp walls
- maintenance of good heating day *and* night. 'Good heating' consisted of increasing the radiator surfaces on the northeast side by 50%, and disconnecting two rising mains from the central heating system, joining them to an independent furnace. During the critical season, this extra heating was designed to function continuously, separate from the rest of the plant and regulated according to the amount of driving rain.

Capillary action can be summarized by the following points:

- The force of capillary action in walls counteracts that of gravity and normally sustains large masses of liquid, sometimes in excess of 300 kg of water per cubic meter of wall.
- The more the water is laden with dissolved substances, the higher it rises.
- Water tends to rise more in cold walls exposed to the north, due in part to the increased constant of capillary action, but especially due to reduced evaporation resulting from lack of heat.
- Capillary humidity, apart from creating health hazards by penetrating a wall, produces specific destruction of certain building materials (erosion).
- Cement renderings employed as a defense against driving rain develop fine cracks after two or three years and draw in rainwater through capillary action.

¶4. Capillarity in the ground. Why, at the same depth, some fortunate constructions have dry footing and others do not.

— If the ground is flat, rainwater and melting snow are mostly absorbed where they fall, except for small amounts lost through evaporation. The more permeable the ground, the deeper and more rapid the penetration of water. In one sense, permeability is the opposite of capillarity. The most permeable type of ground is composed of pebbles and grains that have large spaces between them and, thus, are quite different from capillaries. Imagine a hypothetical type of soil composed of equal-sized, stone spheres (fig. 6) of any diameter – 5 cm, perhaps, or 1 cm, or 1 mm. This ground would have maximum permeability and rainwater would be absorbed very quickly. How far down would it go? Down to where it meets an impermeable layer: compact rock, for example, or a bed of pure clay that is already saturated. The descending water is then blocked and accumulates above the barrier, forming a liquid layer called the groundwater table which flows like a vast underground stream towards the lowest points: valley bottoms, lakes and the sea.

If the water table is not too deep – say four or five meters below ground level – the water can quickly rise upwards again, depending on the ground's capillary properties. Obviously, this would not happen where the water sank in originally, but in a completely different zone with clayey soil, for instance, far from the point of entry. In figure 7, various heights are given for the rise of water from the water table in homogeneous soils (in reality, the soils are almost always mixed). In agriculture, 'light' soils are those without clay that do not stick to a spade, i.e., loose, granular soils. Clinging soils, such as those with high amounts of clay, are called 'heavy' or 'strong' soils.

Fig. 6.

In a hypothetical type of ground formed of spheres in close contact, there are large empty spaces which act in a manner that is opposite to the action of capillaries. This type of ground (like gravel and sand) is extremely permeable.

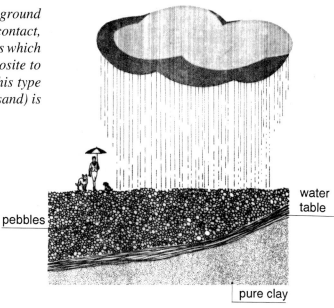

water table

pebbles

pure clay

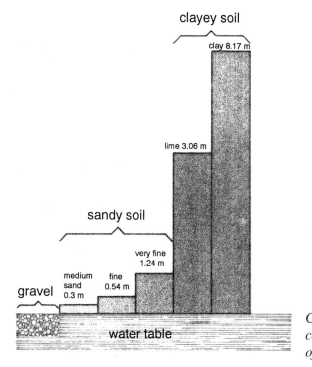

clayey soil

clay 8.17 m

lime 3.06 m

sandy soil

very fine
1.24 m

medium
sand
0.3 m

fine
0.54 m

gravel

water table

Fig. 7.

Comparison of different heights of capillary rise depending on the type of ground: none in gravel, little in sand, maximum in clay.

It can happen that given two buildings, both with three-meter foundations, one will be set in capillary soil and subject to dampness because water rises freely from the water table. The other, perhaps only a few kilometers away, may be set in perfectly dry ground, possibly over a layer of coarse sand. Thus the former building is subject to rising damp if preventive measures are not taken, while the latter will be completely immune, but not because of any merit on the builder's part.

In historic buildings with damp ground floors, it is advisable to dig a vertical shaft outside and inspect the soil at foundation level. This was the case with the Palazzo del Te, constructed by the Gonzaga in Mantua. For military reasons, this city was built in the middle of a vast swamp which had a clay bottom. The magnificent frescos in the upper ground floor were damaged by what was thought to be capillary moisture rising from the water table. After a shaft was dug to the water table, however, it was discovered that the building had been deliberately constructed over a thick layer of sand that had been imported and superimposed on the clayey natural soil of the area. Between the building's foundation level (see fig. 196, p. 276) and the water table, a good 1.70 m of excellent, very pure river sand completely blocked any rise of capillary water. Since the sand was dry to the touch, the moisture attacking the frescos was not rising from the foundation; rather it was entering laterally from the large, square interior courtyard where heavy rainfall collected. For aesthetic reasons, there were no downspouts off the enormous roofs, and even the simplest surface rainwater drainage was lacking. Thus the rain, being trapped in the courtyard, percolated to the foundation walls around the courtyard. If the soil had not been inspected, the problem might have been dealt with by erroneous and dangerous repairs.

When old damp buildings are studied, it is generally worthwhile to study the water table level in the neighborhood as well. Unfortunately, boreholes for this purpose are quite expensive. The most practical system is to inspect wells in the area, if they exist, and record the water level in different seasons.

¶5. Efflorescence on walls: remedies.

— In porous plaster of old damp walls the demarcation line between wet and dry is often clearly marked by surface deterioration. This is due to superficial fragmentation caused by the pressure of salts. The salts crystallize in the capillary veins when drying periods (which concentrate the solution) alternate with periods of wetting (which re-dissolve the salts). In other cases, the changing demarcation line is identified by lavish festoons of continuously progressing efflorescence.

In contrast, efflorescence on brick facings is often random and appears only on certain bricks, while others seem immune. The agent is always moisture, which acts as a vehicle for the soluble salts. The white 'beards' of migrating salts grow at a steady rate until they reach the last stop – where the moisture ends (see fig. 32, p. 68). The principal component of efflorescence is *magnesium sulfate,* one of the most migratory of salts, but sulfates of calcium and sodium are also present. Chlorides are rarely found unless they originate from sea breezes. Nitrates (contrary to the common belief that efflorescence is due to *saltpeter*) seldom appear unless there is a deposit of organic refuse next to the wall, as happens in stables or near cesspools and sewers. Walls in churches may also show nitrate-rich efflorescence because the soil under the floor was often used for burials. Chemically, true saltpeter is potassium nitrate, which is not deliquescent, and once was the basic ingredient of gun powder.

Soluble salts can either be present as original components of brick, stone or mortar, or be absorbed from the ground together with rising damp. In the former case, the quantity of salts is finite; in the latter it is infinite.

The principal components of efflorescence can be divided according to their provenance and solubility in water:

Salts present in the wall

Very soluble in water	*magnesium sulfate* *sodium sulfate*
Not very soluble (1 part in 500 of water)	*calcium sulfate*
Soluble in water only if it contains a certain amount of CO_2	*calcium carbonate*

Salts formed with external supply of nitrogen or chlorine

Soluble in water, not deliquescent	*potassium nitrate* (from foul water)
Very soluble and deliquescent	*sodium nitrate,* idem *calcium nitrate,* idem *calcium chloride* (from sea air)

Intense but random efflorescence on *individual* facing bricks is attributable to the quality of the clay or to the water used in the mix; it is principally and almost exclusively composed of *calcium sulfate*, sometimes with a negligible amount of calcium carbonate. If efflorescent salts come from the water, they can be blocked by adding barium carbonate to the mix, making the sulfates insoluble. Efflorescence on individual facing bricks is also found in dry walls and freestanding pillars, as it needs only occasional wetting with rainwater in order to develop. *Its presence must not be taken as proof that a wall is damp.* In a few years, when the supply of calcium sulfate is exhausted, the disfigurement disappears in most cases.

Efflorescence, erosion and concretion are all attributable to the migration of dissolved salts. This migration is caused by two different agents: the first is *capillarity,* or the phenomenon by which liquid moves successively from damp spaces to dry capillary spaces; the second is *diffusion,* a molecular movement of salts within the liquid, i.e., from one area of the liquid to another or, more precisely, from the area where the solution is concentrated to where it is more diluted. These causes of migration are easily confused, and it is not always possible to tell which of the two, capillarity or diffusion, is responsible for damage resulting in efflorescence, erosion or concretion.

Since efflorescence on brick and tile is always composed of sulfates, the Italian Railways technical manual prescribes a maximum SO_3 content of 0.5% for normal bricks, and 0.2% for facing bricks, as a preventive measure. Some English firms guarantee that their plaster-base preparations for special renderings contain less than 0.1% of soluble salts of magnesium and sodium (calculated as oxides).

There are no easy methods to control active efflorescence, even though special formulas for this purpose occasionally appear on the market. The best approach is to *suppress migrating moisture*, the only vehicle of the salts. Thus it is certainly unwise to wash the wall with water, as some authors recommend, since it will act as a vehicle for the salts. Washing with dilute acids is equally undesirable because it can cause further deterioration. Rather, the wall surface should simply be cleaned with a dry brush.

In short, migrating moisture should be suppressed by preventing its entry to the wall by means of driving rain, condensation or rising damp.

¶6. Deterioration of natural stone.

— Capillary moisture has a deteriorating effect on some natural materials, depending on their position and role in the masonry of a building. For example, **sandstone** performs well in elevated structures but shows accelerated decay in the damp sections at the base of walls (as in Florence). The chemical composition of sandstones is also a factor in their deterioration; those with silica-based cements show better resistance than those with calcareous ones which are liable to attack by CO_2 dissolved in rainwater.

Foundations in Naples are made of soft, porous, **volcanic tuff**, chosen especially for that purpose. When the quality of the material is inadequate for a damp environment, a sort of rot sets in.

In general, one notes that some components of natural building materials provide resistance to moisture, whereas others do not. For example, apart from extreme cases of freezing, **silica** is helpful, **carbonous** or **bituminous** substances are neutral, and colored streaks containing **metal oxides** or **sulfides** (which give marble its variety) are damaging. **Clay** is extremely damaging. In conglomerate rocks (such as breccias), which could be defined as 'concrete' mixed by Mother Nature out of fragments and powder from older rocks, a clayey cement is fatal for conservation.

Even materials such as granite and prophyry, usually thought to be impervious to weathering agents, are prone to disintegration processes. Such feldspathic rocks contain aluminum silicate minerals, which can undergo a chemical process that transforms them into clays under the action of water. In an intermittently damp environment, even granite can easily disintegrate into a pitifully inconsistent paste of quartz and mica particles.

How can this potential weakness be reconciled with the reputation some materials – especially granite – enjoy as being everlasting? The explanation is simple: granite is genuinely durable when it is employed for obelisks and outdoor monuments in dry climates, as has been the case for centuries. But what if granite were used in Venice for wall bases where it would be subject to alternate wetting and drying? Irremediable deterioration would be just as certain there as the long life guaranteed for an obelisk in Egypt.

Another serious form of chemical erosion, which occurs in the presence of moisture and specifically attacks calcareous stone (as well as plaster and mortar, of course), is due to 'saltiness' in buildings exposed to sea breezes. Calcium carbonate is attacked by the magnesium sulfate and chloride contained in sea spray, which impregnates the air with fine aerosol droplets. This leads to the formation of calcium chloride, a deliquescent salt that causes the deterioration of mortar and calcareous stone. Istrian limestone from *Orsera*, which is widely used in Venetian buildings, is one of the few stones that can resist this process.

In order to protect natural stone in buildings or statues of artistic merit, surface treatments or other methods are applied to impede the movement of capillary humidity or the penetration of condensation and salt spray (see ¶59).

¶7. Merits and defects of porous building materials.

— Water's best friends, *ordinary bricks*, as well as numerous varieties of *tuff, light sandstone, soft limestone* and *lime mortar,* are optimum construction materials, principally because they provide good thermal insulation. They lose this quality, however, when they become damp as a result of their high capillary suction power.

In contrast, heavy materials, such as *vitrified brick, basalt* (e.g., Roman cobblestones), or *gneiss,* which are compact and resistant to moisture absorption from the ground, are relatively good heat conductors. They easily overheat in summer, quickly cool in winter, and are cold and unpleasant to the touch. These heavy materials, no matter how thin, obstruct air movement through the walls; this causes the formation of cold bridges and interior condensation, creating another type of humidity problem. Given a choice between compact and porous materials, it is advisable to select porous materials for elevated walls, and compact materials for foundations. The ancient Romans did this by using flint-chip concrete for foundations and brick for elevations. In Holland, where only brick is used, a good practice is to construct the foundations with impermeable engineering bricks. The same result could be obtained by inserting a stratum of some common anti-capillary material (such as vitrified brick or travertine slabs) at the base of the elevated walls. Indeed, *porosity must not be confused with hollowness*; tuff is porous, travertine is holey. Tuff facilitates the rise of water in walls, travertine obstructs it because its holes and passages are so large that capillary phenomena do not develop, while the solid part is not porous at all.

Materials soaked in water have *good capillarity* when water evaporates as easily as it is absorbed (as is the case with brick); in materials with *bad capillarity,* water evaporates only on the surface and is held in the core (see fig. 28, p. 48).

It is possible to obtain artificial materials that are not very absorbent, such as some *cellular, porous concretes.* These are made either by mixing soapy foam with liquid mortar so that the bubbles leave thousands of independent holes in the solidified mass, or by adding substances to the dry mix before the water is stirred in. The additives generate tiny gas bubbles that remain imprisoned in the concrete as it sets. Artificial materials such as these have the precious qualities of thermal insulation and anti-capillarity, but, to date, they have not been widely exploited. Natural pumice has also been neglected, even though it is inexpensive.

¶8.   Molds in paper and books. Remedies.

— Organic materials, such as paper, wood, glue, leather and foodstuffs, are more damaged by damp environments during the warm season than in cold weather; this is the case because the combined action of heat and humidity favors the growth of parasitical vegetation.

Paper, man's faithful working companion, shows a striking similarity to man in its limits of tolerance for humidity; in fact, it keeps well in air with a relative humidity between 65% and 40%. When the RH stabilizes between 80% and 90%, damage occurs almost immediately. Such damage can have two aspects: humidity can act alone, without the assistance of biological agents, or else together with them. When acting alone, humidity progressively softens paper and parchment until the material becomes mushy. Modern paper (especially if it is patinated) is more prone to softening than antique paper.

The action of humidity is almost always accompanied by that of organic agents such as insects, bacteria, fungi, and especially molds, unless the temperature is so low that the biological cycle is hindered.

The typical odor of mold in closed spaces is a sign that the diffusion of spores is already extensive. Yet, well before this dramatic symptom appears, the presence of mold can be ascertained by patient searching in the least-ventilated spots: behind bookshelves or pictures, in the lower shelves of cupboards – wherever the air circulates so slowly that it becomes saturated and forms a microclimate favorable to the development of spores.

Librarians are confronted with two types of mold that flower visibly on the outside of bindings: black mold (*aspergillus*) and green mold (*penicillus*). The amount of damage they cause depends upon how the leather was tanned, but their growth is encouraged by the absence of natural light. Brief exposure to ultraviolet lamps would kill the spores[1], but it is difficult to create permanent installations for sterilization *in situ* in the stacks, at least with the present state of ultraviolet-lamp technology. If indirect sunlight dominates the premises where books are kept, the problem would be nearly solved. It has been found that natural light is a positive factor in the good conservation of paper, given the same RH and temperature.

In London, according to H.J. Plenderleith, 72% RH is held to be the limit below which spores do not develop. In Italy, an instruction to state public libraries, given by Alfonso Gallo (the illustrious founder of the *Patologia del Libro*), fixed the desirable limits of RH at between 65% (maximum) and 40% (minimum), with the proviso that the annual *average* temperature should not exceed 18-20°C. Where there is artificial heating in winter, it should not exceed 14°C, in order to compensate for higher summer temperatures and keep the average to 18-20°C. In any case, it has been proven that *high artificial winter temperatures are much more dangerous* than low ones for libraries and archives located in premises that are damp due to moisture in the walls (the humidity source should

---

1   Paul H. HUEBNER, "Le maladies du papier et leur traitement," in *Mouseion*, III-IV, p. 242, 1934. The author also advises librarians who suspect that their storerooms are damp to ensure that parachlorometacresol is added (1 part per thousand) to the glue used in rebinding. This has a germicide power three times stronger than the pure sublimate.

be ascertained by analysis). Where there are damp walls the simplest and most effective remedy for mold is considered to be energetic forced ventilation of the premises. This must be carried out properly (¶55), with an installation planned so that the bookcases do not create 'dead ends' or compartments where the air stagnates and remains saturated.

On the other hand, if moisture comes from the air (through spring and summer condensation), it is inadvisable to introduce outside air with ventilation. Although it may seem paradoxical at first, the remedy we advise is light summer heating (see ¶56) and contemporaneous good air recirculation, indoors only.

It is possible to control the humidity level of unprinted paper in storage: a maximum moisture content of 12.5% by weight is admissible; this is the amount absorbed by paper when the RH is 65%. By weighing a given amount of paper before and after drying in an oven at 100°C, the moisture content in relation to weight can easily be verified.

To summarize:

- For good conservation of books and documents in temperate climates, the RH must be below 65%, with an average annual temperature below 18-20°C; any winter heating should never exceed 14°C.

- High temperatures are more damaging than low ones for good conservation of paper and parchment in damp environments, because they provoke the development of mold.

- Natural light (or radiation from ultraviolet lamps) arrests the propagation of mold; energetic air circulation achieves the same effect.

- To be considered dry, paper should never contain more than 12.5% moisture by weight.

¶9.   Rot in building wood. Remedies.

— Wood is considered dry when its maximum moisture content remains between 12% and 15%. The limit for fir, one of the woods most commonly used in construction, is usually fixed at 12%. As in the case of paper, where wood absorbs excessive moisture in an unhealthy atmosphere, there are different consequences depending on whether the moisture acts alone or in combination with biological factors. During construction, moisture alone can be damaging to wood because it reduces resistance to compression; resistance to tension is not affected. In a very damp attic, for example, a wooden truss of red fir may continue to hold water until it approaches saturation, causing the whole truss suddenly to give way due to the crushing of the rafters or struts, which were working in compression, while the tie members (working in tension) remained intact. Geiger's graph (fig. 8) shows how the breaking point of red fir varies with its moisture content. At a normal content (12%), the breaking point fluctuates around 470 kg/cm^2, and falls to less than half at about 220-200 kg/cm^2 when the wood is close to saturation.

In general, it may be said that, *due to moisture, wood used in construction is less resistant in autumn and winter than in summer*. This observation can be important in relation to seasonal overloading, such as the accumulation of farm products in attics or the action of snow and wind on roofs.

Yet wood's worst enemy, which forms only in the presence of humidity, is fungus; the danger begins as soon as the natural moisture content of the seasoned wood is surpassed.

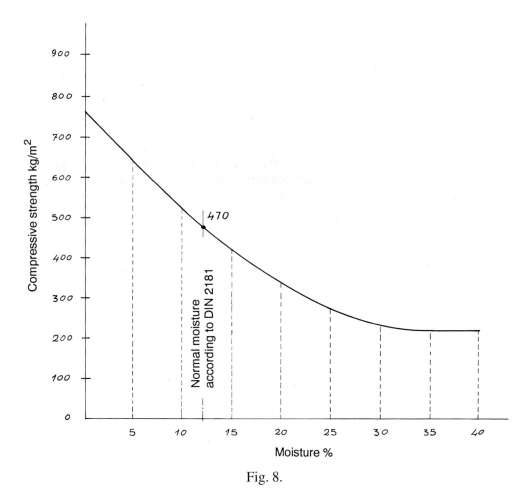

Fig. 8.

Relationship between the compressive strength and moisture content of red fir.

The three conditions that favor fungus attack of wood are:

- moisture content of wood 18% or higher
- lack of ventilation
- enough heat for the development of the mycelium

In homes, domestic fungi develop in the ceilings of very damp basements, in closed, unventilated attics and behind skirting board and wooden counter walls applied on top of damp walls. The most common are as follows:

- *Merulius lacrymans*, commonly called 'brown rot.' This is the most widespread and harmful fungus because it survives at low humidity levels; yet, in the dim light of an attic, it appears bedewed with shining drops of water
- *Coniophora cerebella*, often called 'wet rot' or 'cellar fungus,' which produces a dry putrefaction
- *Lenzites abietina*, also called 'dry rot,' which actually needs the most moisture

Merulius lacrymans, the most widespread of the wood fungi, produces in closed spaces a suffocating odor of mold, even when it is hidden behind wooden fittings and beneath loose plaster. When unexpected environmental changes lower the humidity of the air to the point that other fungi cannot survive, *Merulius* takes their place, and with such vitality that it can even vegetate in dry air (but only when the air is absolutely still). Along with ventilation, high temperatures will kill this fungus since it can live only at temperatures below 27°C.

Fungus attack causes the destruction of either the wood's lignin or its cellulose, but never both at the same time; one after the other may be destroyed due to successive waves of different fungi. Organic acids and carbohydrates are released as a result. If the diseased wood is encased in setting cement, the cement will be disturbed, especially by the carbohydrates produced by *Merulius*, to the extent that its resistance will be lower than expected. This has happened in our experience when a rotten board was used in a concrete formwork[2] for a reinforced concrete construction. (Hypothetically, the same thing could happen if one attempted to consolidate old, rotten beam-ends in trusses or floors by encasing them in concrete. Instead of good consolidation, one would end up with improperly hardened concrete as well as rotten timber).

Generally, good air circulation can prevent fungal attack, even in damp premises. Thus, the presence of domestic fungi is not only an indication of a humidity problem (which one cannot always help), but also a sure sign of insufficient ventilation (which can be remedied).

In homes, the invasion of domestic fungi is often discovered only when a floor or roof gives way. The first action that should be taken is *to investigate the vitality of the fungi*. Before choosing a remedy, it is essential to know whether the invasion is still active or whether the collapse is the after-effect of a previous invasion. This analysis should be done by a botanical or plant physiopathology laboratory, using fragments from the wood in question. What may look like fungi to a layman may be only residues or dried skeletons. If the damage is no longer progressive, one can proceed to replace the rotten wood. On the other hand, if the fungus is alive and the invasion still in progress, it must be arrested before repairing the damage. There is no point introducing new wood which will later be ruined. Such decayed wood from the Palazzo Corsini in Rome felt as light as cork when weighed in the hand.

In combating domestic fungi, it is important to know that the thread-like mycelium works its way deep into the wood and carries away *cellulose* or *lignin* from the inside, leaving the external shape of the board or beam unchanged while weight and resistance are lost.

Impregnation with sterilizing solutions (zinc chloride, Carbolineum, creosote, sublimate) can be carried out in the laboratory or the sawmill with reliable preservative effects. Unfortunately, such treatments are impossible to apply to wood already in place under a roof or in a floor, since the impregnation will not be as deep as required. Even an

---

2   Saviron CARAVANTES, "Un agresor del cemento deseumascardo," *Cemento y Hormigòn*, p. 61. 1942.

artificial rise in temperature above 27°C, to discourage *Merulius,* is difficult to achieve and dubious in efficacy.

There are three useful measures for effective repair: remove all the rotten wood, replace it with already impregnated wood or modify the environmental conditions with good ventilation to eliminate stagnant air.

To summarize:

- Excessive moisture in wood (above 15%) generally causes progressive reduction of resistance to compression, while resistance to tension remains unchanged.

- For the above reason, wood used in buildings that are subject to humidity is weaker in the autumn and winter than in the summer.

- The attack of domestic fungi on wood occurs in the presence of three conditions: moisture content of the wood above 18%, lack of ventilation and assured minimum of heat.

- The most widespread domestic fungus, *Merulius lacrymans*, can live only at temperatures below 27°C; this fungus can survive on a negligible amount of humidity *so long as the air is completely still.*

- Repairs and protective measures should be chosen according to whether the fungus invasion is still active or already complete.

- Sterilizing impregnation of wood is a valid preventive measure but does not arrest fungal attack already active in wood.

- The first remedy, applicable to every case, is good ventilation to eliminate stagnant air.

Chapter Three

LABORATORY TESTS ON INDIVIDUAL CONSTRUCTION MATERIALS

¶10. Experimental procedures.

— In medical texts on hygiene and in technical texts on construction materials, three relationships between material and water are examined:

- *the quantity of water absorbed* by a completely immersed sample. Hygienists call this 'water capacity'; technicians call it 'imbibition coefficient'
- *the rate or absorption power* of a completely immersed sample – sometimes called 'capillary absorption power'
- *the evaporation rate* of a sample removed from the water

In all three experiments, the sample is submerged beneath the water surface. In every country in the world, local materials have been tested for the quantity of water they can absorb when submerged – a test that is easily made.

These generally known imbibition coefficients are only of relative interest for the study of moisture in walls. In a real structure, the material is not totally immersed in water as it is in a laboratory test, except for rare cases where foundations are below the water table or houses are built on the banks of a canal or in a lagoon.

It is more relevant to determine the quantity of water that a material can draw up when a limited portion of its surface touches water, i.e., *the amount absorbed by capillary suction in the dry part above water level.* This type of examination more closely reproduces the case of an elevated wall that absorbs water from the ground. Unfortunately, such research has had few proponents and there is a paucity of data on suction.

To classify the behavior of construction materials with respect to wall dampness, we carried out research to determine:

- the quantity of water a material absorbs by capillary suction, expressed as a percentage referring either to volume or weight, which we shall call *'suction capacity'* (or suction percentage)
- the quantity of water by weight a material absorbs in a given time period from a surface unit, which we shall call *'suction rate'*

In natural building stone (but not brick), there is a significant difference between the percentage of water the material holds when it has been submerged below water level and that which it draws up when only one face of it touches the liquid surface. In other words, there is a difference between the absorption capacity and the suction capacity. *The property we call 'suction capacity' is a property of porous, permeable materials that are fine-grained and homogeneous,* such as brick, tuff, soft limestone and some sandstone. In contrast, materials such as travertine that are visibly riddled with holes, and become totally filled with water when submerged, show a very low suction capacity when they are only partially submerged in water.

Finally, the present data on evaporation curves and drying rates are very uncertain and have no practical value, as far as we know.

All told, for tests of construction materials in water, it would be useful to have uniform criteria and laboratory apparatus to reproduce, as closely as possible, the condition of the material in use, as is done for resistance tests in another field.

¶11. Absorption during immersion.

— The following is a general division of construction materials according to the percentage of water they absorb when completely submerged (the water percentage refers to the volume of the sample):

- from 0% to 0.1%: very compact rocks, e.g., granite, Carrara marble, and compact limestone in general
- from 0.1% to 5%: the same rocks, but less compact, e.g., flint, ordinary compact limestone
- from 5% to 20%: sandstone, semi-hard limestone, travertine, cement-sand mortar, lime-sand mortar, hard brick, and brick facings
- from 20% to 35%: molasse, soft sandstone, good quality tuff, lime-pozzolana mortar, common machine-made brick
- from 35% to 55%: calcareous tufa and volcanic tuff, handmade brick, gypsum plaster structures

Not surprisingly, the natural materials with the greatest absorption capacity are the lightest ones, i.e., those with specific gravity between 1 and 2. In general, these materials are good for house construction as they possess maximum thermal insulating power and good adherence to mortar; because of their porosity, however, they are also more subject to invasion by moisture. Dampness can be inherent, and thus brought with the materials, or acquired, and thus produced while the wall is being built. If a recently constructed stone wall does not dry out within a normal time limit, the persistence of dampness can be due either to a supply of water from some source, or to residual 'quarry water' in parts of the material used. (Some blocks of stone tenaciously hold onto this water, particularly in damp climates and in sunless exposures.)

In compact and heavy rocks, the amount of inherent water, absorbed over millennia in the quarry, is greater than the amount the material can take in during absorption experiments.

Humidity damage can be substantial when blocks of stone that still contain quarry sap are used.

¶12. Capillary suction.

— As previously mentioned, *suction capacity is a measurement of the capacity of a partially immersed material to become damp in the portion of the sample above water.*

Suction characteristics can be expressed either as a percentage of water acquired (*suction capacity*) or as grams of water absorbed in a given time (*suction rate*).

For every construction material (including dry mortars) two indices can be determined: one measuring the quantity of water acquired and the other the rate at which the material 'drinks.' Since most damp walls drink from the foundation and become progressively damp in the part above ground, experimental suction tests (on a small scale in the laboratory) can reproduce what happens on a large scale to walls in their natural environment (fig. 9).

Fig. 9.

The sample is set in a tank of water in order to reproduce, on a small scale in the laboratory, the absorption that occurs on a large scale in damp walls.

During a series of practical experiments conducted in a worksite laboratory at the Accademia dei Lincei in Rome, the following criteria were applied:

- Fairly large-sized samples (the same size as bricks, 28 x 14 x 5 cm) were used instead of the small cubes previously employed.
- Instead of being dried in an oven at 100°C, the samples were dried naturally in the open air. They were spread out and exposed to dry winter wind or full summer sun for 20 days, and kept sheltered from bad weather; after such seasoning, the materials can be considered '*nominally dry*,' or as dry as they would be when used in construction.
- Normal drinking water at room temperature was used instead of hot, distilled water.
- Finally, the observations were repeated in various seasons and at different temperatures in order to obtain a representative average of annual behavior.

Each sample was placed upright in a few centimeters of water in a special closed tank (fig. 10) and rested on runners which kept it slightly above the bottom. The water level in the tank was occasionally replenished so as to keep a fairly constant area of the sample's surface in contact with the water. Most of the sample was exposed to the air.

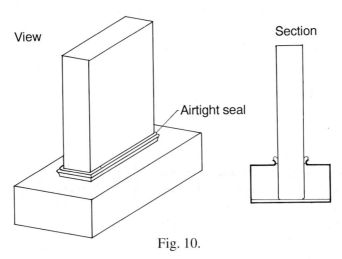

View

Section

Airtight seal

Fig. 10.

The enclosed water tank for suction tests allows the 28-cm sample to stand upright in 4 cm of water.

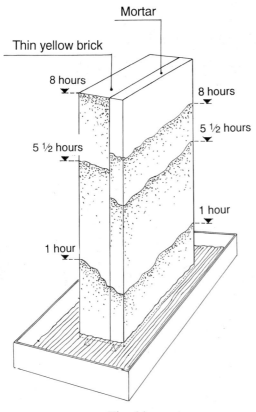

Mortar

Thin yellow brick

8 hours

8 hours

5 ½ hours

5 ½ hours

1 hour

1 hour

Fig. 11.

Differing suction rates in brick and the mortar adhering to it.

Of the samples tested, the greatest absorption occurred in pozzolana mortar (31%) and soft yellow brick (30.4%). It was found that lime-sand mortar drinks less than lime-pozzolana mortar and that common hydrofuges mixed with mortars reduce absorption by about half, but do not arrest it altogether. As far as dampness is concerned, therefore, a building of soft yellow brick and lime-pozzolana mortar is liable to have the greatest problems.

It was interesting to note the behavior of a sample obtained by applying a bed of mortar to the back of a thin brick. The differing velocity of the water's rise was clearly visible, and much more rapid in the brick than in the mortar, even though the two materials adhered closely together (fig. 11).

Whereas brick has high suction power, tuff and mortar absorb moisture much more slowly. The absorption rate of lime-sand mortar is greater than that of lime-pozzolana mortar, although the lime-sand mortar absorbs less water. Cement-sand mortar is ten times slower in suction than lime mortar, and becomes 60-70 times slower when hydrofuges are added.

Suction height differs greatly from one material to another, and might be explained by the hypothesis that capillaries vary in type and diameter, depending on the structure of the material.

Of all the materials tested, soft brick and tile showed the greatest suction height. Three groups of natural stone – *granites, compact limestones, basalts* – can be considered to possess *excellent anti-suction properties*. In most regions, it is easy to find local materials with pronounced anti-suction characteristics; these are good for constructing foundations.

Kettenacker has made the interesting observation that, in brick and tile, the quantity of water absorbed by suction is uniformly divided throughout the damp portion; in natural stone samples, however, the upper layers contain progressively less water than those below. This fact can be understood if we suppose that natural absorbent stone (such as the calcareous limestone studied by Kettenacker) possesses large and small capillary tubes side by side; these draw water up to different heights. Figure 12 shows the capillary structure of natural stone schematically, using only two capillary sizes. In contrast, since brick capillaries presumably have a constant diameter, water is uniformly distributed up to the maximum attainable height. Due to this consistency in capillary diameter, the behavior of brick remains unchanged no matter whether it is totally or only partially immersed in water; in fact, the percentage of water absorbed in either case is almost equal. The opposite is true of natural materials, notably sandstone and tuff, and porous artificial cement, all of which absorb much less by suction than during immersion. Experiments by J.S. Cammerer have confirmed this observation. Samples of various materials, immersed in water for $\frac{1}{5}$ their height, showed the following distribution of water absorbed in each fifth of their total height:

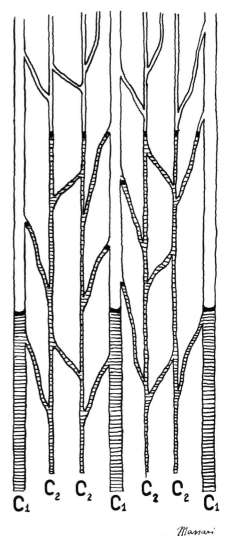

C_2 C_2 C_2 C_2
C_1 C_1 C_1

Massari

Fig. 12.

In natural building stones, in contrast to brick, the capillaries (C_1, C_2, etc.) are not all of the same diameter and, therefore, the quantity of water absorbed diminishes with height.

CHART II – MOISTURE CONTENT PERCENTAGE BY VOLUME

Material		Portion in water	Portion above water			
		1/5	2/5	3/5	4/5	5/5
Normal brick	(sp.gr. 1650)	30.4	29.7	29.7	29.7	20.7
Light sandstone	(sp.gr. 1750)	28.1	26.7	25.6	23.7	18.0
Cinder brick	(sp.gr. 1350)	13.9	12.0	9.1	5.8	5.5
Porous cement	(sp.gr. 1040)	21.7	15.8	15.8	15.0	14.5

¶13. Evaporation of damp materials. Bending point.

— When moisture invasion has stabilized at a given height in a wall absorbing water from the subsoil, the wall has reached *a condition of equilibrium in which a certain amount of water enters at the bottom and an equal amount exits by evaporation from the parts exposed to the air.*

It would be useful to know the operative coefficients for the surface evaporation of different wall structures in order to calculate (for a damp wall under given conditions of temperature and RH) the average humidity supplied to the environment over a given time period. Even though conditions change progressively, one could at least project how many changes of air would be needed to lower the RH of the air in a room to an acceptably healthy level. To date, few conclusions about this phenomenon have been made, and it would be difficult to take into account the mutability of external circumstances sufficiently well to make accurate calculations and predictions.

In practice, one finds *average evaporation rates of between 0.4 g and 10* $g/m^2/h$ in most damp walls or floors. For example, in the floor of the temporary library storeroom of the Archaeological Institute on Via Lungara in Rome, an average evaporation rate of about $1 g/m^2/h$ under normal conditions of average air humidity was measured.

The evaporation rate increases from three to five times when the wall or floor is exposed to a mild breeze, and increases two or three times under exposure to the sun; moreover, these conditions of wind and sun cause the evaporation rates of various saturated materials to increase together in almost parallel fashion.

The results of experiments by Kröll, Krischer and Görling make a practical contribution to the problem of wall repair. These are summarized below.

When a damp material with no water supply is subjected to strong evaporation and begins to dry out, two phases must be distinguished. At first, the loss of moisture from the surface is constant while the percentage of humidity contained in the mass progressively declines. This is the first drying phase, in which evaporation occurs at a constant rate and temperature from a saturated surface.

At a certain point, however, inappropriately called the '**bending point**,' there is a rapid decline, indeed a sharp fall in the water rate. This is the second drying phase, which begins suddenly when the moisture content percentage falls below a given, critical limit.

Every porous material behaves in this way when its moisture evaporates. There are differences between one material and another, but the pattern can always be translated into an evaporation graph such as Figure 13. It is composed of a virtually horizontal section (constant evaporation during first drying phase), and an almost vertical section (evaporation rate in rapid decline during second drying phase).

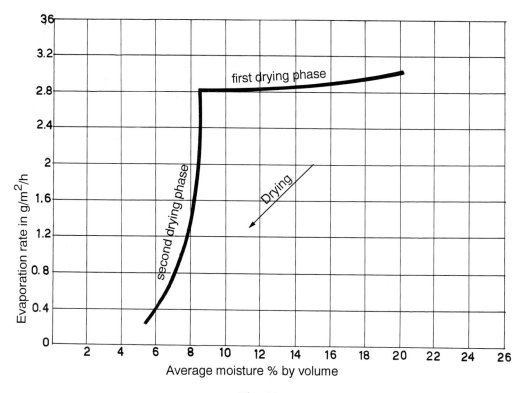

Fig. 13.

Krischer and Görling's graph of the variation in evaporation rate as a function of the moisture content in a brick: in the first drying phase there is a virtually constant evaporation rate; in the second, this rate declines rapidly.

In Figure 13, the first phase begins when the moisture content is 20.1% by volume, and continues until the moisture content is reduced to 8.8%. During this first period, the surface evaporation rate is virtually constant at around 2.9 g/m²/h, but the moisture content continues to decrease.

At the bending point, i.e., when the moisture content falls below 8.8%, the second phase begins. Here, the evaporation rate declines much more rapidly than the moisture content of the material.

To understand why two such different phases occur, one must realize that when the surface of the material is saturated, it acts almost like a pool of water where the evaporation rate depends entirely on whether the air can absorb the water vapor being given off. The air's absorption capacity will vary with its saturation deficit, i.e., the difference between the actual amount of water vapor present and the maximum amount the air could hold at the same temperature. In other words, *evaporation during the first drying phase depends solely on the air's capacity to absorb vapor and is independent of the properties of the material* being dried.

At a critical point (bending point), when the surface is no longer saturated, new water still comes from the interior layers, but too slowly to maintain full evaporation because the water reserves have been depleted.

Here, the material's capillary conduction properties come into play. The resistance the water must overcome to reach the surface depends on the material's specific structure; in consequence, the evaporation rate depends on the characteristics of that structure.

As far as wall moisture is concerned, the first drying phase is the more dangerous to health on account of the constant and high evaporation power of a saturated wall, while in the second phase the evaporation power falls rapidly.

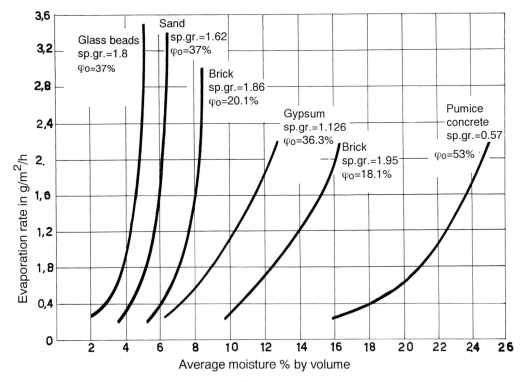

Fig. 14.

Variation of evaporation rate as a function of moisture content for several materials. The more homogeneous the structure of the material itself, the more closely the curve comes to the vertical (sp.gr. = dry specific gravity; φ_o = initial moisture)

Figure 14 shows the bending curves developed by Krischer and Görling for various materials. *The more homogeneous the structure of the material, the closer the second drying phase comes to the vertical*; indeed, the steepest rates are those of fine glass beads and sand.

From this we can deduce that in walls constructed of very fine-grain, homogeneous materials, the first drying phase will last considerably longer than in walls made of irregular, heterogeneous materials, while the second phase will be short and steep. In other words, a damp wall made up of regular, carefully laid courses of high-quality bricks with homogeneous mortar will continue to give a high and constant rate of surface evaporation despite the fact that its moisture content percentage gradually diminishes; only when the percentage is reduced to 6-8.8% by volume (for brick with a specific gravity of 1.86) – that is, at the start of the second drying phase – will the rapid decline of surface evaporation begin and actual drying occur.

In contrast, an uneven tuff wall, with different-quality blocks and crude, unsifted mortar, will have a relatively brief phase of constant evaporation rate. Then a very slow decline in surface evaporation will begin with the second drying phase while the moisture content percentage is still quite high – we can assume perhaps 15 or 20% moisture by volume.

From a health viewpoint, brick walls are much more dangerous than most stone walls because even at low percentages of moisture content, the water they contain is dissipated at a high rate. Walls of light stone, however, such as tuff, tenaciously retain water, even at high percentages.

One can further deduce from figure 14 that the maximum evaporation rate of the four construction materials shown (two types of brick with different specific gravities, construction gypsum and pumice concrete) is nearly the same for all the materials when their surfaces are saturated; the usual rate is between 3 and 2 $g/m^2/h$.

Experiments conducted in 1929 in England by the Building Research Board (*Report*, 1929, p. 9) confirm the somewhat unexpected finding that an equal evaporation rate will take place in different materials when their surfaces are kept saturated. This is very important because *when they are very damp, walls constructed of different materials produce the same amount of evaporation and, therefore, cause the same damage.*

Thus, it is fundamental to any study of the moisture condition of a wall to ascertain whether the evaporation is in the first or second drying phase. As already mentioned, *a wall in the first drying phase can cause more damage than one in the second.*

If, for instance, a structure of heavy bricks had a bending point in the drying curve corresponding to a moisture content of 8.8% by volume (as in fig. 13), the health situation would not be affected by lowering the wall's moisture content from 17% to 10%, because the surface evaporation would remain about the same. If, through repairs, the moisture content could be lowered below 8%, a real improvement would be made owing to the reduction in surface evaporation.

From what we have been able to deduce from the Krischer and Görling graphs and other experimental data, the passage from one phase to the other, for other materials, should occur with the following moisture content percentages by weight: normal light brick, between 4.7% and 3.2%; tuff, between 14% and 8%; gypsum plaster, between 9.5% and 5.3%. This means that where there is also heat or ventilation the walls could begin to decrease in surface evaporation when their moisture content goes below:

- 5%   by weight, for normal light brick
- 14%   by weight, for tuff
- 9.5% by weight, for gypsum plaster

The above considerations provide a simple method for quantifying the task of wall repair. Unfortunately, however, each of these percentages is related to a single material and not to a wall as a composite structure made up of many materials. If the exact *bending point* of each normal type of wall construction, complete with plaster, were known, then the corresponding moisture content or the demarcation line for effective restoration could be determined. Below that percentage, provisions for heating and ventilation would accelerate the drying of the wall as well as the air. Any additional steps to lower, even slightly, the moisture content of the wall would then become truly effective.

In summary, *damaging evaporation in a damp wall is proportional to the moisture content of the wall, so long as it is relatively low* (below 5% for light brick, 14% for soft tuff, and 9.5% for gypsum plaster); *evaporation becomes constant and independent of the moisture content when the latter is high.*

¶14.   Practical deductions on the behavior of materials.

1) A brick absorbs the same quantity of water when immersed as by suction (above the water surface), but naturally porous materials, such as sandstone and tuff, absorb much more moisture when immersed than by suction.

2) Water is absorbed easily by light brick, soft limestone, tuff, lime mortar – all the materials that are good heat insulators; they lose this valuable property when they are wet. On the other hand, compact, porous materials, such as travertine, do not absorb liquid above the water surface. Other compact materials, such as granite, saccharoid marble, compact limestone and basalt, do not absorb liquid at all.

3) Light yellow brick and lime-pozzolana mortar absorb the greatest quantity of water by suction – between 30-32% by volume – but at quite different rates; *lime-sand mortar absorbs less water than pozzolana mortar, but absorbs it faster.*

4) In the group of materials examined, light yellow brick has the maximum suction rate; red brick about half the maximum; lime-sand mortar about ¼; lime-pozzolana mortar ⅕; soft tuff about ⅐. Cement-sand mortar is ten times slower in water suction than common lime mortar, and about fifty times slower than yellow brick.

5) On comparing the overall absorption behavior of brick and mortar, one sees that mortar 'drinks' water much more slowly, but eventually takes in as much as, if not more than, brick. *Mortar has more inertia than brick, both in absorbing and in losing capillary water.* Therefore, in restoring damp brick walls, an excellent way of speeding up the drying process is to remove the plaster.

6) Due to the variations in the suction rate of different construction materials, dry walls placed in equal contact with water will become wet in different lengths of time. A

wall of yellow brick, well constructed with fine joints, shows the first signs of dampness after a year. A tuff wall will show dampness after six or seven years.

7) The addition of common commercial hydrofuges to a mortar mixture reduces the quantity of water that the mortar (after it has dried) can reabsorb by more than half, and notably slows down the absorption rate as well. Lime mortar's absorption rate is reduced to a tenth of its normal rate, and cement mortar's to a sixth, using common products and normal working methods.

8) Diverse materials with very high moisture content percentages (saturated) evaporate almost equal amounts per surface unit. Therefore, when a wall is so damp as to approach saturation, it is of little importance, in terms of health, whether the wall is made of tuff, sandstone, brick or some other material. On the other hand, when the wall is not very damp, its behavior varies because the evaporation rate tends to be proportional to the suction rate of the dry material. In slightly damp samples, where the evaporation rate of soft yellow brick is equal to 1, that of harder red brick will be $\frac{1}{2}$, lime mortar $\frac{1}{5}$, tuff $\frac{1}{7}$ and cement mortar $\frac{1}{50}$; thus, *the most damaging damp wall is one of soft yellow brick and lime mortar* when it is continuously supplied with water, as happens when moisture rises from the water table.

9) The effect of a light wind, about 8 km/h, increases surface evaporation three to five times, other conditions being equal.

The effect of sunlight is weaker than that of light wind; other conditions being equal, it increases surface evaporation two to three times.

10) Analogous to the behavior of a sample, the quantity of water a damp wall can absorb from the ground will vary within broad limits and will depend (other conditions being equal) on surface evaporation. The more a wall is forced to evaporate above ground, the more it will absorb from the foundation; if the foundation touches the water table, *ventilation, even if accelerated, is unlikely to dry the wall completely.*

11) The reverse is also true: when a wall is damp due to *driving rain or condensation*, complete drying can be obtained with ventilation.

Chapter Four

HOW TO MEASURE AND INTERPRET HUMIDITY

¶15. Measuring the humidity of the air.

— The best way to assess the healthfulness of an environment is to determine its atmospheric humidity, by using instruments such as hair hygrometers or psychrometers. The water vapor that is always present in air can be measured for different purposes. It interests us as relative humidity (RH) because this is what causes the typical sense of discomfort we feel upon entering a damp place. Relative humidity (also called 'hygrometric state') is expressed as a percentage; this means that if the RH is 80%, the air contains only 80% of the water vapor it would hold at that temperature if it were completely saturated. By subtracting this percentage from 100, we obtain what is called the *saturation margin or deficit* – 20% in this case.

Different aspects of this physical phenomenon can be measured as follows:

- **absolute humidity of the air**: the total weight of vapor in grams actually contained in a cubic meter of air; this weight varies from 1-2 grams to 30-40 grams at common temperatures.

- **water vapor pressure**: the part of atmospheric pressure expressed in millimeters of a column of mercury which is exerted by the vapor itself. This pressure varies from 1-2 mm to 30-40 mm of mercury at common temperatures. The pressure increases directly with the quantity of vapor present, i.e., with the absolute humidity; it also increases with the temperature.

- **relative humidity of the air (RH)**: the percentage ratio between the humidity actually contained in the air at a given temperature and the maximum amount of humidity the air could potentially contain at the same temperature. The ratio between the two vapor pressures (actual and maximum potential) gives the same result.

Suppose that at 10°C in a given environment the air contains 6.6 g of water per cubic meter. We know from the tables that it could hold 9.4 g if saturated, so the ratio $\frac{6.6}{9.4} \times 100 = 70$ gives us the relative humidity – expressed as a percentage: 70%.

It is helpful to remember that the maximum absolute humidity expressed in grams per m^3 is almost equal to the pressure expressed in mm of mercury. For example, the maximum figures are:

temperature °C	0	5	10	15	20	25	30
max. pressure in mm	4.57	6.51	9.14	12.67	17.36	23.52	31.51
max. absolute humidity g/m^3	4.85	7.61	9.32	12.71	17.11	22.79	30.03

The RH can be calculated either as a ratio between two absolute humidity figures – the actual and the potential maximum – or as a ratio between the two corresponding vapor pressures.

In an enclosed space, where part or all of the wall surface evaporates moisture, the RH of the air will tend to rise. If the space is perfectly closed, so that there is no exchange with the outside air, the air inside will eventually reach saturation. In most cases there is a continuous exchange between inside and outside so the damp internal air, diluted with some regularity by dry external air, cannot reach saturation. It tends to stabilize around an intermediate RH level – usually 3-15 percentage points higher than that of the outside air in spring and summer; but in winter and autumn, the indoor air (since the space, though damp, is warmer) is almost always lower in RH than the outdoors.

Air nearing saturation is important for health reasons because once it is saturated the phenomenon of condensation begins to act, i.e., water in excess above saturation passes from the vapor to the liquid state and is subsequently deposited on cold bodies. This phenomenon occurs partially even in a room where the mass of air has not quite reached saturation; it happens, for instance, in the air layer cooled by contact with a cold floor or wall. In that layer, which is continuously renewed, saturation is easily reached by the lowering of temperature, and dew or condensation is formed as a result. One commonly says the air '*is damp*.' The floor or wall becomes covered with an opaque, damp veil, especially when its surface is not absorbent, as is the case of painted walls and floors of cast stone, tile or marble.

As opposed to this '*wetting*' property, the air has a '*drying*' property when it is far from saturation. The lower the RH of the circulating air, the faster damp walls or goods dry out. The true drying capacity of the air and thus the degree of desiccation it can effect on damp walls or articles depends, therefore, on the absolute humidity, because the less humidity a cubic meter of air holds at the outset, the more it can take on. As the absolute humidity at saturation decreases with lowered temperatures, cold air will have the maximum drying effect on damp, warm materials. All told, *the volume being equal, initially cold air can carry away (given enough heat for evaporation) a greater amount of moisture than air that is already hot* at the start. This is why a cold winter wind often has a greater drying effect than a hot summer wind. Industrial drying plants exploit this feature.

The two instruments most often used to measure the relative humidity of the air are the **hair hygrometer** and the **psychrometer** (fig. 15). For details of the many other instruments available, the reader can refer to textbooks on meteorology or climatology and suppliers' catalogs.

The hair hygrometer is based on the fact that certain types of human hair and some other organic fibers stretch according to the amount of humidity in the air. This instrument gives rather approximate figures and, depending on the model, often has considerable inertia, sometimes requiring as much as 20 minutes to give a new reading when moved from one place to another. The instruments currently on the market are liable to lose their accuracy if moved or otherwise disturbed and are, therefore, furnished with a regulating screw so they can be periodically calibrated to a basic instrument. A good hygrometer should not err by more than three or four percent. Another, very modern type of hygrometer is based on variations, caused by RH, in the electrical conductivity of a salt or a resin. This instrument, however, is apparently no more accurate than the traditional hair hygrometer.

The psychrometer, on the other hand, is both accurate and easy to use. It includes two identical thermometers, side by side in the same holder. One of the two is called the *dry bulb thermometer* and its bulb is exposed like any normal thermometer. The other is the *wet bulb thermometer*, and its bulb is covered with a little sock, which must be kept wet when the measurements are taken. The end of the sock can be dipped in a small bottle of water, or dampened with an eyedropper. Although plain water works perfectly well, it is advisable to use distilled water to avoid building up mineral encrustations that could eventually affect the reading.

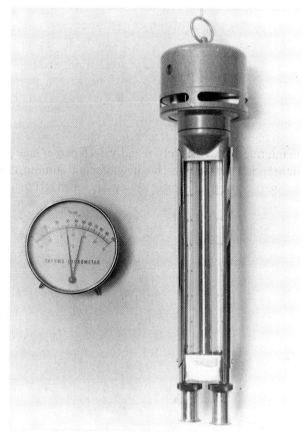

Fig. 15.

The psychrometer (right) uses the differential readings of two thermometers – one dry, one wet – and is much more accurate than the hair hygrometer (left).

When a psychrometer is used, the evaporation of the wet sock is accelerated with light ventilation (simply fan it with a piece of cardboard), which cools the bulb. The dry bulb, meanwhile, remains insensitive to the air movement. The dryer the air, the greater the evaporation will be, and thus the greater discrepancy in temperature shown by the two thermometers. Two measurements are recorded: the difference between the readings of the two thermometers and the temperature of the wet bulb thermometer. The instrument comes with a table which gives the corresponding RH for each pair of readings. The best instruments have the temperature scale incised on the glass and are graduated in at least fifths of a degree; some types have built-in fans powered either by winding or batteries, and some have a rubber bulb to blow air.

When the temperature of the wet bulb thermometer falls below zero, the measurement becomes unreliable, partly because ice is a poor heat conductor and keeps the wet bulb thermometer from reaching the low temperature it might otherwise attain.

At temperatures below freezing, therefore, the readings given by a well-calibrated hair hygrometer are better; at normal temperatures, psychrometer readings are always preferable.

Other auxiliary instruments deriving from those above are the **hygrograph**, a hair hygrometer attached to a lever that marks on a drum, and the **thermohygrograph**, which marks the movements of both RH and temperature together on one sheet, on a daily, weekly or monthly basis (fig. 16).

Fig. 16.

The thermohygrograph registers both the RH and the temperature of the air.

These recording instruments are very useful in keeping track – hour-by-hour and day-by-day – of variations in the RH, and perhaps the temperature, of a damp space. A comparative study of indoor and outdoor air calls for two identical instruments set up in the same way. As a rough guide, when the RH is below 50%, the air is considered very dry; between 50-65% it is dry; above 75% it is damp.

Another type of hygrometer which seems to be very sensitive at medium and high temperatures is the **diffusion hygrometer;** it works according to the phenomenon of the diffusion of water vapor through a membrane. This phenomenon is directly related to RH. The instrument is composed of a small container of distilled water covered by a membrane and directly linked to a manometric tube which registers pressure differences in millimeters. A dial thermometer gives the temperature at the moment of observation. The instrument comes with a table which lists the RH corresponding to each pair of temperature and pressure values.

¶16. Measurement of wall moisture. The two simplest methods.

— The second kind of measurement, which is indispensable and decisive in assessing the humidity of an environment, is that of wall moisture. There are two ways to take this measurement: with an electric meter and with the weight method.

It is possible to ascertain, with an electrical measurement, the humidity of plaster (fig. 17) up to a depth of 15-20 mm without further investigating the condition of the wall's internal fabric. It is also possible to concentrate directly on the fabric, by taking small samples from the inside of the wall and examining them in the laboratory. The amount of water in the samples is found by weighing them immediately after extraction and then noting the weight loss after oven drying.

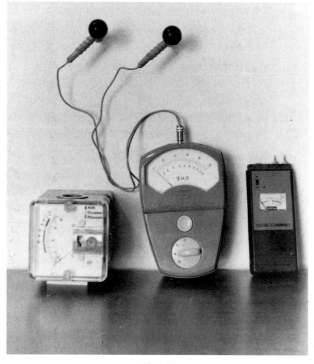

Fig. 17.

Various types of electric meters for measuring plaster moisture.

Surface measuring instruments are based on variations in the plaster's electrical resistance, which changes according to its moisture content. The measurements are taken between two points separated by a given distance. Some of these instruments work with pin electrodes which are stuck into the wall; others work with electrode plates pressed against its surface. These electric meters can also be used inside a wall after opening a hole ⅔ of the wall thickness and exposing a horizontal bed of mortar where the pin electrodes can be conveniently inserted at various points. A series of measurements is usually made, working from the inner wall face towards the outside; thus one can check whether the percentage of moisture in the mortar increases or decreases from inside out.

In looking after public housing projects in Italy, we have found occasionally that the foremen mislead administrators and maintenance offices by insisting that driving rain is passing through the walls – a highly unlikely occurrence in Italy. In such cases, a *measurement taken inside the wall demonstrates that the core is dry* because the rain has not passed through.

Electric humidity meters are inaccurate because the electrical conductivity of plaster or mortar does not depend solely on its moisture content, but also on the salts dissolved in the water. If the electric meter registers a 12% moisture content when it is actually 9%, the error is of little practical importance, for a wall is still quite damp whether it contains 12% or 9%. When the meter shows 'dry,' the reading *can be trusted* because the salts lose their electrical conductivity without water. The meter can guarantee, without fear of error, that badly stained plaster, which at first glance looks damp, has become perfectly dry although it must have been damp in the past. All told, despite their inaccuracy, these instruments are very useful.

Other excellent portable electric meters, which anyone can use, do not require sticking pins into the plaster; their electrodes are simply pressed against the wall (Paquet's meter, for instance). These meters are based on variations in the wall's dielectrical constant, which depends on its moisture content. Still others are based on measurement in decibels of the weakening of a microwave band that is sent through the entire thickness of the wall. This last technique is laborious and can be used only by specialists.

Common surface meters have become standard equipment for interior decorators and painters, who use them to judge whether the plaster is dry enough for painting. This helps them to avoid having colors destroyed by basic calcium salts because the plaster is still setting and damp.

In cases where so-called 'cavity' walls are concerned, a comparison between two measurements – superficial and in depth – is always useful, especially when they are in

Fig. 18.

To remove samples from the wall fabric, a serrated boring rod can be used.

contrast. If the plaster is found to be wet while the internal fabric is dry, one is certainly dealing with a case of condensation due to water vapor in the air.

Depth measurement samples for weight analysis can be easily taken as follows:

a) The material is collected by penetrating the wall 15-20 cm with a serrated *boring rod* (fig. 18), which makes fairly uniform cylindrical holes. The crumbled bits of wall sample remain inside the rod and can be dropped, untouched, into a dry glass or plastic jar, which must be tightly sealed at once. It is preferable to take samples entirely of mortar from the bed between two bricks.

b) Taking samples is much easier with a normal electric drill. Excessive pressure against the wall should be avoided, as well as high revolutions (not above 200 rpm), causing heat that might make some moisture evaporate and alter the results of the analysis.

c) Unless one is looking for surface condensation, the samples must be extracted some *15-20 cm inside the wall, where the material is no longer subject to the variable influence of atmospheric humidity.*

d) Numerous samples should be taken in order to obtain reliable averages. For official surveys, or in cases of litigation, two samples should be taken for every figure reported.

e) This operation is inadvisable for structurally unstable walls. In such cases, it is better to take more superficial samples with a plain chisel.

f) In new buildings, which should have virtually uniform humidity conditions, three samples taken a meter above the floor for every bearing wall will suffice; the extraction should be taken from one in every five or six rooms on each floor, reducing proportionally for large buildings.

g) As a rule, in old buildings, at least three samples should be taken a meter apart along a vertical line on the wall. Heights of 0.40, 1.40 and 2.40 m above the floor (fig. 19) are practical since it is awkward to work below 0.40 m and it is possible to reach 2.40 by standing on an empty box or a table.

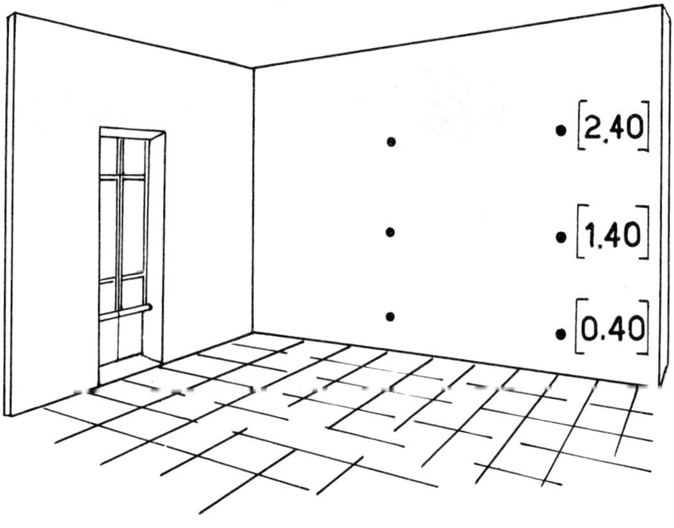

Fig. 19.

Samples are taken along a vertical line at various heights above the floor: the heights shown (0.40, 1.40 2.40 m) are convenient since no ladder is required.

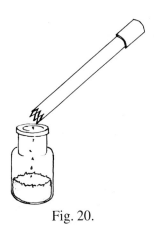

Fig. 20.

The crumbled sample material is collected in glass or plastic jars with sealed tops.

h) When examining masonry floors, lift mortar samples with a chisel to some depth beneath the flooring material.

The crumbled sample material can be collected (fig. 20) in completely dry glass or plastic jars with airtight stoppers. If these receptacles are stored away from excess heat or cold, the analysis can be postponed for a month or more, if necessary.

The containers must be carefully numbered to correspond to the list of locations made when the samples are taken; it is also advisable to mark the sample number and date on the wall beneath each test hole.

According to Bianchini's research, humidity only ceases to be affected by fluctuations in the hygrometric state of the ambient air at a depth of 15-20 cm beneath the wall surface. This is why normal samples are taken at that depth.

To find out how much water the samples contain, it is advisable to take them (tightly closed) to a public health laboratory. The laboratory can follow two methods to measure the moisture content:

The weight method and the alcohol method.

With the weight method, the sample's moisture content is measured as the difference in weight before and after oven drying. The alcohol method uses alcohol's thirst for water to withdraw all the moisture the sample contains, whereupon the amount is calculated.

These practical laboratory procedures are named after the persons who have developed them and are described in detail in basic hygiene textbooks[1]. The moisture content of the wall, given as a percentage of the sample's weight, can range from 0.5% to 30%. If the moisture content is given by volume, the figures grow in proportion to the specific gravity of the wall – from one-and-a-half to two-and-a-half times.

Not all the water contained in a wall is damaging. The interpretation of the analysis should clarify whether there is an excess above the normal amount that is specific to every type of wall structure. This subject is treated in Chapter Five.

¶17.   **Graphic representation of the absorbent state of a wall.**

— The distribution of water is different in old and new walls. The difference can be summarized in two words: *uniformity* in new walls, *irregularity* in old ones. As one can

---

1   A. SCALA, *Applicazioni di fisica e chimica all'igiene*. Turin: U.T.E.T., 1926. – P.L. FIORANI GALLOTTA, *L'igiene della casa*. Padova: 1932.

Fig. 21.

Representation of the moisture content of a wall as a function of its height, along a vertical line.

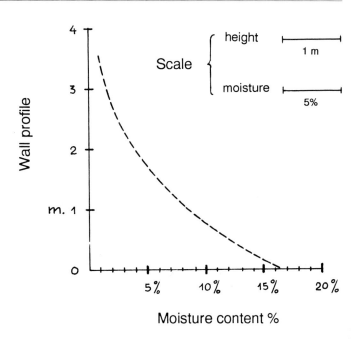

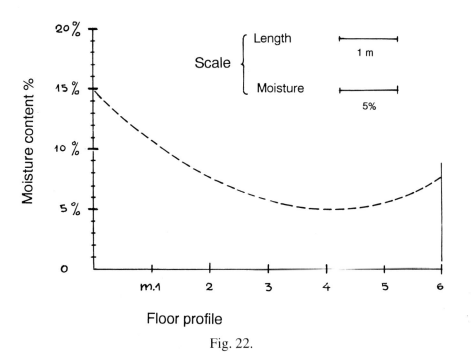

Fig. 22.

Representation of the moisture content of a floor as a function of distance from the wall, along a horizontal line.

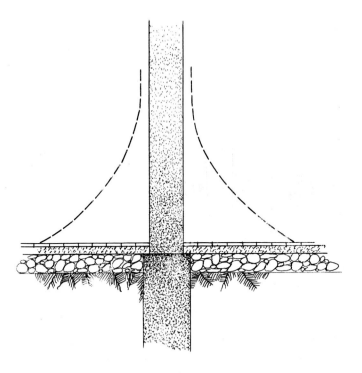

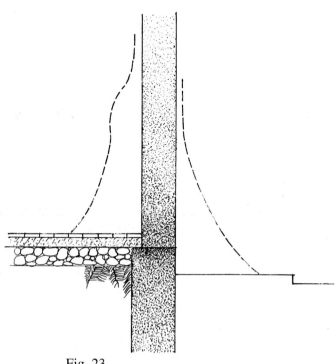

Fig. 23.

The moisture content of an interior wall (above) is often relatively symmetrical on both faces. Graphs of the two faces of an exterior wall (below) are always dissimilar.

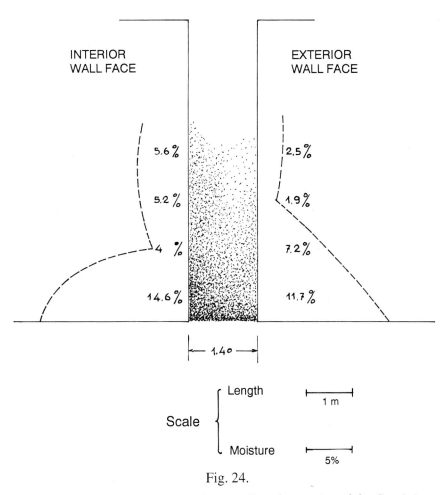

INTERIOR
WALL FACE

EXTERIOR
WALL FACE

5.6%

2.5%

5.2%

1.9%

4 %

7.2%

14.6%

11.7%

1.40

Scale
{ Length — 1 m
Moisture — 5% }

Fig. 24.

Irregular graph of the two faces of the base wall in the portico of the Corsini garden in Rome (see exterior wall in fig. 1).

imagine, it is much easier graphically to represent the humidity condition of a wall structure in the former case than in the latter.

One good way to illustrate wall moisture is by means of a *graph of the damp section*; this is based on the results of the percentage analysis of the moisture content, as shown in Figures 21-22.

When the complete vertical section of a wall is shown (fig. 23, top), graphs can be made for both its faces. If an interior wall is involved, the graphs will generally be symmetrical and almost equal. With an exterior wall, however, (fig. 23, bottom) the graphs are always dissimilar, for the humidity in the external face tends to decrease faster as it rises above ground, on account of natural, outdoor ventilation.

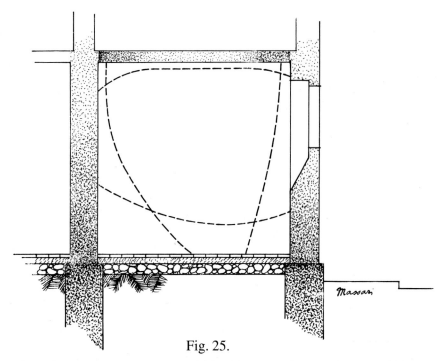

Fig. 25.

The humidity of an entire room (in an old building) is illustrated graphically by four somewhat irregular curves.

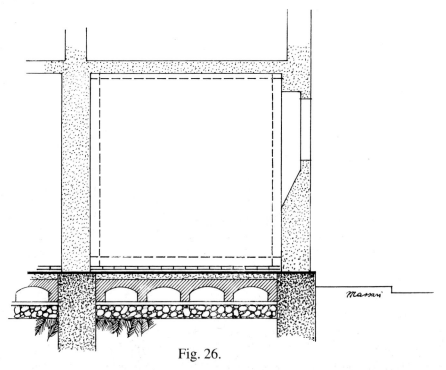

Fig. 26.

The humidity of a room in a newly constructed building is graphically illustrated by four lines which are regular and parallel to the walls, ceiling and floor.

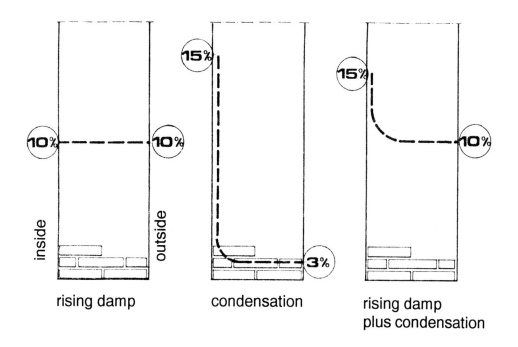

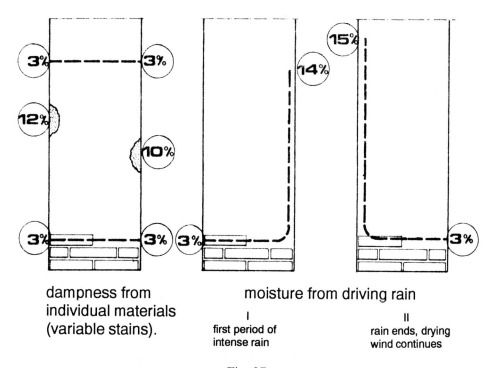

Fig. 27.

Graph of the transverse distribution of moisture from the inner to the outer wall face (in a horizontal section) of a wall with good capillarity, depending on the water source.

The graph can be broken and also irregular as in figure 24, which shows the humidity in the base wall of the portico in the Corsini garden in Rome. A photograph of the same wall is shown in figure 1.

Finally, one can summarize the humidity state of an entire room by using a typical section, which generally includes the interior bearing wall and the exterior wall (fig. 25). The three graphs of the walls and floor are usually sufficient to represent the humidity of a typical section. The ceiling graph has been added to the figure for demonstration purposes, but it is seldom plotted. In some cases, the two wall graphs will suffice.

All the examples provided so far deal with dampness in old constructions, where the moisture content percentage of one wall jumps from maximum to minimum values at some distance apart. Thus, the graphs are composed of strongly curved lines.

If, instead, we look at the section of a newly built room (fig. 26), the graph lines are almost straight, parallel to the walls, because the moisture content percentage is virtually constant in every point examined.

While a representation of wall humidity by means of a graph of the damp section is not very illuminating if the moisture content percentage is virtually constant in all parts of a wall (as in newly constructed buildings), a graph is extremely useful to show the irregular and capricious distribution of humidity in older buildings.

How can the severity of a humidity problem be evaluated by examining the graph of a humidity section? How can graphs of different walls be compared? Which is more dangerous: barely 5% humidity diffused over a vast wall surface, or a high percentage (18%) affecting only the wall base? How can the same yardstick be applied to both cases?

From a technical viewpoint, one can certainly not claim that the 18% moisture content is more serious than the 5%. Indeed, humidity invasion is not so much characterized by the maximum percentage as by the extent of territory conquered and by the average percentage content; the limit of the advance is marked on a wall by the height it has reached. From the point of view of health and according to the criteria given on evaporation, *the extent of evaporating surface has a greater damaging effect than a high moisture content.*

When the wall's internal moisture content is plotted on the basis of samples taken in depth throughout the wall, a diagnostic diagram of the humidity source is obtained. The principal cases are shown in figure 27.

Chapter Five

WHEN TOO MUCH HUMIDITY
MAKES A HOUSE UNHEALTHY

¶18.   Drying of newly built houses.

— Traditional masonry construction, without a reinforced concrete frame, has a moisture content of 20-25% by volume before drying begins. This water was artificially introduced in the materials while the wall was being built; it is gravitational, i.e., it tends to sink downwards inside the walls, leaving an ever more slender rear guard of capillary water behind. Later, there is a small amount of water produced gradually as calcium hydroxide $Ca(OH)_2$ sets under the action of carbon dioxide in the air and turns into carbonate. This amount, which is overvalued by some scientists, represents only 1-2% of the total water and thus 0.5% of the wall volume at most.

$$Ca\,(OH)_2 + CO_2 = CaCO_3 + H_2O$$

This water, which is forming continuously, is the last to leave; it serves to dissolve more lime and so on until the entire mass has set. The process is rather slow, but the quantity involved is, as we have seen, below a fiftieth part of the total construction water. The latter is what is truly worrisome. Cadiergues provides the following proportional drying time coefficients for various types of walls, all equally thick, in still air and at 70% RH (the coefficients for brick and lime mortar are optimum):

Brick	0.28
Calcareous stone	1.20
Cement concrete (250 kg)	1.60
Cement and pumice concrete	1.40
Cellular cement	1.20
Cement mortar	2.50
Lime mortar	0.25
Cork	0.14

All building materials can be divided into two categories: those with *good capillarity*, which dry quickly and well throughout (brick, tile, lime mortar, wood fiber or cork board) and those with *bad capillarity,* which dry well only on the outside while remaining impregnated inside for an incredibly long time (cement concrete, calcareous stone, pumice, tuff, rock wool). Ideally, materials with bad capillarity (among which are some of the best thermal insulators, such as pumice) ought to be worked only when they are *dry*, and with a mortar of minimal fluidity. Naturally, this is not possible; yet, whenever these materials are used, it should be borne in mind that if water reaches the material's inner core it will remain imprisoned in a labyrinthine structure, unable to return to the surface and evaporate – or it will do so extremely slowly.

The opposite occurs with brick, where the strong capillarity promptly redistributes the slightest amount of water, no matter where it enters, throughout the entire mass. Drying is rapid because water is continuously brought to the surface and, as it evaporates, is quickly replaced by more arriving from within.

The different drying patterns of two new walls, one with good capillarity and the other with bad, are schematized in figure 28. Four successive stages are shown. In stage four, moisture is evenly distributed horizontally in the first wall, which is completely dry, whereas only the sides of the second wall are dry. The second house may seem dry, but if it is occupied too early, condensation will quickly appear on the inner wall (along with stains and plenty of mold) and further delay the drying process..

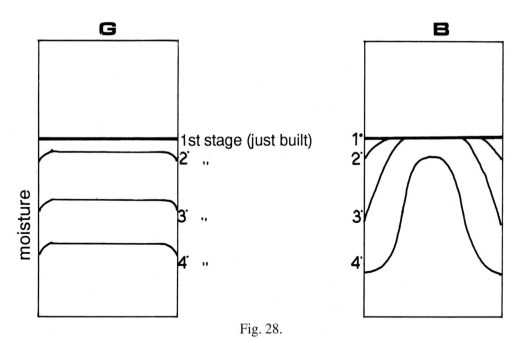

Fig. 28.

New walls dry differently depending on whether the material has good (G) or bad (B) capillary conductivity. Wall G may be of solid brick; wall B of tuff, concrete or pumice.

As the interior walls of a building dry much more slowly than the exterior walls, the health inspector of new construction must primarily consider the interior walls, although winter condensation is found mainly on the exterior walls.

Walls built of pumice blocks require particular attention. After being cut, pumice blocks require long seasoning to rid them of water. Unfortunately, technical handbooks do not have standards, based on seasoning control, for testing and evaluating these blocks.

Expanded clay granule blocks, being porous and having better capillarity, do not require as much seasoning as pumice. Whatever size granules are used, cement blocks must contain *at least three internal air cells,* running the same direction as the wall, if one wishes to avoid winter condensation (especially in bedrooms and in cold climates).

In practice, from the viewpoint of drying speed, it is desirable for the wall to be left unplastered for several months: *ventilation, more than hot, still air, favors drying.* Finally, new, reinforced concrete framed buildings dry in about half the time required for traditional masonry with solid bearing walls.

Attempts to accelerate the setting of mortar by deliberately introducing carbon dioxide are not worth bothering with. Ventilation, however, should never be omitted.

During rainy seasons, to avoid retarding the drying process or, worse, having more condensation deposited on walls and cold floors, the only effective measure (if few rooms are involved) is to keep some kind of dry heat source going in the center of each room – charcoal braziers. or more costly electric heaters. To activate air exchange, it is important to keep the windows partly open at all times.

¶19. Damage caused by damp walls to people and furniture.

— Damage to occupants' health results from three separate physical phenomena:

- The evaporating water passes from the damp wall to the air in the room.
- The wall cools when subjected to this continuous surface evaporation – sometimes by several degrees.
- The exterior wall, soaked with water, loses its nonconductivity with respect to heat, as if its thickness were reduced to two thirds or even half.

The three phenomena coexist to a maximum degree in walls of brick and sand mortar, which, the water content being equal, *are the most damaging* until they dry out.

The first phenomenon of surface evaporation is immediately felt by anyone staying in an unhealthy room. The addition of cold provokes the well-known series of bronchial complaints and also rheumatic afflictions that involve more or less all the body organs.

Kettenacker experimented with the passage of humidity from a wall to still air, in order to measure the distance at which the evaporation effect of a wall surface is felt. The results are given in figures 29-30 and refer to walls that contain 27% and 4.5% water by weight, respectively. The horizontal scale gives distances in cm from the wall, and the vertical scale gives the water vapor content x in g/m^3 contained in the air affected by evaporation from the wall; the x_0 water vapor value is the normal ambient value at such a distance as to be no longer affected by the wall.

Two facts of great interest can be pointed out from Kettenacker's graphs:

- Still air reaches saturation in the layer directly in contact with the wall, whatever the wall's moisture content.
- The direct damaging effect of the wall on the air ceases at a distance of 6-8 cm.

Fig. 29.

*A very damp wall (17%
water by weight)
increases the amount of
water vapor in the air up
to about 6 cm away. The
wall's influence ends at
8 cm, where a water
vapor weight x_0 identical
to that in the middle of the
room is found.*

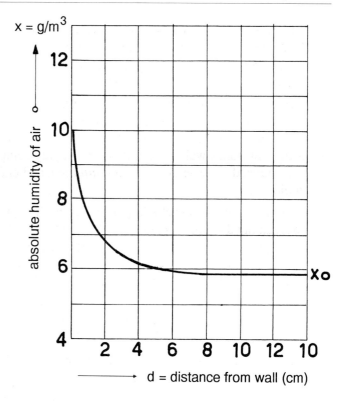

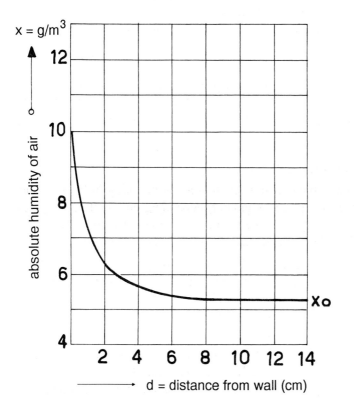

Fig. 30.

*The influence on the air is
the same even when the
wall is not very damp
(4.5% water).*

From this one draws the conclusion, surprising at first, that all damp walls are equally damaging, no matter what material they are made of or what their water content percentage may be, because the wall's evaporation always produces saturation of the contact air layer. Of course, the air must be still.

This explains why certain molds flourish behind a picture or on the back of furniture against the wall or inside a closed cupboard even when the air in the rest of the room can be considered dry, having low humidity overall. When books or a pair of boots are placed less than 8 cm from a wall (even if it is only slightly damp), they will be immersed in a layer of saturated air *when there is no ventilation*, and understandably become covered with mold.

In our view, Kettenacker's graphs can be interpreted in the sense that the air becomes saturated within 8 cm of the wall regardless of the wall's water content, but the time involved can be long or short depending on the evaporation rate. That is, depending on whether the wall's construction material is in the first or second evaporation phase according to Krischer and Görling's criteria (see ¶13).

To put it another way, when a tap is turned on, the container beneath it always fills up regardless of how much water comes out, but the time it takes to fill the container will vary greatly, depending on the tap's rate of flow.

From Kettenacker's experiments we can deduce the following practical conclusions on the passage of humidity from a wall to the air:

- *There is an immediate and serious effect at a distance of 6-8 cm from the wall*, even when the wall's humidity percentage is relatively low.

- *After a certain time, if the space has no air exchange with the outside, a minimum amount of wall humidity will suffice to produce spectacular effects*, as if an extremely damp wall were involved.

The observation on the saturation of air up to 8 cm from the damp wall should be kept in mind when rehabilitation by ventilation is planned; a radiating ventilation action on the evaporating surface and avoiding stagnation in corners is preferable to activating a violent but restricted air flow.

¶20. Building and health regulations.

— Most major cities nowadays have health regulations on humidity in houses. Such regulations vary greatly from one place to another, depending on the climate, typical construction materials and living habits of the community. Often they are confused and incomplete, but Article 236 of the Turin Health Regulations is quite specific:

"A building is considered habitable if its mortar, taken from within the internal walls, does not contain more than 3% water in the months from June to September, and more than 2% in the other months of the year; when premises are to be occupied only by day (shops, laboratories, workshops, etc.), the mortar should not contain more than 4% water in any month of the year."

This courageous and precise standard should serve as an example. Not surprisingly, it was first introduced in Turin because, about half a century ago, Turin and Naples were the two major Italian centers for study of the health problem of dampness in homes.

Regulations have not been updated since that time in relation to condensation – a problem posed by new construction techniques using reinforced concrete frames with infilling and roofing; builders keep on reducing the weight of materials in order to economize. Excessive reductions in thickness are detrimental to thermal insulation and cause condensation, which, contrary to what is believed, cannot always be eliminated by forced heating. Rather, good thermal protection should be obtained through the use of light insulating layers and panels – all somewhat costly and delicate materials. In Italy, the few building regulations to have tackled this problem contain prescriptions that are either ambiguous or counter-operative. Take article 44 of the Rome Building Regulations, which permits a thickness of "three layers of insulating material" instead of an air chamber (under flat roof coverings): someone with few scruples could slap in three superimposed tarred cardboard sheets and be completely within the law.

Just as for stability we must respect *numerical* limits on the stresses in concrete and steel, so in the health sector we must learn to respect *numerical* limits on the thermal resistance of the walls enclosing our dwellings. One must be responsible in matters of health.

To summarize, two contemporaneous limits must be set for health protection:

- maximum acceptable water content in the walls
- minimum guaranteed thermal protection of the exterior walls and roof systems.

With regard to the first criterion, the following maximum water percentage by weight that walls may safely contain from a health viewpoint is:

- no more than 3% for common brick walls
- no more than 6% for walls of tuff, sandstone or other, very absorbent light stone with specific gravity below 1.9

It should be remembered that each different material in a damp wall has imbibed moisture in its own way, and that the components of a wall are not all alike in absorption behavior (fig. 31). An average between brick and mortar is often used.

As to the second criterion, it is clearly not possible to fix a single, legal minimum thermal protection figure for exterior walls everywhere in the world; even if we limited ourselves to temperate zones, there is too great a difference between the rigors of the climate in Frankfurt, for instance, and Naples.

A SHORT DISCOURSE ON HOW COLD IN BUILDINGS IS MEASURED

Some formulae are unavoidable when dealing with humidity from cold and the thermal protection of buildings. The European decimal metric system has been generally adopted in recent years and the old English B.T.U. has lost ground as a measuring unit for heat transfer. The basic formula for measuring the amount of heat that passes through a wall is commonly based on the kilo calorie – known as kcal:

$$K = \frac{kcal}{m^2 h \, ^{\circ}C}$$

IN VERY DAMP MASONRY
THE COMPONENTS AGREE

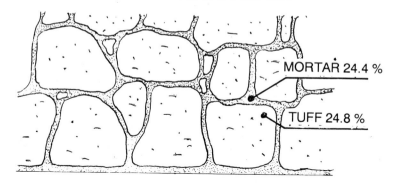

MORTAR 24.4 %

TUFF 24.8 %

IN MEDIUM DAMP MASONRY
THE COMPONENTS DIFFER

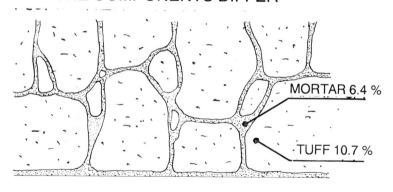

MORTAR 6.4 %

TUFF 10.7 %

IN NEARLY DRY OR WELL-VENTILATED
MASONRY THE DISPARITY INCREASES

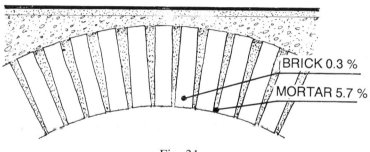

BRICK 0.3 %

MORTAR 5.7 %

Fig. 31.

Differences in moisture content between mortar and adjacent material in damp masonry.

In this formula, K represents the number of kilo calories (heat flow) that pass through 1 m of wall in an hour due to a 1°C difference in temperature between the two faces of the wall.

Even more recently, a new measuring system has been adopted.

This is known by the abbreviation SI, i.e., International System of Units. Here the watt (W) replaces the calorie, and the preceding formula becomes:

$$K = \frac{W}{m^2 \, °C}$$

with 1/kcal/h = 1.160 watts.

In revising this book, especially the tables, watt values have been added next to the old calorie values, in conformity with the International System. *These new watt values are always given in brackets.*

¶21.   Massari and Talenti's practical assessment of habitability from a health standpoint.

— After carefully studying the European climate tables, we feel that Italy can be considered as an excellent model, for every type of European climate is found between the Alps and Sicily. For simplicity in this study of health conditions, we reduce the Italian climate (and, analogously, that of any other nation in the temperate zone) to just two typical zones. In what will be called climate zone 'A,' the average temperature of the *coldest month* (January in the northern hemisphere) is below or equal to 6°C; in the other, which will be called climate zone 'B,' the January isotherm is above 6°C. Naturally, in zone A, the outer walls and roofs of houses must have much more protection against cold than in zone B. As a result of numerous experiments carried out with Professor Talenti in the Institute of Health at Rome University, we have established that, to avoid condensation, the protection or thermal resistance of outer walls must not be less than:

$$1 \, \frac{m^2 h \, °C}{kcal} \text{ or } [0.9] \, \frac{m^2 \, °C}{W}$$

in climate zone A; and not less than:

$$0.8 \, \frac{m^2 h \, °C}{kcal} \text{ or } [0.7] \, \frac{m^2 \, °C}{W} \text{ in climate zone B.}$$

On the basis of the preceding observations, we have formulated the following practical rules, which are valid both technically and legally.

Living quarters should be declared unhealthful due to humidity in either of the two following cases:

1) when wall analysis confirms that the moisture content exceeds 3% by weight in brick walls, or exceeds 6% in walls of light, absorbent stone, such as tuff. Maximums of 4% for brick and 7% for light stone are still tolerable in two cases: ground-floor premises open to the street (where the occupants do not stay overnight)

or premises that enjoy full sun in southern and southwestern exposures (even when occupied at night);

2) when, due to proven construction defects, the premises are found to be inadequately protected against heat losses and subject to condensation. To claim insufficient protection, the calculation for total thermal resistance,

$R = \dfrac{1}{K} = \dfrac{m^2 h\,°C}{kcal}$ per square meter of at least one of the masonry surfaces enclosing

the premises should give the following values: below 1 [0.9] in climate zones where the average temperature of the coldest month is below or equal to 6°C; or below 0.8 [0.7] in zones where the average temperature of the coldest month is above 6°C.

In summary, three possibilities can be encountered:

- The masonry contains more than the admissible moisture content: the premises are *unfit for habitation*.

- The masonry is dry but the usual symptoms of dampness appear and, due to a construction defect, the thermal protection is inadequate for the local climate: the premises are *unfit for habitation*.

- The masonry is dry but slightly scarred by signs of moisture (discolorations, stains, mold, varied flaws), perhaps from the past: the premises are *habitable* if there are no construction defects that reduce their thermal protection.

¶22. Cold walls and the body's temperature sense.

— Sometimes a mysterious thing happens: upon entering a storeroom, a church, or a museum with a temperature of 17.5°C, or any empty space, or an uninhabited but still heated house, one has a strong sense of discomfort, of damp chilliness, even if all the masonry seems intact and there is no trace of mold, spots, or damp. The atmospheric humidity is high, while measurement of the wall's moisture content shows it to be within the limits of tolerance given above. Why, then, this sense of discomfort?

It is known that our subjective sensations of hot and cold, well-being or malaise, depend *not only* on temperature, as registered by a traditional mercury thermometer, but also on the RH and the stillness or motion of the air, and finally on the temperature of the surfaces surrounding us, if it differs from the air temperature. Thus the common thermometer registers only one of the factors of the temperature we feel – or the true temperature for us, which Missenard and the French school have called *resultant temperature*. In summer, the floor and walls of a half-basement may be much colder than the air, due to excessive heat dispersion through the ground; this is just the opposite of winter radiant heating from the floor. It could be called 'radiant cold' (paradoxically and with scant technical accuracy), in that a person's skin *feels* the cold of the walls and floor even though the air is at sufficient temperature. The importance of this cold component in determining the *resultant temperature* one feels seems evident if we consider a breakdown of how a person gives off heat. Take the case of a lightly clothed adult who spends some time in the above-mentioned basement, immersed in air of average humidity at a temperature of 17.5°C on the mercury thermometer. Of the 2,700 calories per day that an adult emits under such circumstances (plus a bit for various other small losses):

- *About 30% is lost through conduction* (which depends on the temperature and RH of the air).
- *About 20% is lost through evaporation* (which depends on RH and air speed).
- *About 43% is lost through radiation* (and this is due exclusively to the temperature gap between the skin and surrounding surfaces – floor, walls and ceiling).

Thus, it is possible to understand the enormous influence the temperature of surrounding walls exerts on an individual's sensation of well-being or discomfort. In these cases, one has to identify the 'cold surface,' which may be the floor, ceiling or wall.

A new diagnostic procedure was proposed by the author for quickly finding the 'cold wall' of premises where condensation caused by inadequate thermal protection was suspected. Before this, the thermal imbalance between wall surfaces and the air was completely ignored in hygienic testing in cases of supposed condensation – either because it was not considered important (compared to the ease of measuring RH) or because it was difficult to measure the surface temperature of walls with ordinary thermometers. Not only was a certain ingenuity needed to hold the bulb or thermoelectric pair to the wall surface, but above all, a lot of time was lost due to the inertia of the thermometers and having to take the large number of readings required.

The use of wide-range optical scanning, using new infrared thermometers that have no inertia allows surface temperatures to be measured at a distance. There are good grounds to believe that the instantaneous measurement of thermal imbalance – applied to floors, walls, ceilings, facades and the ground surrounding the building – is the key that was lacking until recently in borderline cases of habitability. This measurement permits identification of structural conditions that are liable to produce irregular occurrences of condensation. In this way it is possible to predict condensation based on environmental conditions, without waiting for it to occur.

With this equipment it is possible to make a safe judgment in many cases, not only regarding habitability, but also in the difficult sector of conservation of art works, frescos in particular.

Apropos the tendency of condensation to be deposited on the 'cold wall,' we have noted a curious similarity between economic and physical phenomena. For instance, on the hectic floor of a stock exchange, all the capital at stake runs upwards to garner the highest interest rates, whereas in the courtyard of a building, all the rainwater runs toward the lower center by force of gravity. In the nocturnal silence of an empty church, with still air and high RH (say 85%), all the condensation is exclusively deposited on one cold surface – the dome, perhaps, or the apse or the marble floor. Not a drop appears on any of the other walls, even if the surface temperature is only one or two tenths of a degree higher than that of the cold wall. Yet, in a courtyard with exact gradients, the rainwater cannot even climb a centimeter or two from the low center toward the base of the building.

¶23. Summary hygienic classification of various types of walls.

— To judge the maximum hygienically tolerable moisture content in new materials (natural or artificial) of unknown behavior, a relatively simple empirical test can provide accurate results. Brick-sized samples are taken, i.e., 15 x 30 x 5 cm (constant dimensions are important for time reference) of already *seasoned material (at least six months should have passed since the material was quarried, or cast*, if artificial).

After seasoning, the samples are left *outdoors for twenty more days* in summer sun or dry winter wind and kept sheltered from bad weather at all times. They should never be artificially dried in a laboratory oven.

After such treatment, materials can be considered 'naturally dry,' and it is possible to measure their residual moisture by weight, this time with the usual laboratory oven-drying method. This moisture is considered native to the material tested and is thus innocuous because it no longer can be mobilized at the ordinary temperatures and ventilation encountered when the material is used in the wall of a building.

As a guide, to calculate the hygienically tolerable moisture content of any building material in place, one *adds 2% to the material's own humidity after natural drying in the open air in whole samples the size of a common brick*.

Table I gives the normal moisture content limits for habitable and uninhabitable premises.

TABLE I . – HYGIENIC CLASSIFICATION OF WALLS ACCORDING TO MOISTURE CONTENT BY WEIGHT

Type of wall	Perfectly dry (native humidity)	Hygienically dry	Hygienically tolerable in some cases	Damp	Very damp
Common brick	1%	up to 3%	up to 4%	from 3% to 9%	above 9%
Light, absorbent stone (sp.gr. 1.9)	up to 4%	up to 6%	up to 7%	from 6% to 15%	above 15%
Other materials, natural or artificial	native humidity must be measured after drying in open air	up to 2% above native humidity	up to 3% above native humidity		

To facilitate checking in doubtful cases, the most common structures are classified in Table II on the basis of the thermal protection they assure in the two typical climates, A and B (average January temperature below 6°C or above 6°C) respectively.

An indication of 'sufficient' or 'insufficient' in the table should not automatically be taken to mean that premises are definitely habitable or uninhabitable, but as a double check in relation to the presence or absence of objective symptoms: odor or signs of mold, efflorescence, stains, erosion of walls or plaster, warping or loosening of furniture, etc. If there is no observable trace of humidity in any season of the year, the premises should be considered habitable, even though some individual element thereof might be classified as 'insufficient' according to the table.

Table II refers to the three surfaces through which loss of heat can occur: walls, floor and roof. The protection provided by each of these three surfaces depends on its total thermal resistance ($R = 1/K$), which includes, in addition to the specific resistance of the structure itself, the resistance inherent in its location; the latter involves resistances of induction and emission between the surface and the air. As explained in ¶21 on *Practical assessment of habitability,* the protection given by a structure in zone A is considered sufficient when its minimum resistance is $R = \dfrac{1}{K} = 1$ [0.9]. In other words, when it takes at least 1 hour to let a kilo calorie pass through each m^2 per °C of temperature difference between the inside and outside air. In zone B, the minimum resistance must be at least 0.8 [0.7], i.e., requiring 48 minutes for the same passage of heat.

[Note that the values indicated in Table II have been estimated in view of *health* requirements only. These figures may not coincide with the values required by local legislation with regard to energy savings.]

TABLE II. – HYGIENIC CLASSIFICATION OF MASONRY ACCORDING TO PROTECTION AGAINST HEAT LOSS

	TYPE OF MASONRY	Thickness m	Total thermal resistance $R = 1/K$		Protection coldest month	
			$\dfrac{m^2 h\,°C}{kcal}$	$\dfrac{m^2\,°C}{W}$	T < 6°C	T > 6°C
	Exterior walls:					
1.	Wall of solid, common brick ($\lambda = 0.67$ [0.78]	0.55	1.00	0.86	Sufficient	Excellent
		0.50	0.90	0.77	Tolerable in some	Excellent
		0.45	0.83	0.71	cases	Sufficient
		0.42	0.80	0.69	Insufficient Insufficient	Sufficient
2.	Wall of heavy stone (sp.gr. 2.5÷3) gneiss, basalt, marble, hard limestone	0.75	0.46	0.39	Very poor	Very poor
3.	Walls of sandstone, soft limestone (sp.gr. 1.8÷2.2)	0.75	0.82	0.71	Insufficient	Sufficient
		0.60	0.70	0.60	Insufficient	Insufficient
4.	Walls of light tuff (sp.gr. 1.4÷1.6)	0.65	1.28	1.10	Sufficient	Excellent
		0.60	1.18	1.00	Sufficient	Excellent
		0.50	1.00	0.86	Sufficient	Excellent
5.	Walls of common hollow brick (with cells running parallel to walls)	0.40	1.00	0.86	Sufficient	Excellent
		0.30	0.80	0.69	Insufficient	Sufficient
6.	Cavity walls: outer leaf of solid brick (15 cm), inner leaf of hollow brick (15 cm), cavity ca. 10 cm, airtight	0.40	1.00	0.86	Sufficient	Excellent

	TYPE OF MASONRY	Thickness m	Total thermal resistance $R = 1/K$		Protection coldest month	
			$\dfrac{m^2 h \,°C}{kcal}$	$\dfrac{m^2 \,°C}{W}$	$T < 6°C$	$T > 6°C$
7.	*Idem*: Outer leaf of hollow brick, inner leaf of thin hollow brick (8 cm) on edge; airtight cavity ca. 10 cm	0.30÷ 0.33	0.80	0.69	Insufficient	Sufficient *
8.	Beams or columns of reinforced concrete; common frame	0.40	0.50	0.43	Very poor	Very poor
9.	*Idem*: column 0.40 m lined with bricks on edge (8 cm), actually detached ca. 1 cm from the column	0.50	0.80	0.69	Insufficient	Sufficient
10.	*Idem*: columns 0.30 m thick of cement with counterwall of flat hollow brick and 5 cm air cavity, airtight	0.50	1.00	0.86	Sufficient	Excellent
11.	Walls of pumice or slag concrete (sp.gr. ≤ 1), 30 cm thick	0.30	1.00	0.86	Sufficient	Excellent
12.	*Idem*: of pumice or slag concrete 20 cm thick with counterwall of hollow brick on edge (10 cm), and airtight cavity 5÷6 cm thick	0.35	1.09	0.94	Sufficient	Excellent
Floors of premises overlying cold basements:						
13.	Floors of r.c. and brick. Bearing thickness 10-15-20 cm. Paving of terrazzo or terrazzo tiles, plaster. Total thickness: 10 + 7 cm 15 + 7 cm 20 + 7 cm	0.17 0.22 0.27	0.58 0.62 0.65	0.50 0.53 0.56	Very poor " "	Insufficient " "
14.	*Idem*: with linoleum flooring 3 mm thick instead of terrazzo tiles; same protection as preceding case	0.15 0.20 0.25	0.58 0.58 0.65	0.50 0.50 0.56	Very poor " "	Insufficient " "
15.	*Idem*: with parquet flooring on framework forming air chamber	0.17 0.22 0.27	1.08 1.12 1.15	0.93 0.96 0.99	Excellent " "	Excellent " "
16.	Brick vault (one-brick, 12 cm) with levelling filler and flooring of linoleum, terrazzo, or terrazzo tiles	0.19÷0.26	0.72	0.62	Insufficient	Tolerable in some cases

(*) Sufficient only in theory, because the cavity must be *completely* airtight.

TYPE OF MASONRY	Thickness m	Total thermal resistance $R = 1/K$		Protection coldest month	
		$\dfrac{m^2 h \,^\circ C}{kcal}$	$\dfrac{m^2 \,^\circ C}{W}$	$T < 6^\circ C$	$T > 6^\circ C$
Floors on ground and walls against banked earth:					
17. Asphalt on concrete of lean cement which combines with earth to form solid mass	0.10	0.50	0.43	Very poor	Very poor
18. Fired tiles laid over asphalt overlying a bed of lean cement forming solid mass with ground	0.15	0.60	0.52	Very poor	Insufficient
19. *Idem*: with bricks laid on edge	0.22	0.70	0.60	Insufficient	Doubtful against summer condensation
20. Planking or parquet on timber joists which form air chamber over structure in N° 17	0.15	1.10	0.95	Excellent	Excellent
21. Paving of cement or terrazzo tiles or terrazzo or linoleum on bearing structure of small vaults or large hollow tiles (1.5 m) with underlying air space		0.83	0.71	Insufficient	Doubtful against summer condensation
22. *Idem*: on common, light bed superimposed on subfloor of gravel, stone or tuff	0.40	0.72	0.62	Insufficient	Doubtful against summer condensation
Roofing:					
23. Flat roof of r.c. and brick, bearing thickness 10, 15, 20 cm; overlying common light bed (of pozzolana pebbles or crushed brick) *average* thickness 8 cm for formation of falls; asphalt and paving of baked tile or cement paving tile, average total thickness	0.27 0.32 0.37	0.60 0.66 0.70	0.52 0.56 0.60	Very poor " Insufficient	Very poor Insufficient Tolerable in some cases
24. *Idem*: and false ceiling of metal lath and plaster on framework of timber joists that forms air space beneath roof. Average overall thickness (apart from air space)	0.27 0.32 0.37	0.82 0.88 0.92	0.70 0.76 0.79	Insufficient Tolerable in some cases "	Sufficient Excellent "
25. Flat roof of r.c. and brick, thickness as in N° 23, but with bed of pumice or slag , 8 cm average thickness	0.27 0.32 0.37	0.74 0.80 0.84	0.64 0.69 0.72	Insufficient " "	Tolerable in some cases "

	TYPE OF MASONRY	Thickness m	Total thermal resistance $R = 1/K$		Protection coldest month	
			$\dfrac{m^2 h\ ^\circ C}{kcal}$	$\dfrac{m^2\ ^\circ C}{W}$	$T < 6^\circ C$	$T > 6^\circ C$
26.	*Idem*: but with false ceiling of metal lath and plaster: avg. thickness (apart from air space)	0.27 0.32 0.37	0.94 1.00 1.06	0.80 0.86 0.91	Tolerable in some cases Sufficient "	Excellent " "
27.	Flat roof in r.c. and brick; 5 cm thick layer of tarred cork interposed between roof and usual bed	0.25÷0.35	1.20÷1.30	1.03÷1.11	Excellent	Excellent
28.	*Idem*: with cork 3 cm thick	0.25÷0.35	1.00	0.86	Sufficient	Excellent
29.	Flat roof of iron beams (poutrelles), with usual bed for falls, asphalt, paving; underlying air space with false ceiling of plaster /metal lath	—	0.90	0.77	Tolerable in some cases	Sufficient
30.	Simple pitch roof with timber joists and rafters, cladded with roof tiles, or slate, or 'Eternit' or corrugated sheet iron, with sealed or soldered joints – airtight but without ceiling	—	0.20	0.17	Very poor	Very poor
31.	*Idem*: with ceiling of boards attached below the joists	—	0.58	0.50	Insufficient	Insufficient
32.	*Idem*: as N°30, with flat under-roof of boards linked to light attic floor	—	1.10	0.95	Excellent	Excellent

It is important to avoid making snap judgments or going by tactile impressions of the thermal resistance of a surface; confirmatory calculations must never be omitted.

Thermal resistance $\dfrac{d}{\lambda}$, and thus the protection of the environment, depends on thickness (d) and increases linearly in relation to it. Although one can 'feel' conductivity, one must 'measure' thermal resistance. For all practical purposes, a 3 mm thick linoleum flooring, although pleasant to the touch, gives the room the same thermal protection as a flooring of common terrazzo tiles, 20 mm thick.

In pathological cases of stains or mold on walls and ceilings, or intermittent dew on floors, it is necessary to discover how much thermal resistance is lacking (the deficit) in relation to the local climate. The deficit is made up by adding structures such as those given in Table III below.

TABLE III. – THERMAL RESISTANCE OF THE MOST COMMON STRUCTURES ADDED AS PROTECTION AGAINST HUMIDITY DUE TO COLD

Type of additional structure	Thickness (including air layer, if any) cm	Thermal resistance	
		$M^2h°C/kcal$	$M^2 °C/W$
I. – For interior walls			
Adherent lining of any kind of dry wood boards, net thickness 2 cm, without formation of cavity	2	0.10÷0.15	0.09÷0.13
Idem: wood panelling with cavity behind less than 1 cm thick (airtight)	3	0.22÷0.25	0.19÷0.21
Idem: airtight, with cavity 2÷5 cm thick	4÷7	0.30	0.26
Lining of fiber insulating board 5 mm thick, airtight cavity behind, 2÷5 cm thick	3÷5	0.27	0.23
Adherent lining of tarred cork panels 5 cm thick, lined, smoothed or plastered on front face	6	0.80	0.69
Idem: of wood – cement particle board ('Heraclit' type), 3 cm thick, plastered	4	0.44	0.38
Idem: with cavity behind, airtight, 2÷5 cm thick	5÷8	0.60	0.52
Common counterwall of hollow brick on edge, plastered only on front face, with 3÷5 cm cavity behind, free of rubble or fill	≈ 13	0.35÷0.38	0.30÷0.33
Idem: replacing cavity with semi-rigid panels of mineral wool or polystyrene, 3 cm thick, applied with mastic	≈ 12	0.70	0.60
Idem: advisable to use 'heavy' type, long lasting polystyrene or other expanded resin - sp.gr. between 20 and 35 kg/m^3. Brick counterwalls can be replaced by **ribbed p.v.c. sheeting or other rigid sheet** that can be applied dry to reduce encumbrance to less than 4 cm	3.5÷4	0.70	0.60
Idem: of very light, small blocks, sp.gr. no greater than 0.6, and 10 cm thick (cellular cement, pumice, slag, expanded clay granules), with 3÷5 cm thick cavity behind	≈15	0.80	0.69
N.B.: to be effective, the cavities must not be filled with debris or traversed by bonders.			
II. – For floors			
Planking of any rough kind, 2.5 cm thick, juxtaposed without cracks or tongue-and-grooved and nailed to tarred stringers which leave air pockets 2÷5 cm deep, free of debris	5÷7	0.35	0.30
Idem: superimposed over a filler of 20 cm loose dry pumice, without debris or lumps (fig. 79)	23÷25	1.35	1.16

Type of additional structure	Thickness (including air layer, if any) cm	Thermal resistance	
		$M^2h°C/kcal$	$M^2 °C/W$
Light bed, 10 cm thick, of lean mortar mix of lime and pumice or slag, over layer of asphalt 16 mm; flooring of linoleum or terrazzo tiles or terrazzo	≈ 12	0.25	0.21
III. – For roof coverings			
Usual false ceiling of plaster and metal lath on joists. Air space 10 cm thick or more	≈ 12 or more	0.22	0.19
Idem: of light fiber building board, for ex. 8 mm thick and weighing 3 kg/m^2 with cavity 10 cm or more	11 or more	0.32	0.28
Idem: of expanded cork panels 2 cm thick with cavity above, 10 cm or more	12 or more	0.60	0.52
Lining of ceiling (from below) with 3 cm thick panels of very light expanded resin applied with mastic to ceiling without leaving air space	≈ 4	0.65	0.56
Quick lining of top floor from below with tarred cardboard, or softwood plywood 3 mm thick that forms a closed air space 4÷8 cm thick	≈ 5÷9	0.18	0.15
IV. – Air layers (see fig. 104)			
Net thickness from 4 to 20 cm		0.18	0.15
" " about 2 cm		0.17	0.15
" " at least 1 cm		0.15	0.13
" " less than 1 cm		0.10	0.08

N.B.: A series of thin air layers is more effective than one alone, doubly thick. The maximum value R = 0.18 can be obtained with a 4÷8 cm cavity so long as the air is still. Increasing the thickness may be disadvantageous in vertical cavities because currents may form. Ventilation is only useful for summer protection against heat in horizontal cavities (under flat roofs), because the thermal resistance of the air diminishes with each degree of temperature increase. For the possible advantage of filling the cavity with light, loose material, see chart in ¶ 47.

V. – Preferred expanded resins

There are two expanded resins widely employed today against cooling in buildings. One is polystyrol or polystyrene (which has closed cells and therefore blocks the dangerous passage of water vapor by diffusion). However, the heavy variety must be used (at least between 20 and 35 kg/m^3) and preferably the boards formed directly by extrusion rather than the ones sawed out of blocks.
The other widely used expanded resin is polyurethane, which has the defect of open cells. For this reason it must only be used in sheets having both sides protected by impermeable bitumenized paper, glued on.

¶24. Drawbacks of reinforced concrete.

— Table II holds some surprises because it illustrates the unexpected thermal insufficiency of some structures that are normally considered optimum. For instance, the traditional flat roof covering of iron beams and small arches or large hollow tiles, even if perfectly executed and completed with a false ceiling beneath (N° 29 of table), offers barely $0.9 \frac{m^2 h \,°C}{kcal}$ [0.77] $\frac{m^2 \,°C}{W}$ thermal resistance, which is only just tolerable in certain cases for climate zone A; it promptly becomes insufficient as soon as dispersion increases due to adverse conditions of frequent fog or wind. This is a borderline structure, in health terms. When rolled steel I-beams were first used in construction, they represented technical progress in terms of both statics and fire protection, compared to the classic pitched roof of centuries past – a roof with a wooden attic floor beneath, the well-known attic 'catchall' of our grandparents. *Nevertheless, the older roofing system offered thermal protection of: 1.10* $\frac{m^2 h \,°C}{kcal}$ *[0.95]* $\frac{m^2 \,°C}{W}$.

The result: progress in construction and regression in health. Nowadays, when insulating materials are better known and more widely used, the protection given by steel girders need only be improved with a small mass of expanded granulate or vermiculite or cellular concrete or cork or any other over or underlying stratification, as long as it is calculated to bring the total thermal resistance R up to at least 1 [0.9].

Speaking of the thermal resistance of roofs (although the observation holds true for all air chambers), it should be stressed that the values given in the table for structures having false ceilings (N°s 24, 26, 29) presuppose that the chambers are airtight. If they are ventilated *in winter*, the values should be reduced by at least half. The old builder's habit of ventilating air spaces in the false ceiling without providing enough insulation is erroneous in terms of both winter heating expense and the efficiency of the heating plant.

The thermal insufficiency of some very modern structures is an even greater surprise, as can be seen from examination of the resistance of *infilling* for case structures, and *floors* and *roofs* of reinforced concrete (N°s 7, 13, 14, 24, 25 in the table).

With the advancement of building technique, the exterior walls, which as bearing walls had to be quite thick, have declined in function; every static requirement is brilliantly resolved with reinforced concrete. Among the masonry techniques that still exist, the two most delicate are the infilling and the roof protection, which today must satisfy requirements of a health nature almost single-handedly. Table II shows that *although reinforced concrete technique has made giant strides, health standards have been left far behind* because the masonry structure that fills in the frames does not ensure the minimum of thermal protection.

Yet even the planning of the reinforcing frame, although ably calculated, sometimes seems to be conducted with blinkers on: saving on iron seems the only goal in view. The edge beams become ever more slender and tall; the area to be occupied by infilling tends to be reduced; ever more frequently one finds parapets or the housings of rolling shutters incorporated in the bearing beams to simplify construction. Where space is at a premium, bedrooms are left with exterior walls of reinforced concrete only 10-12 cm thick. Out-thrust features, ever more popular in public housing architecture, are thermal sieves; heat escapes in winter and enters in summer through various thermal flaws, completely unbeknown to the naive designer.

Cost economy per room? From the viewpoint of social economy, what is saved in construction is lost three times over in health care and energy. On one account there is a saving, certainly, but those who build with public funds cannot ignore the health side of the balance.

To return to particulars, the points most exposed to condensation in reinforced frame constructions are as follows:

- rolling shutter housings
- windowsills
- columns, especially corner ones (fig. 91)
- tall thin beams
- floors over open spaces (porticos, jutties)
- stairwells cast in cement to comply with fire regulations
- thin walls (too thin) of small courtyards and projecting features
- embanked, reinforced concrete walls
- roofs

The traditional foundations of basement floors (subfloor of air spaces between parallel sleeper walls, or subfloor filled with gravel, stones or tuff – N°s 21 and 22 of table) are also antiquated structures that give very poor protection against spring and summer condensation. Just 10 cm of dry pumice or light cellular cement, and only 2 cm of rock wool, well applied, would suffice to reclaim entire basements that are damaged by summer humidity – even in brand-new buildings.

The northern and eastern exposures of reinforced concrete constructions are highly subject to winter condensation; any side exposed to driving rain is subject to condensation from cooling.

In the *planning phase* for reinforced frame constructions, condensation can be safely forestalled by allowing for lining the whole inner face of exterior walls with a 2 cm layer of insulation giving *high protection*, i.e., with an internal heat transmission coefficient (λ) between 0.04 and 0.06. Rock wool, cork, fiberglass, expanded resins, are all excellent and interchangeable in buildings so long as (to repeat) they are at least 2 cm thick and applied equally on the reinforced concrete and the infilling.

Unfortunately, it is difficult to line reinforced concrete columns and beams because the insulation protrudes into the rooms and is extremely unsightly. Moreover, the insulation itself must be protected against impact and needs to be covered, but not compressed, by metal lath and plaster or, preferably, by a thin wall of Perret tiles (only 3 cm thick), which are then plastered. This all adds up to an encumbrance of 5-6 cm, for which the prudent designer must allow in order to shield the frame from thermal excesses. Though modern structures may not collapse during earthquakes and explosions, they are still very sensitive to heat and cold.

The two basic rules of coordination between the thermal protection of reinforced concrete walls and their frames can be stated as follows:

- the thermal protection must be uniform on the reinforced concrete and on the infilling
- the reinforced concrete with its protective lining must not protrude from the infilling

As a result, it is advisable to design the columns as thin as possible, with their long sides parallel to the direction of the wall.

To summarize: humidity rising from the ground is never encountered in framed constructions (set on columns); on the other hand, there is abundant humidity from spring-summer condensation in semi-basement stories, and from winter condensation in the northern and eastern exposures, even though the in-fill wall is dry – being made usually of hollow bricks in a 'cavity' structure. Condensation from cooling on sides beaten by driving rain is also frequent.

When an expert is asked to pronounce on mold and humidity stains in a reinforced concrete building, he or she can be 99% sure that condensation is at fault, caused by the building's inadequate protection against cold. Table III indicates the simplest additional structures that are useful in these cases.

Chapter Six

CHARACTERISTICS OF HUMIDITY RISING FROM THE SUBSOIL

¶25. Identification of water source.

— Figures 32-35 show examples of rising damp, some more serious than others. Moisture that rises from the ground can be distributed in two ways:

- by dispersed water
- by groundwater

The first type is accidental and often intermittent, but can at least be intercepted with suitable measures and cut off. The second is a subterranean tide that cannot be dried or contained. A completely different approach is needed to rectify in each case.

It is most difficult to ascertain the presence of *dispersed water* in contact with a foundation, because it comes from localized, restricted sources and not from a uniform, general situation. Localized causes are always more obscure.

A choice example of rising damp from dispersed water is that of San Bernardo (fig. 35), which was formerly one of the corner towers of the Baths of Diocletian in Rome.

Dispersed water is usually due to improperly drained rainwater, leaks from wells, water mains and sewers, or even condensation – all factors that produce localized soaking of the ground in contact with foundation walls. Sometimes the dispersion is superficial and the water penetration occurs at ground level, or slightly below; in fact, rainwater is often conveyed by downspouts from the roofs to the base of the building and collected in drains which, due to poor maintenance or faulty construction, assume the inauspicious function of distributing the water along the outer walls instead of carrying it away. When complete information on the water's provenance is lacking, it must be obtained from systematic inspection around the perimeter of the building. This includes the following activities:

- digging a series of holes next to the damp walls until dry zones are found
- checking whether wells, cisterns, internal or external drains are leaking
- meticulously inspecting whether rainwater drainage and street sewers are well connected
- exposing water pipes under pressure and verifying possible leaks with a manometer, closed gate valve or some other means; likewise verifying whether the pipes cause condensation

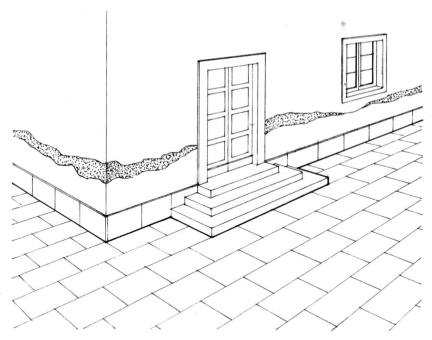

Fig. 32.

Sometimes a damp strip of plaster remains between two dry areas, even when rising damp has ceased; this is due to hygroscopic salts which draw moisture from the air.

Fig. 33.

A typical example of rising damp in the facade on the palazzo of the "Sapienza" in Rome. The absorption level surpassed the 3 m height of the leveling rod.

Fig. 34.

The same wall as shown in the preceding figure. When analyzed from the inside face, it shows that the moisture content percentage decreases with height – behavior typical of rising damp.

Fig. 35.

Rising damp is also demonstrated in the church of San Bernardo in Rome (photo Alinari).

The two types of water source can be distinguished by the following characteristics:

Moisture drawn from dispersed water:

- has striking manifestations, but is often localized on one side or in one part of the building (fig. 36)
- is typical of only one building or a limited group of buildings close together
- often fluctuates annually in height

Moisture drawn from the water table:

- attacks the entire building with almost perfect uniformity, unless the carcass is constructed of different materials
- reaches maximum height in N and NE exposures, minimum in sunny exposures
- is common to all buildings in the same zone, built at the same time with similar materials
- does not fluctuate in height during the year

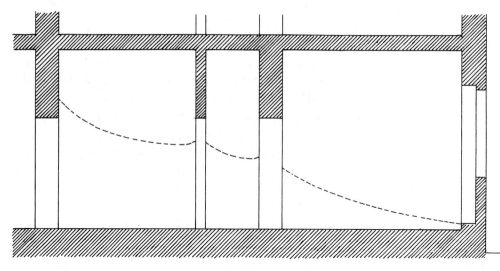

Fig. 36.

It is sometimes possible to deduce where dispersed subterranean water is infiltrating by analyzing graphs of the damp section of the walls in a series of rooms.

The contact between groundwater and a building's foundation may have occurred a considerable time after construction. In Rome, for instance, the construction of the Tiber embankments, which were built on continuous, very deep foundations, intercepted the flow of subterranean water descending from the Gianiculum hill to the river and induced rising damp in the basements of all the buildings in between. Previously, judging by their functions, these basements had been dry. The water table is also often raised by urban projects involving ground fill above the original level.

The opposite case happened in Milan, where the groundwater level was lowered over a number of years as water was continuously extracted by artesian wells.

The normal annual fluctuation of groundwater is usually not very great. In Italy, it ranges from 1 m in the Po Valley and Campania region to above 2 m in the Pontine plain and Palermo region. Such seasonal fluctuation, however, does not greatly affect walls already saturated with moisture drawn from the water table.

In free-draining, calcareous, karst terrain, wall moisture from groundwater can be ruled out, as the water table is extremely deep.

¶26. Walls that accept or reject invasion by damp.

— In laboratory tests, equal-sized samples of individual building materials attain different suction heights. Each material in place affects a wall with its behavior, although the surrounding mortar acts as a unifying agent in some masonry structures. *The overall absorption power of a structure tends to become like the specific power of the basic material*: the thinner the joints (and therefore the less mortar used), the more the wall's overall behavior will resemble that of its basic material; a brick wall with little mortar will behave much more like brick than an irregular wall of large sandstone blocks but a great deal of mortar will behave like sandstone.

Since common brick has a suction power three to five times greater than mortar, one arrives at a rather discouraging conclusion for builders: the higher the quality of the brick wall construction – with very little mortar spread in thin joints and well-made beds, using choice, homogeneous, properly baked bricks – the more the water will rise if the building should be attacked by humidity in later years.

The basic ingredient (brick or stone) can cooperate with the mortar actively or passively: actively when it carries humidity on its own account, at a rate equal to or greater than that of the mortar; passively when it retains humidity at the mortar's expense. *If a structure contains anti-capillary stone (flint, for example), the wall complex becomes slow to accept humidity invasion because the humidity's only route is through the mortar, which is quite sluggish in absorption.*

In a brick wall, on the other hand, the brick acts as a shortcut between one mortar layer and another; a true conveyor belt mechanism occurs because the brick, which absorbs faster than the mortar, preempts the mortar's function as a vertical connection. Brick takes the moisture directly from the horizontal mortar bed on which it rests and conveys it to the covering bed above; the invasion (fig. 37) thus follows the quickest routes – A or B – through the brick courses. In this way remarkable heights of humidity, characteristic of brick walls, are reached in a relatively short time.

Humidity's progress in stone walls is always much slower than in brick walls; moreover, the active cooperation of the material depends on the size of blocks used. If an individual stone block becomes soaked throughout when set with its lower side in water, then each block of that size in a wall will transmit water by itself as actively as brick, even though much more slowly. However, if the size of the piece exceeds its suction height by a considerable amount (H_s in fig. 38), the piece will not contribute to humidity's progress because it tends to hold the water subtracted from the nearby mortar, while keeping a dry or almost dry core; indeed, because of the excessive thickness of the piece with respect to its suction power, a long time is required for the mortar's humidity to permeate it after

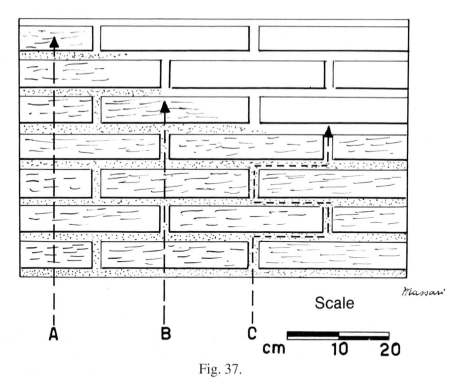

Fig. 37.

An invasion of damp follows the shortest route (A) or (B) when the material is more absorbent than the mortar; it follows the longest route (C) and makes little progress when the material is anti-capillary.

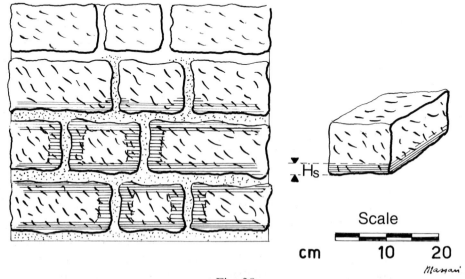

Fig. 38.

If the height of the block is much greater than the suction height H_s, the material does not contribute to humidity's progress and the core will remain dry or almost dry.

passing and surrounding it on all sides. In such cases the advance of the wall's moisture is extremely slow and the maximum height it can gain is rather low.

As a result, one often finds that two walls – equally situated with respect to the water source and constructed of the same material – will behave differently because in one the material was cut in large blocks (> H_s height) and in the other it was cut in small blocks (< H_s height). The former wall will reject humidity invasion and the latter accept it.

Going to extremes, one might ask whether, in the case of an absolutely anti-capillary building material, *rising* damp can occur on the strength of the mortar alone. The answer is no. As noted above, *rising* damp is always dependent on the coexistence of two factors:

- continuous water supply from ground to wall, and
- high suction power of the building material surrounded by mortar

Both conditions are necessary: if the material is hostile to absorption, the capillarity of the mortar alone is insufficient to produce a rising invasion, even with a constant water supply. If the water supply is intermittent, the humidity does not rise but spreads uniformly in all directions, prevailingly downwards, even if capillary material is used. In the case of the Pincio wall in Rome, near the Popolo gate (fig. 39), the humidity stain descends, instead of rising. One must diagnose whether an intermittent water source is involved (from rainwater dispersion, perhaps), or a continuous source in a wall hostile to absorption because it is constructed with hard, anti-capillary material.

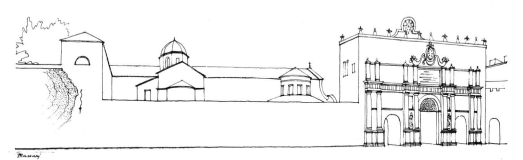

Fig. 39.

Humidity descends, rather than rises in the large wall of the Pincio in Rome, near Porta del Popolo.

Further evidence that a rising invasion depends on both conditions together was obtained by experimentally injecting several hectoliters of eosin-colored water into a large pillar built of yellow, high-suction bricks (this experiment was done in cooperation with Talenti). For 20 consecutive days, 17-18 liters were introduced daily through a 60 cm deep hole slanted down towards the inside of the pillar (fig. 40). After five days the first red eosin stains appeared in the outer rendering; these stains later expanded and flowed

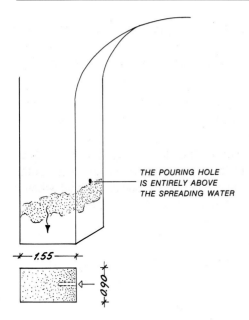

Fig. 40.

Experimental dampness in a dry pillar, obtained by injection of eosin-colored water (Talenti).

THE POURING HOLE
IS ENTIRELY ABOVE
THE SPREADING WATER

together until they formed a wide band all around the pillar. Although the humidity might have been expected to rise, the entire stain remained beneath the pouring hole, demonstrating that the water spread quite rapidly, due to the high absorption power of the structure, but spread only downwards.

From this rather elementary test, one can draw a conclusion that is helpful in diagnosing the origin of rising damp: that *humidity tends to rise, i.e., it assumes the characteristic pattern of rising damp only when it is sustained by a capillary column with its base in subterranean water.*

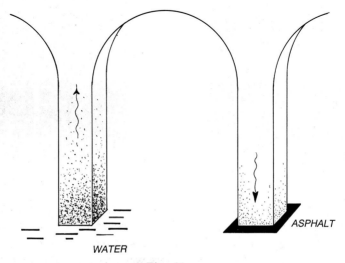

WATER

ASPHALT

Fig. 41.

Moisture rises (left) so long as it is sustained by a capillary column based in subterranean water; it reverts to gravitational behavior (right) as soon as the supply is cut off.

In every other case, the humidity invasion assumes a gravitational pattern and the result of the movement is definitely downwards; *only if a wall is already saturated, with continuity in the lower part, does humidity rise*, expanding in the only free direction, upwards (fig. 41).

Rising damp begins attacking a dry wall with a relatively fast advance in the first decimeters of the conquest, but then gradually becomes slower due to the counter effect of surface evaporation. The fact that maximum absorption heights are found in very old structures would lead one to think that beyond a certain limit the greatly retarded advance ceases to be continuous, but rather proceeds in leaps whenever, over the years, some combination of circumstances favors a resurgence – perhaps reduced sunlight when a new building is constructed or a grove of trees is planted nearby. Humidity conquests would then be occasional but, once made, they would not regress.

Concerning the average rate of rise, Salmoiraghi cites the case of the brick pylons in the large cistern in Leghorn. It was built in 1828, and by 1887 the humidity trace had reached 2-2.40 m above the water surface, thus rising about 4 cm a year.

¶27. Height of rise.

— In the Farnesina in Rome (a small sixteenth-century building of tuff construction), humidity reaches 1.50 m on the south side, which is well insolated; on the north side (fig. 42), the dampness reaches a height of 3.10 m. As there is no other reason for this difference, we can deduce that sun exposure reduces the absorption height by 1.60 m in this case.

Fig 42

On the south side of the Farnesina in Rome (left), the height of moisture is 1.50 m; on the north side of the same building (right), moisture reaches a height of 3.10 m. This suggests that sun exposure can reduce absorption height.

Fig. 43.

*The border line of moisture follows the line
of a stairway attached to the wall.*

Whatever height humidity gains, we can suppose that the water passes through the wall as if flowing in a true *capillary conduit.* The quantity of water absorbed in a given time unit through the horizontal section of the wall at ground level can be considered as the *rate of flow, or intake, through the absorbent section.* When the height reached by the

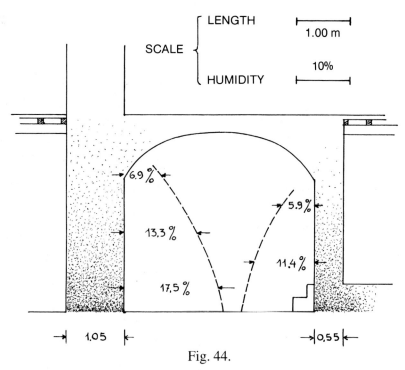

Fig. 44.

*The thicker of two parallel walls in an entryway is the damper one (hallway on the ground
floor of Palazzo Corsini, Rome).*

moisture is stabilized, every wall must have a hygric balance in which the intake of the lower absorbent section equals the total evaporation of the wall. In other words, *the same amount of water enters by absorption as exits by evaporation.*

As soon as the wall's evaporating surface is reduced for any reason, moisture will start to rise again. One sees, for instance, how the border line of humidity follows the outline of a stairway attached to the wall in the Buon Pastore convent in Rome (fig. 43).

If we consider walls that are of consistent construction and orientation, but of different thicknesses, the absorbent section, and therefore the rate of flow as well, will grow directly with the increase in thickness. Then, other conditions being equal, the thicker wall would need a greater extent of evaporating wall surface to balance the greater absorption. Therefore, *the thicker the wall, the higher the humidity will rise.* This fact has already been pointed out by several authors; further evidence can be found in the Palazzo Corsini, where two walls parallel to a damp entryway have moisture contents in proportion to thickness (fig. 44). Another example is the aforementioned church of San Bernardo, where the moisture reaches the exceptional height of 5.30 m; this is understandable when one learns that the wall is 4 m thick (fig. 45).

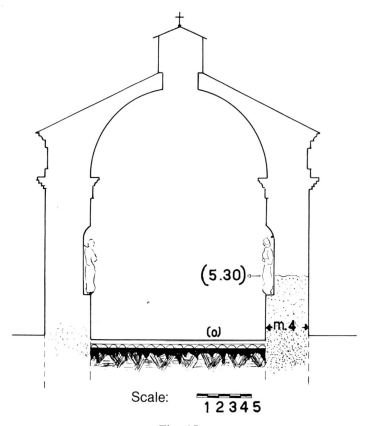

Scale: 1 2 3 4 5

Fig. 45.

In the church of San Bernardo in Rome, the exceptional suction height (5.30 m) relates to the equally exceptional thickness of the wall (4 m).

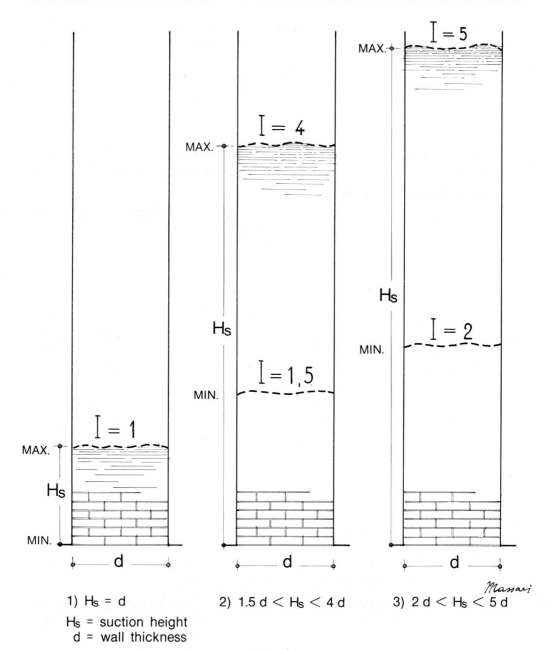

1) $H_s = d$

H_s = suction height
d = wall thickness

2) $1.5\,d < H_s < 4\,d$

3) $2\,d < H_s < 5\,d$

Fig. 46.

The climb index ($I = H_s/d$) depends on the thickness of the masonry and the ventilation to which the structure is exposed: 1) freestanding pillars; 2) walls with an exterior face; 3) interior walls.

The relationship between the evaporating surface and the absorbing surface, derived from various observations on damp walls in Rome, is the following, on average:

- in freestanding pillars $\dfrac{evap.surface}{absorb.surface}$ = from 2 to 3
- in walls with an exterior face   "   = from 3 to 8
- in interior load-bearing walls   "   = from 4 to 10

Perhaps it is more convenient to relate the maximum suction height (H_S) to the wall thickness (d); we can call this ratio of two linear measurements the 'climb index' = H_S/d.

Figure 46 demonstrates that:

- In *freestanding pillars*, which are exposed to ventilation on all sides, the suction height is equal to the pillar's thickness, and therefore the climb index is 1.
- In *walls with an exterior face*, the suction height goes from 1.5 to 4 times the thickness, and therefore the climb index is between 1.5 and 4.
- In *interior load-bearing walls,* the climb index varies from 2 to 5 and more.

In practice, the greatest suction heights are found in winter in north-facing brick walls when the imbibed water is loaded with dissolved salts, which increase (together with the effect of low temperature) the capillary constant. The maximum is reached if the air is saturated, or nearly so, as happens in unventilated, closed environments.

¶28. Kettenacker's hypothesis.

— Concerning the way in which surface evaporation hinders and finally arrests humidity's upward progress, one might think that an increase in ventilation, or the sun's direct action, would produce uniform drying over the entire wall surface so that while the upper limit reached by moisture remains stationary, the part of the wall below that limit would lose its moisture content uniformly.

According to Kettenacker's hypothesis, however, the drying action occurs quite differently. In the experimental tests on individual materials kept partially in water, we have already seen that the action of ventilation and sunshine forces surface evaporation, and that as the amount of water evaporated increases, there is a corresponding increase in the amount of water absorbed from the bottom of the tank.

The same thing happens in a damp wall; if we induce a higher evaporation rate, the water's rise also increases to keep pace. At higher speeds, however, the water must also overcome greater resistance in the wall's capillary spaces. All told, considering a wall as a capillary conduit, the same loss of load occurs as that produced in any water pipe when the water flows faster. Therefore, the height reached by water in a wall tends to decrease as the surface evaporation rate increases. Thus, according to Kettenacker, *drying begins at the top and is complete*, while below the moisture demarcation line the wall remains as wet as before. The onset of drying is entirely due to the loss of load by friction as a result of the increased mass of water moving through the wall, called to the surface by increased evaporation. Strange as it may seem, the greater the amount of water a wall evaporates, the more the height of ascent drops.

Moisture reaches its maximum height when the air is saturated, i.e., when evaporation is no longer possible. In such a case the water's rise depends entirely on the wall's structural characteristics and thus on its materials. The finer and more regular the capillaries, the higher the humidity will climb.

Chapter Seven

MEASURES TO COUNTER HUMIDITY RISING FROM THE SUBSOIL

¶29.   Reduction of the section. The Koch method.

— This method consists of hollowing out the wall with a series of small arches cut through the wall beneath the part to be restored. This reduces the passage of rising damp to the contact points between the arches. The horizontal area through which the humidity can pass is thereby limited to such an extent that the small amount of rising damp still able to pass through the bottleneck is rendered harmless by evaporation. The method is of limited use, however, because it alters the distribution of the wall's structural load and concentrates it onto a reduced wall area.

   In the example in figure 47, the wall, steeped in water from the canal, is shown hollowed out by a series of arches; the zone within the outline ABCDE, left without a water supply, is destined to dry out.

Fig. 47.

Reduction of the absorbent section with a row of arch-like openings.

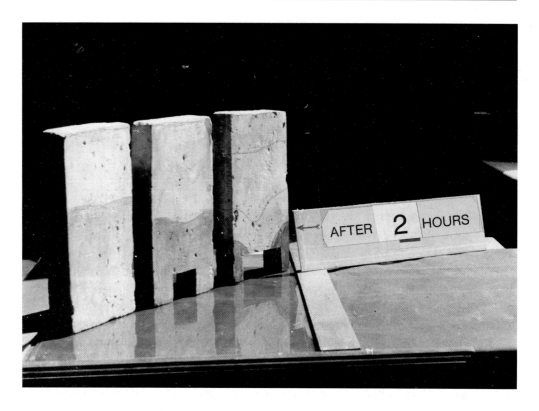

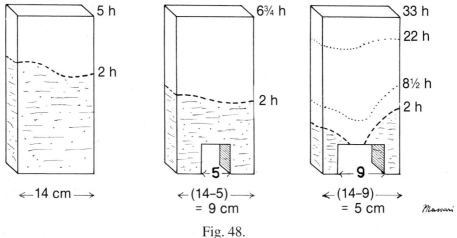

Fig. 48.

Common bricks with reduced absorbent section. When the absorbent section is reduced to a third, the speed of moisture invasion is reduced to a seventh.

To obtain an idea of the behavior of a wall in which the absorbent section has been reduced, a simple laboratory test, such as is shown in figure 48, can be conducted. This test involves taking bricks from the same kiln and the same batch (as homogeneous as possible) and observing their suction power when the absorbent section at one end is cut down and set in water. With soft yellow brick we have had the following results:

CHART III – WATER ABSORBED BY A BRICK WITH REDUCED SECTION

Sample	Suction section	Ht gained by water after 2 hrs	Time needed to soak entire sample	Comparative speed of water's rise
I. Control	Entire	18 cm	5 h	1.00
II With reduced section	0.74	14 cm	6 h 45 m	0.75
III With more reduced section	0.36	8 cm	33 h	0.15

In sample III, the suction rate is reduced to 15%, i.e., about ¹/₇ of the first sample, which has a complete absorbent section. Nevertheless, even the third sample eventually becomes totally soaked.

In practice, structural considerations make it difficult to reduce the section enough to cut off the passage of moisture completely. Usually, wider supports are left, but an anti-capillary material is inserted throughout the original wall thickness. In this way the supports, while barring moisture, can be large enough in section to meet structural requirements. The work is done in three phases. In phase one, a cut is made through the wall base and impermeable material, on which the plinths will rest, is inserted. In phase two, the arches themselves are constructed, again with breach cutting, but anti-capillary material is not inserted. In phase three, the damp wall beneath the arches is removed.

In the church of San Luigi dei Francesi in Rome, the architect Koch left a perfect example of restoration by reduction of the absorbent section. In the 1890s, Domenichino's frescos (in the chapel by the same name) were deteriorated by the action of humidity, which caused dramatic spalling of the intonaco. To restore the most damaged wall (the left-hand one bearing the fresco of St. Cecilia's death), Koch decided to isolate the frescoed wall as much as possible by separating it from the underlying wall mass. He cut three arches beneath the fresco, leaving the wall resting on only four plinths at the base of the arcade (fig. 49). He constructed the plinths with Roman selce (basalt), a very compact and completely anti-capillary material, and thus moisture was unable to pass those four possible points of contact between the foundation and the wall.

¶30. Barring humidity through the entire wall thickness. The Massari mechanical method.

— If any city in the world has a problem of 'rising capillary moisture,' that city is Venice, where the buildings literally stand in water. It was the Venetians who invented a system called *cuci e scuci* (sew and unpick) to bar the rise of water inside their walls, which are uniformly constructed in regular brick courses. The system involves chiselling a section of the wall straight through its entire thickness, until a sort of peep-through slot is obtained. A sheet of lead is carefully spread on the sill of the slot, and the hole is subsequently refilled with wedged bricks. After a few days, the mortar is set and an adjoining slot can be opened and treated in the same manner. This continues until the entire wall is finished (figs. 50-51). One can imagine how slow and tedious this procedure is. Moreover, it cannot

Fig. 49.

Koch saved a Domenichino fresco from ruin in San Luigi dei Francesi by reducing the absorbent section at the wall base and opening vertical slits to hinder lateral moisture penetration from the damp pillar.

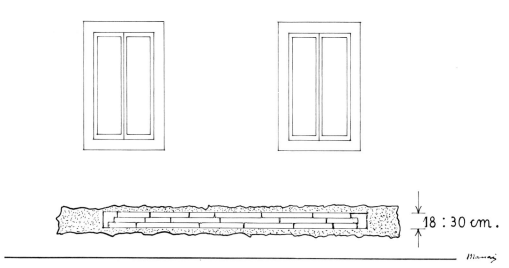

Fig. 50.

In barring moisture throughout the wall thickness, a horizontal strip of anti-capillary material is inserted through the entire wall.

Fig. 51.

The barrier through the wall can also be made with arches.

be used if the wall is damaged or if it is not constructed of brick (because hard stone and compact mortar call for dangerously heavy blows to open the gap). Nor can it be used when the wall is thicker than 75-80 cm because the slot would have to be too high.

The Massari mechanical method represents a technological updating of this traditional technique. Laborious handwork with hammer and chisel is replaced by the rapid and quiet work of an electric core drill. Lead sheets, which are subject to erosion from unpredictable electric currents, have been replaced by polyester resin, which is chemically and electrically inert, absolutely impermeable (boats are made of it), and both longer lasting and more resistant than reinforced concrete.

The resin or, more accurately, a resin mix in the liquid state, is introduced into the horizontal fissure that has previously been drilled through the wall. The space is then filled completely until the resin reaches the top of the slot. The mix subsequently polymerizes, or hardens, in three or four hours, with minimal shrinkage. No wedging is needed, and the moment the resin sets it can carry the weight of the wall above, no matter how great the load.

Fig. 52.

A core drill in use on a brick wall.

With a small, horizontal-axis core drill (fig. 52), a uniform slot is obtained by boring a series of holes side by side, followed by a second series to clear out the remaining material, as shown in figure 53. No rubble is left in the slot because the core drill extracts the material in compact cylinders or 'cores.' With 15 holes, for instance, one obtains a standardized, clean slot that is 42 cm wide and as deep as the wall is thick. The use of polyester resin as a damp-proof course brings with it the enormous advantage of introducing an elastic material instead of a plastic one such as bitumen; this is a precious quality for the stability of a building that must be cut along its base. With this method it is possible to prevent further humidity damage in historic buildings, including those in poor static condition, since the elastic strain of a 4 cm layer of polyester resin is negligible, even under the maximum load concentrations found at the base of the pillars of a dome.

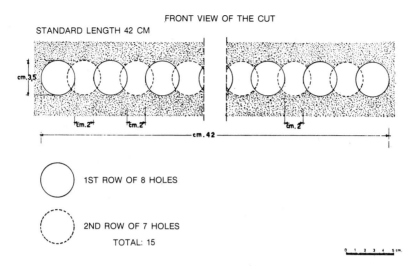

Fig. 53.

An even horizontal cut is obtained by making a first row of adjacent holes; the second row overlaps the first holes, clearing out the remaining material.

Commercial polyester resin base concrete should be composed of:

- skeleton-forming grains of dry marble dust or fine sand, corresponding in volume to the size of the breach cut
- commercial polyester resin (with up to 50% dry calcium carbonate dust), corresponding in volume to the voids between the skeleton-forming grains.

This formula assures that the resin concrete meets the requirements for the special task of barring rising damp – so long as the operation is carried out carefully and the ambient temperature is no lower than 14°C.

The following precautions should be taken:

- Fluidity should be varied according to the depth of the breach cut.
- Complete polymerization should occur in 3-4 hours.
- The compressive strength 24 hours after casting should be no less than 800 kg/cm^2.
- There should be no cracks.

Instead of polyester resin, epoxy resin (with a different filler) can be used but it is much more expensive.

Restoring a damp structure by this method is simple and quick, especially if two core drills are used in different parts of the same building. Once the horizontal cut is made, its interior surfaces must be dried with a large industrial dryer. A sheet of polyethylene, 0.05 mm thick, should be spread on the lower bed of the cut; finally, the resin concrete is poured in, after having been mixed with its catalyst. Since moisture greatly disturbs the polymerization of this resin, the cut, as well as all the ingredients of the resin concrete must be dried thoroughly. As soon as polymerization occurs (or, as builders say, the resin 'sets' or 'hardens'), the layer can be put under pressure. The next cut, adjacent to the one already filled, is then drilled.

Current prices [1992] for restoration work done with rapid mechanical cutting are about Lit.1,000,000-1,400,000 (about US$ 900-1,100) per square meter of wall area treated, depending on the wall material. Valid and less expensive alternatives, such as using a chain saw, have also been developed for simple cases (e.g., brick, soft stone).

This updating of a traditional technique means that the problem of preventing rising damp can now be considered solved for all historic buildings where the true obstacle was the lack of a valid operating technique. In Florence, for instance, the Massari Mechanical Method enabled Perugino's famous fresco of the Crucifixion, in the convent of Santa Maria Maddalena dei Pazzi, to be saved from an incipient humidity attack. The supporting wall ranges from 80 to 85 cm in thickness and is a fruit salad of square blocks and roundish stones. While the traditional method would have shattered everything, including the fresco, the mechanical cut was made without causing damage in a 'U' around the base and sides of the fresco (see fig. 201, p. 281).

In Venice, the admirable church of Santa Maria dei Miracoli was rapidly, and simply, saved from further damage due to rising damp with this new method. The church is faced, inside and out, with polychrome marble slabs, so hand cutting was impossible. Mechanical breach cutting immediately reached the soaking wet brick structure, passing through the marble facing without disturbing any of the slabs, and at minimum expense.

In the grandiose church of Santa Caterina in Galatina (Lecce), with its wealth of mural paintings that were deteriorated by humidity, no other technique could have blocked the rising ground water in such thick and heavily loaded structures. The pillars of the central nave were systematically cut and restored despite the fact they were 3.20 m thick, allowing the possibility of restoring the paintings in the future (see fig. 206, p. 287).

¶31. Capillary interception with resins, or a 'bread and water banquet.'

— The mechanical method described above is advisable when the restoration must be so foolproof that expense is a secondary consideration – as in the case where art works and historic buildings are at risk.

If one is dealing with apartment buildings, however, or individual rental properties – shops, storerooms, basements (perhaps to be used as nightclubs, etc.) – there are other, less expensive commercial reclamation methods that use the technique of capillary interception. If the client wants to economize too much, however, the work is likely to be useless and result in little more than a superficial 'face lift' of the wall plaster. Technically, this process involves expelling water from the capillaries of the wall material by filling them with suitable substances: these include silicone resins dissolved in xylol, latex rubber and ethyl polysilicate (which absorbs water and deposits silica). The solvent should be able to displace water from the pores and allow deposition of the intercepting substance. Although this makes sense in theory, the outcome in practice depends upon execution and the condition of the wall, which – if it has cracks and internal cavities – dissipates the intercepting liquid unbeknown to the operator. The liquid is usually injected into the strip of wall adjacent to the floor through horizontal or slanted cylindrical holes of small diameter (10-12 mm), which are made with an electric drill and aligned in two or more quincunxial rows along the wall. These holes can be about 10 cm apart. Some firms employ horizontal, crisscross holes, 3 cm in diameter and 30-60 cm apart. Either system will do. In any case, the liquid must be under a certain pressure, and each hole must be fed for several days until it will take in no more liquid.

As it is always difficult to achieve such *consistent and perfect diffusion that an entire strip of wall is rendered impermeable*, the rising damp is often only partially barred. It is known that even drastically reducing the absorbent section (fig. 48) does not impede water from rising through the bottleneck. Figure 48 shows that it takes 33 hours for the water to reach the top in brick with a reduced absorbent section, i.e., to reach the height it would normally attain in only five hours through a complete absorbent section. Therefore, *the interception of moisture must either be obtained in 100% of the wall's horizontal section or it is worthless* because it only delays the inroads of moisture.

Another weak point of this type of treatment is the *technical impossibility of controlling the outcome of diffusion within the treated wall*. As a result, there are no certain contractual guarantees. For major work, one can fall back on the cautionary formula suggested in ¶61 to safeguard the public agencies in charge of restoring historic buildings. This formula protects prudent clients who are unwilling to be taken in when on unfamiliar ground. They should secure the services of (and pay for) an inspector to measure the moisture content 20 cm deep in the wall fabric (not simply on the surface). The measurement should first be taken before the injections are made, in the presence of the operator, and then again at least a year after completion of the resin treatment. The client should bear the full expense of the testing. Final payment of not less than 50% of the cost of the work should be contingent on a proven and significant reduction of the moisture in the wall. If the person applying the resin interception treatment is unwilling to accept such a contract, it's a bad sign.

¶32. Doubtful traditional treatments for rising damp. The perimeter trench.

— External perimeter trenching, either open or closed, has been proposed for centuries as a way to counter rising damp (fig. 54).

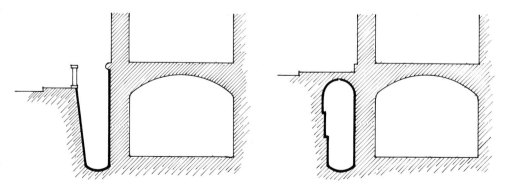

Fig. 54.

The two types of external perimeter trenching: open and covered.

In checking the moisture content of masonry walls before and after construction of a perimeter trench, it has been found that open trenching produces a decrease, if only a small one (10÷15 cm), in the height to which the dampness arrives.

In contrast, covered trenching has no effect whatsoever, yet this method is used today throughout the entire civilized world.

Let us examine the case illustrated in figure 55. If the wall's humidity is due exclusively to dispersed surface water, carried by capillarity from the ground onto side AB, and if the water does not go deeper than point 'B' (which can be ascertained by digging an inspection hole against the wall being restored), the trench will perform what we shall call an 'intercepting function.' Such cases are rather rare.

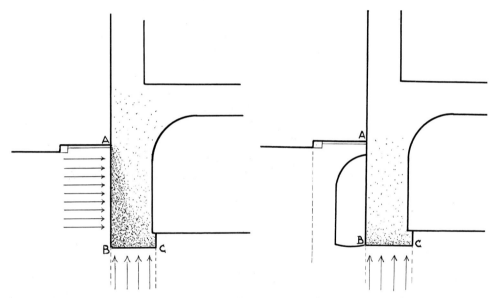

Fig. 55.

Moisture enters the wall not only from the AB face, but also from below the foundation BC. The trench cannot cut off the moisture coming from the BC foundation, but partially evaporates it through the AB face (drying function).

But what if the humidity is not only absorbed through the AB face (fig. 55), but is also drawn up through the BC foundation? The trench will then have a double task. Apart from interfering with the inflow on the AB side, it must also eliminate (by evaporation from the exposed AB surface) all of the moisture absorbed by the base of the wall, so the water no longer has sufficient reserves to continue its rise above ground. Of course this is impossible. Under the best of circumstances, the surface evaporation rate of the side of the wall in the trench is four or five times less than it is above ground, so a trench would have to be at least four or five times deeper than the height the humidity reaches above street level. If the humidity has risen 1.20 m above ground, a functional trench would have to be at least 5 or 6 m deep and energetically ventilated to avoid air saturation. All told, this would be absurd and dangerous. Actually, conventional trenching, as is still done today, is powerless against true rising damp, which comes from deep in the ground.

¶33. New and worthless pseudoscientific methods. Knapen siphons and fanciful variations.

— A. Knapen of Belgium has suggested drying walls with the so-called 'atmospheric siphon.' His idea is based on a simple theoretical principle, often cited in the technical literature.

Fig. 56.

Knapen's atmospheric siphon.

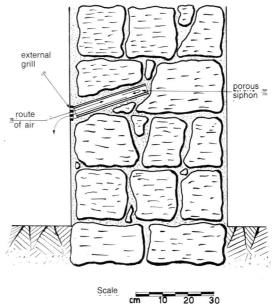

Knapen maintains that moisture can be extracted from walls by means of porous tubes, about 30 cm long and around 3 cm in diameter, which are put into the wall at a downward slant towards the outside; he calls these tubes 'atmospheric siphons' (fig. 56).

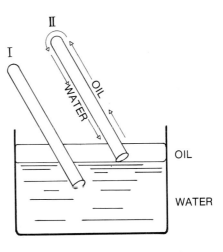

Fig. 57.

The experiment that inspired the Knapen siphon. In position I the test tube remains full of water. When the tube is moved to position II, the water exits and the tube fills with oil.

The phenomenon that inspired Knapen is illustrated by the following simple physics experiment (fig. 57): if an open test tube, full of water, is inverted in a container of water covered by a layer of oil, the oil (which is lighter) will rise in the tube and the water (which is heavier) will exit from it.

Just as the lighter oil rises, he said, so the external air (which is dryer and therefore lighter) rises in the 'atmospheric siphon,' pressing out the damp, heavy air that has accumulated inside. The parallel between the behavior of oil and dry air (both being light and thus rising) has no basis in the reality of the two phenomena Knapen has linked. The truth is that there is a constant ratio between the specific gravities of water and oil, and the exchange of the two in the test tube is constant and independent of other parameters.

In contrast, the specific gravities of free outside air and the air contained in the wall siphon vary according to temperature, and the water vapor loads also vary, so that the weight ratio is changeable and the consequent reciprocal movement can go in either direction, as can the subtraction of water vapor. The situation presents a puzzle to be solved anew each time; the movement of air in the siphon is an *unknown variable* and not a fixed phenomenon such as the behavior of oil and water. In order for the air to leave the slanted siphon, it's not enough for it to be loaded with water vapor, for the more vapor air contains at a given temperature, the lighter it is. Contrary to expectations, the dryer the air, the more it weighs. Thus it does not exit from the siphon because it is wet, but only when it is cooled enough to become heavier than the outside air. In winter, however, the walls are warmer than the outside air, so the siphon would have to *slant upwards* for the warm, damp air to exit; this solution is ridiculous when one considers rain, snow ... and the toilet habits of young rascals.

In summer, if the wall is flooded with sunshine, the air in the siphon is also heated and remains inside because it is lighter, though damper, than the outside air. To make matters worse, if a wall is too cold (which can happen if it faces north or is shaded) while the external air is temporarily warm and humid (as can happen during a mild, rainy 'sirocco' wind in winter), condensation is inevitably produced inside the siphon, similar to the weeping described in ¶41.

To summarize: For a large part of the year the siphon will be inert; in some cases it will store condensation and be counter-productive; and finally, it will function ideally (as in fig. 57) only under two conditions, when the wall temperature is slightly lower than or equal to that of the outside air or when the outside air is very low in RH, a rare and intermittent occurrence.

Other authors have pointed out the absurdity of Knapen tubes and the damage they frequently cause. A. Watson of England (who created a new system for measuring the variable humidity rate inside a wall on the basis of absorption of microwaves) verified after two years of careful observations that *there was no reduction of the initial moisture content* in walls treated with tubes. This negative result is given in the proceedings of the RILEM symposium held in Helsinki in August 1965 for brick manufacturers from all over Europe.

Even prior to this, Günter Mall of Germany, in *Bauschaden* (Editions Bauverlag GMBH, Wiesbaden, Berlin, 1963) showed that the tubes are not only useless, but often damaging because, being exposed to phenomena of internal condensation, *they can make the humidity rise* within the wall.

Despite all this, the image of the oil and water appeals to the lazy-minded with the suggestive power of simple, predigested solutions that do not cause one the trouble of thinking for oneself. Such power of suggestion works in certain advertisements in popular

magazines that claim to resolve the unhappy reader's major problems: how to grow 10 cm taller with a limb-stretching machine or how to fill out the bust line with plastic, pneumatic depression cups. In this way, Knapen tubes have spread all over the world, supported by the advertising of a solid commercial organization.

In old cities, rows of siphons can often be spotted at ground level in historic buildings; the walls, however, have remained as damp as ever. Sometimes the siphon's small external grills are surrounded by a greenish mold color – a proof of failure; ones like this can be seen in the base of Michelangelo's Porta Pia in Rome. An application, solemn in intent but humorous in outcome, is described in Chapter 15 (see ¶74: the Palazzo of the Accademia di San Luca).

The Knapen siphon has given rise to many fanciful variations, even though the neo-inventors no longer credit the master's name. Such products are available in Italy, Switzerland, Hungary, Belgium and France as the last word in science, and find faithful adherents among rural homeowners and poor parish priests. The new versions come in all sorts and sizes (fig. 58): in tile, with circular or semicircular sections (the prism form Knapen prescribed has long been forgotten); in inexpensive plastic that can be

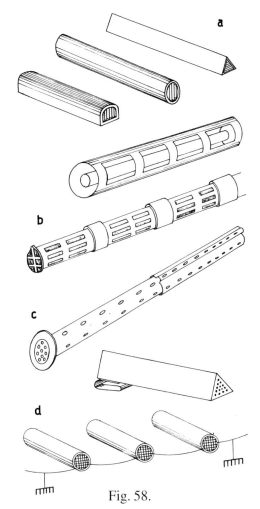

Fig. 58.

Among the variations on Knapen's tile siphons (group a), are siphons with cylindrical and semi-cylindrical sections. Other innovators, forgetting the porosity Knapen prescribed, use economical and unbreakable plastic (group b) or even stainless steel (type c). Yet others re-introduce tile (group d), garnished with mysterious tongues and copper conductors, sometimes with grounds, under the protection of a new divinity: electro-osmosis.

adjusted to fit any wall thickness; in stainless steel, because 'the bimetallic pair of nickel-steel accelerates osmosis.' (Clearly, until recently, no one knew that a homogeneous alloy of metals formed a bimetallic pair, not to mention that this triggered an electro-osmotic process.) Other inventors have added a mysterious folded copper tongue to the tile tube, and some other colleagues link the siphons with copper wire and ground the whole system. One never knows! The publicity flyers provide glib explanations larded with words like 'potential,' 'electro-osmosis,' and 'catalyzers,' which sound as good as the impressive medical terms once used by clever hucksters at county fairs for selling snake oil as a cure for rheumatism. As a protection against all this nonsense, see the specific contractual directives (¶61) based on checking the wall moisture content before and after treatment. Figure 59 shows a lighthearted caricature of Knapen tubes, as if they were steam valves or even taps that pour out the wall water at will.

Fig. 59.

Even today, restoration firms and public works departments that are behind the times apply an old pair of exorcisms against rising damp in ground floors: external perimeter trenching (as shown by the arrow in the figure) and Knapen-type dehumidifying tubes. These are caricatured here as if they were steam valves or even taps that pour water out of the wall. We cannot help but laugh at these kindergarten techniques.

¶34. Drying walls with electro-osmosis.

— We know that passing a continuous electric current through a conducting fluid can, by electro-osmosis, make liquid pass through porous or semi-porous membranes at a speed independent of the thickness of the section. This physical principle has been brilliantly applied in industry for the dehydration of various materials, the extraction of juices and the partial drying of clay and peat. Naturally, some researchers have thought of utilizing the same principle for drying damp walls in buildings (fig. 60).

The most relevant application is the temporary consolidation of clay banks (while retaining walls are being built) with the vertical emplacement of perforated iron tubes,

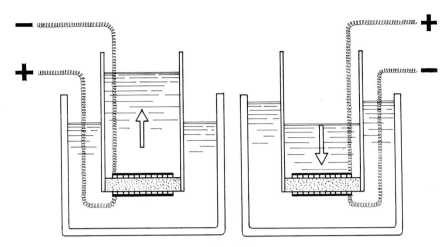

Fig. 60.

Electro-osmotic transport of water from positive to negative through a porous membrane, on either side of which are applied the two poles of a direct current.

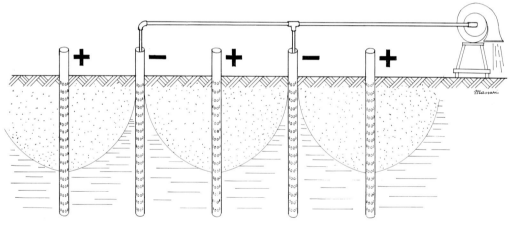

Fig. 61.

Application of electro-osmosis to the drying of clayey soil. Perforated iron tubes are set in quincunxial rows and connected alternately to the positive and negative poles of a direct current supply.

which are connected alternately to the positive and negative poles of an adequate power supply. The water impregnating the clay is gradually transferred by electro-osmosis from the positive to the negative iron tubes, from which it is then extracted with a centrifugal pump. The escarpment is kept dry for as long as necessary to set up the retaining wall. Direct current is used (fig. 61). Electro-osmosis has also been usefully employed in drying peat; starting with peat containing 90% water, one can obtain remarkable results, with removal of 50% to 70% of the water.

These two examples have been singled out because they are somewhat similar to walls in terms of mass, coarseness and simplicity of materials. Yet, a notable difference always remains. The initial moisture content of clay and peat is very high (90-70%) compared to walls (even of brick), which rarely contain a water volume higher than 30%. A 25% reduction of water in clay and peat is more than adequate and represents great success; in a brick wall, however, one could speak of drying and success only if the original 30% were reduced to 5% (by volume, of course). In brief, the starting point for electro-osmotic drying in walls is the finish line for clay and peat. Experimental results have not yet clarified whether electro-osmosis can force the drying of walls as far as necessary, but there are doubts as to whether it can overcome the rapidly increasing electrical resistance that the wall mass puts up as drying proceeds.

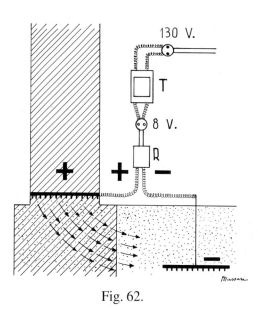

Fig. 62.

Elementary diagram of the application of electro-osmosis to a damp wall. Water is supposed to be drawn from the upper, positive area (wall) towards the lower, negative area (ground). T = transformer; R = rectifier.

Nevertheless, the restoration of damp premises with electro-osmosis is done commercially today with patented methods, which go under various proprietary names. The method has nothing mysterious about it, being simply the application of a physical principle (fig. 62), and can be easily carried out with a light direct current of 6-8 volts obtained from the regular power supply with the interposition of a small doorbell transformer and a rectifier. Personal experience, however, suggests that the electro-osmosis method has not produced any significant results despite repeated trials.

According to the physicist B.H. Vos,[1] all porous substances, and therefore walls as well, have a *critical point* of moisture-content percentage. Above this point, 'diffusion' is possible, i.e., the movement of water under an adequate force such as electro-osmosis; below the critical point, the water moves only by evaporation. We maintain that Vos's critical point coincides with what we have improperly termed the *bending point* in the Krischer and Görling graph referred to in ¶13. For brick walls in Venice, Vos fixes the critical point at 18% water content; below this it is no longer possible to move the water except by evaporation. This figure seems a bit high in our view. In any case, we advance the hypothesis that electro-osmosis is truly valid and useful in the first phase (saturated surface and constant evaporation) of Krischer and Görling's graph, and totally worthless in the second phase (declining evaporation) because true drying does not take place. Seen

---

1   *Studies in Conservation*, XVI, 4 (1971) 136. IIC, London

in this light, the contradictory results obtained by various researchers – the Russians in particular – can be understood. It also explains the results of tests done under our supervision, in cooperation with ICCROM, on very damp walls in Ostia Antica and moderately damp walls in the Farnesina Palace in Rome. There was a slight initial improvement (water reduction between 1% and 3% by weight), followed by a complete halt in any further drying, no matter how much we persevered with electro-osmosis. In both experiments we had reached the Krischer and Görling bending point.

PASSIVE ELECTRO-OSMOSIS

Up to this point, so-called 'active osmosis' has been discussed. With this method, it is necessary to supply electric current to effect the transfer of moisture from one part of the damp mass to the other – a transfer that works primarily well in clay. Indeed, electro-osmosis allowed the consolidation of the foundations, set in clayey soil, of St. Anne's in Warsaw. This method has been described by M.P. Bieganski since 1950.

There are, however, patents and simplistic systems on the market that claim to return the capillary wall water to the ground, without using electric current, by making it follow a capillary path in reverse. This type of electro-osmosis goes by the name of '*passive*' or '*short-circuit*' electro-osmosis and, in our view, is completely worthless.

The commercial proponents of passive electro-osmosis like to discover solemnly, in the client's presence, the difference in potential between the base and the upper part of the wall, pointing out that this discrepancy (which can reach up to 300-400 millivolts) starts to diminish a few days after their miraculous method has been applied, and then disappears altogether. Their claim is that the short circuit established between the base and the top has annulled the current *that was producing the capillarity*. In truth, the difference in potential is always there. Just measure it with clean, new electrodes inserted in the wall, and it will be the same as ever. The difference in potential between the old electrodes left more than 24 hours in the wall first diminishes and then disappears simply because *the electrodes have been polarized*. One can always find differences between any two parts of a damp wall, chosen at random – high, low, or at the same level. These are due simply to irregular saline concentrations in the water. Every wall is a complex of small batteries of salt concentrations, which generate tiny currents. As a reclamation system, 'passive' electro-osmosis is utter nonsense; its advertisement is based on a misunderstanding of the *apparent* cancellation of the difference in potential between the base and top of a damp wall.

An experimental test was carried out on a large wall afflicted with serious rising damp in the ground floor of the building where the Central Restoration Institute is housed in Rome. This test was made in cooperation with Professor Rotondi, then director of the Institute, and Professor Talenti of the Rome University Health Institute. A passive electro-osmosis restoration system, installed by a representative of the company holding the patent, was kept under observation for 30 months. The amount of water contained 15-20 cm deep in the wall was measured before the electro-osmotic device was applied, and periodically thereafter, up to the end of the 30 months. It was found that the *moisture content inside the wall was always precisely the same*. The experiment, as has been said, was strictly controlled.[2]

In Paris, with the kind assistance of the Louvre Museum technician, the author had occasion to examine another passive electro-osmosis system, installed around 1960 without any preliminary testing, simply on the ground of 'common sense.' This was an attempt to combat dampness in the Jeu de Paume building, which housed the Impressionist Painting Museum. The passive electro-osmotic device that was used, according to the patent, is only valid against humidity *'de remonte,'* i.e., rising from the ground. At the Jeu de Paume, appearances and 'common sense' suggested that the humidity was *de remonte*. Samples had not been taken from the stone wall, and moisture content had not been measured because everyone was convinced the wall was saturated with rising damp. In any case, either because the humidity was not truly rising or because passive electro-osmosis does not work, the treatment did not bring about the slightest improvement, even after five years. Finally, the Museums Direction, tired of waiting, installed simple, traditional counterwalls inside the building and had no further humidity problems.

In short, the passive electro-osmosis method, without electric current, is not recommended.

¶35. Interior counterwalls.

— Unlike Knapen siphons and electro-osmosis, this measure does not claim to eliminate the water from the wall. It is inexpensive, however, and, when properly carried out, adequately protects those who must live or work in damp premises. It involves the construction of a thin wall, as thick as a brick laid flat or, more commonly, on edge, constructed at a short distance (5-10 cm) from the damp wall *without touching it*. This detail, *'without touching it,'* is vital to the success of the counterwall; if it is joined by several brick bonders to the damp wall (as is often done for support in tall rooms), every linking brick becomes a bridge where capillary moisture can cross from the old damp wall to the counterwall. (We shall see below how ancient Roman builders solved the stability problem by resting the counterwall against the damp wall while also immunizing the former against the contagion of capillary humidity.) In order to avoid absorption at the base, the counterwall must rest on a damp-proof course, and the bottom of the air space must be carefully cleared of any debris that has fallen in during construction.

A common construction error is ventilation of the cavity (which is formed between the damp wall and the counterwall) with two rows of air vents – one slightly above the floor and the other along the top, not far from the ceiling – made in the counterwall itself and thus communicating with the room being rehabilitated (fig. 63). By creating air circulation between the room and the damp space behind the counterwall, the positive effects of the counterwall are annulled as the saturated air spreads through the room. What, then, is the point of the counterwall? It simply masks the unsightly wall behind, which is often scarred by erosion, mold, blisters and the whole range of flaws produced by

---

2   Giuliano Colombo, "Esperienze sul prosciugamento elettrosmotico delle murature umide," *La Ricerca Scientifica*, 33 (II-A) 1963.

Fig. 63.

It makes no sense to open air vents in the counterwall because the damp air then flows into the premises being restored.

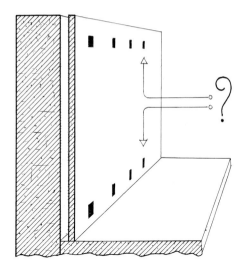

moisture. Thus the counterwall, which is very effective when sensibly built, becomes merely a screen.

The three types of counterwall that work best as protection against rising damp are as follows (fig. 64):

- with a totally closed air space
- with the air space open to the outside through the damp wall (this is the classic Vitruvian type)
- with air space communicating with the room at the top and with the outside at the bottom, with forced expulsion of the moist air

We shall examine the three types separately.

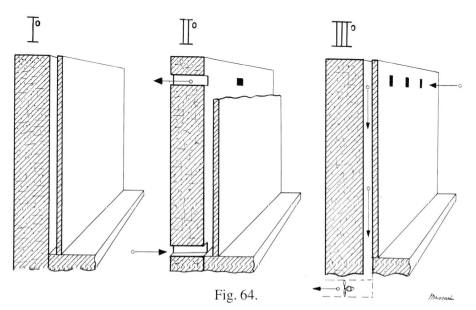

Fig. 64.

The three types of sensible counterwall.

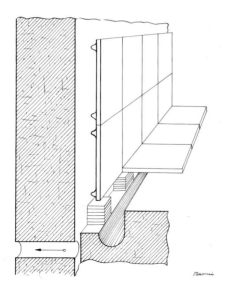

Fig. 65.

A type II counterwall as built by the ancient Romans.

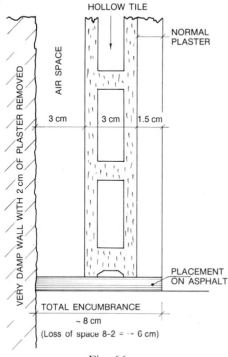

Fig. 66.

Hollow tile counterwall advised to keep to a minimum the loss of space in the premises being restored.

The first, with a totally closed air space, is used when it is impossible to ventilate the air space through the outer wall – in cellars, for instance. This must be considered a drastic remedy because, although it may assure improvement of unhealthy premises, it can also prevent evaporation and provoke the rise of moisture to the floor above. As a precaution, it is advisable to fill the bottom of the air space up to 10-15 cm high with well-dried charcoal while the counterwall is being built, so the charcoal can absorb any condensation that forms on the floor between the two walls.

The second type of counterwall is described in Book VI of Vitruvius's *Architettura* (fig. 65). He must have been thinking of the worst cases – walls underground or dripping with water – because he suggests building a drain along the damp wall and below the floor (to collect the water). The drain is then connected with the outside through weep holes in the outer wall at floor level, and another series of holes is cut in the exterior wall slightly below the vault or ceiling. This double row of air vents, one high and the other low, assures natural ventilation and continuous replacement of the damp air between the two walls.

Even today, a fully effective counterwall depends on the ventilation of the air space to the outside, as Vitruvius suggests, and **not** to the inside in the mistaken manner shown in Figure 63. The subfloor drain is only necessary for underground walls.

To construct light, thin counterwalls, present-day builders often use hollow bricks on edge. This calls for a considerable use of mortar because our bricks are small, and it is known that mortar absorbs moisture easily. It is preferable, therefore (fig. 66), to use larger bricks or hollow clay blocks with fewer joints and hydrofuge cement mortar, or else large, thin slabs of any inorganic material. Another excellent precaution is to paint the cavity side of the counterwall material with impermeable paint before putting it into place. Waterproofing should also be installed whenever condensation from behind is expected, such as if the premises are very cold in winter.

The ancient Romans had a special type of tile, called *tegula mammata,* for this work. The adjective 'mammata' caused translators and technicians some perplexity, inducing them to imagine the strangest shapes. In the Rome Antiquarium, we found some examples (fig. 67) of the Vitruvian *tegula mammata.* They are large, square tiles, 58 cm per side, and have a teat, or knob, projecting about 5 cm from each corner. Some knobs were solid; others were pierced for nails. It should be stressed that these tiles were laid on edge, resting against the damp wall (fig. 65) after having been carefully *tarred on the side exposed to the moisture*, so water could not be transmitted from the wall to the tile through the four points of the knobs.

Fig. 67.

Examples of 'tegula mammata,' the tiles used by the ancient Romans to build counterwalls (photos by Dr. Petrangeli of the Antiquarium of Rome).

An air space of 5 cm, the depth of the projection of the knobs, was thus created between the damp wall and the counterwall. This space communicated with the outdoors through two rows of air vents, one at the top and one at the bottom of the exterior wall.

The last type of counterwall (No. III in fig. 64) is used only in connection with an exhaust system, which permits intermittent, energetic removal of the saturated air accumulated between the two walls. Experience has shown that this solution is somewhat complex and subject to mechanical failure. In any case, the air vents must be cut into the top of the counterwall (never at the bottom), so that damp cold air does not flow back into the room when the fan is off.

To summarize, the building requirements of a good counterwall are:

- no contact between the damp wall and the counterwall unless the contact is made with impermeable material (bitumen, for example)
- no contact between the damp air in the cavity and that in the room
- a layer of asphalt or other waterproof material under the counterwall base

- continuous exchange of damp air from the cavity to the outside, either through natural ventilation or forced exhaust (only if rising damp is involved)
- if there is condensation, the cavity must be *airtight in both directions*

For practicality and economy it is always advisable to build a stable counterwall of brick and mortar (excepting gypsum, which suffers damp), as in the old days. Light structures composed of a wooden framework supporting sheets of plywood or particle board, such as the various types currently on the market, are not recommended. With these materials, which are themselves very sensitive to moisture, the structures constantly 'move' with variations in temperature and RH. Regardless of manufacturers' assurances, the weak points of such products are always the joints; and good utilization of such slabs can only be made if airtight joints are not important.

In contrast, inorganic, self-supporting sheets (sufficiently thick to stand up without a wooden support) are excellent for building counterwalls. These slabs are made of cellular cement, pumice mixtures, cinders, vermiculite, etc. To save space, 3 cm thick Perret tiles can also be used in constructing counterwalls. (These are normally used in roof construction.) See figure 79 for the scheme for dry restoration of the ground-floor breakfast room of a cottage that had become uninhabitable due to moisture rising from saturated, clayey soil. The work included construction of a subfloor, isolated from the clayey soil by the interposition of a damp-proof membrane, a wooden floor with lining of semi-rigid, taut panels of rock wool, and a counterwall of Perret tiles. To avoid a recurrence of rising damp, the sleeper walls and the first two courses of the counterwall were laid with a synthetic sealant in trielin solvent, so *no mortar or water was used* in the lower part of the room.

In order to minimize the loss of space and increase the cooling effectiveness of the counterwall, the air space (resistance $R = 0.18$) can be replaced by light, semi-rigid insulating panels, average thickness 2.5 cm, of mineral wool, fiber glass or foam resins ($R = 0.60$) as suggested in Table III on additional structures for thermal resistance (¶23).

Chapter 15 gives examples of other alternatives to the air space, such as the foamed polystyrene used in Geneva, and the loose pumice or charcoal sticks used in Calabria.

¶36. Possible damaging side effects of counterwalls or commercial waterproof coatings.

— Sometimes the construction of a counterwall on the ground floor suffocates evaporation from the wall and pushes the rising damp to the floor above. The same effect is caused by adherent coatings of cement or bitumen, or by those excellent waterproof sheets produced by the elastomer industry.

Whatever material is used, it causes a detour of the moisture already contained in the wall; soon after, the moisture malignly reappears, either at the sides or higher up. Furthermore, the coating does not hold up against the mechanical strain produced by variations in heat and tension, or by the pressure of internal efflorescence on the contact surface between the capillary plaster and the protective coating.

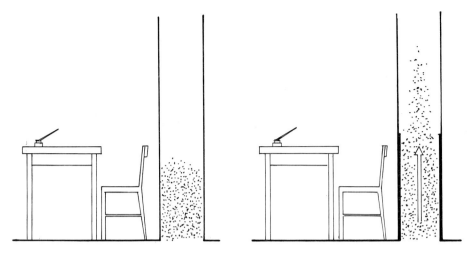

Fig. 68.

Before and after the cure: misguided application of waterproof lining which causes the rise of moisture in the wall.

The commonly applied horizontal layer of asphalt (or similar) should be ruled out because it causes:

- aggravation of the moisture condition in spring and summer, due to cooling of the air by the walls
- rise of moisture from the subsoil into the outer walls and transferral of the affliction from the floor to the walls

In truth, asphalt, tar, cement and hydrofuges are used today, inside and out, by builders with rather confused notions about the function of waterproofing materials.

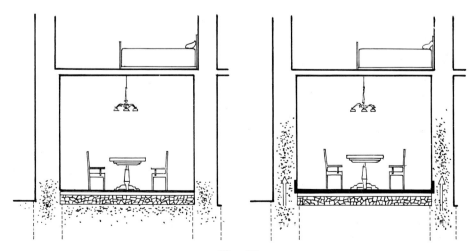

Fig. 69.

Before and after the cure: another erroneous application of a waterproof layer.

Figures 68-70 illustrate some of the most common instances of misguided water-proofing. The first figure clearly shows the formation of what can be called a *capillary conduit*. The rising damp, which was previously balanced by corresponding surface evaporation from both sides of the wall, finds itself channelled upwards to appear directly above the waterproofed strip. Make no mistake: this occurs when the wall is very absorbent, no matter what type of waterproofing is used – whether marble, ceramic, mosaic, linoleum, rubber or paint, as well as asphalt and hydrofuge mortars.

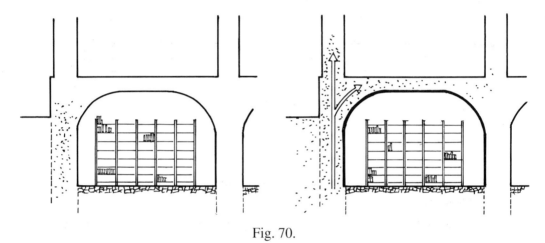

Fig. 70.

Before and after the cure: the total lining of the walls of a semi-basement causes moisture to rise to the floor above.

Similarly, a capillary conduit is formed under the floor, as in Figure 68, when the highly absorbent walls have not been preventively immunized with a good damp-proof course to bar the possible inroads of rising damp. Such disastrous attempts to repair damp floors are often made on the ground floors of country houses and, within a few years, cause an irreparable invasion of the walls themselves. To repair ground floor premises wisely, one must construct a good, anti-capillary subfloor with good ventilation. Unfortunately, this sensible and foolproof approach takes more time and money than a quick, routine application of tar, which explains why the right solution is less popular.

Even a complete lining of the walls of a semi-basement, as in figure 70, can cause moisture to rise at the expense of the adjacent or overlying premises when there is an unfortunate combination of circumstances such as abundant subterranean water, minimum distance above the water table, high suction power of the wall material and lack of winter heating.

¶37. Damp floors caused by erroneous traditional construction. Should subfloors be ventilated? How to improve rooms below street level.

— Analysis has shown that in ground floors and mezzanines the moisture content of the floor alone represents more than half the total moisture of the structure. In fact, the floor's

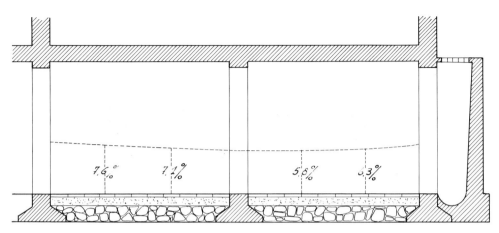

Fig. 71.

Distribution of moisture is almost perfectly uniform in cellar floors.

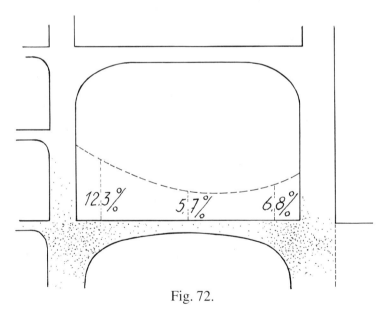

Fig. 72.

In floors over vaulting, a moisture graph takes a catenary form.

moisture content is almost greater than, or equal to, the moisture content of all the walls together.

The graph of moisture distribution is nearly horizontal in cellar floors (fig. 71), where the moisture is virtually uniform at all points; the graph shows a catenary form, instead, in floors over vaulting where water is drawn from the large bearing walls (fig. 72).

In very damp premises, water evaporates from the entire floor surface, whereas water in the walls evaporates from a strip only 1-2 m high. If, for reasons of time or money,

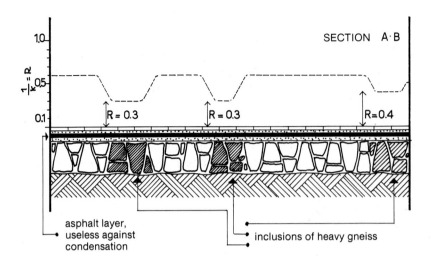

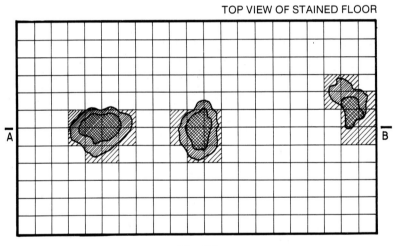

Fig. 73.

Intermittent condensation stains on a floor. Here, these are caused by the inclusion of heavy gneiss in a subfloor of light limestone.

one must forego some part of the restoration work, it is better to pay less attention to the walls. *The floors must never be neglected.*

A good subfloor system is the specific remedy for ground or basement floors where moisture can show up either as an overall darkening of the color or as large stains. The tone of the stains almost always varies with the amount of RH. If the air is near saturation (warm, damp winter days), and thus loses its ability to take on vapor, the stains become a little darker. When the air is dry and cold, and thus has a strong drying capacity (dry, windy winter days), the stains seem to diminish. The stains disappear if the dry spell lasts more than a week.

One of three causes will be found: usually moisture rising from the subsoil, condensation, or the presence of hygroscopic materials, which cause intermittent dampness (fig. 73). A proper analysis of the source must include measurement of the moisture content, not only of the flooring, but of the **layer on which it rests**. *Samples should be taken at two depths:* the more superficial from the bedding layer, i.e., the mortar that holds the paving elements or is a base for the cement; and the deeper at 15-20 cm beneath the first, on the same vertical line.

If the water percentage found by the analysis is greater in the deeper sample, one can be sure that there is moisture rising from the subsoil. If, however, the more superficial

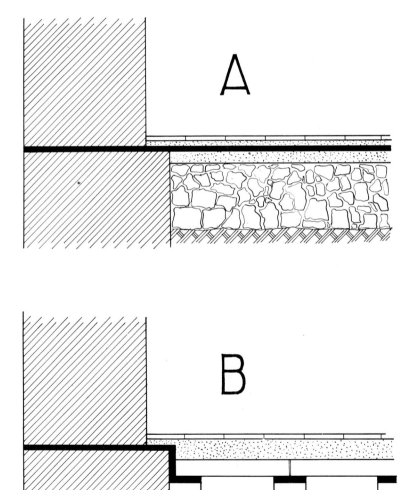

Fig. 74.

Types A and B traditional subfloors, as built to date (either filled or with sleeper walls and air spaces) offer protection against rising damp but not condensation.

sample reveals a higher moisture content percentage, the moisture is due to condensation and can derive from the atmosphere if it is warm and damp while the ground is cold (spring and summer, warm winter wind), or else from telluric air if the ground is warm and the outside air is cold (winter). In the former instance the condensation is deposited above the floor; in the latter, beneath.

In general, moisture rising from the subsoil is constant and produces high moisture-content percentages of 15÷25%, whereas condensation is intermittent and produces much lower percentages (5÷15%).

Sometimes the condensation stains are so clearly outlined on the floor that one can compose an X-ray of the underpinnings; individual materials of high specific gravity betray their presence with dark, clear shadows (fig. 73). These are like the phantom stains on frescoed walls that madden restorers of old churches. An unsuspected fragment of granite mixed with the brick structure under the intonaco may be causing the trouble.

Traditional floors directly above ground have always been empirically built in either of the two ways, A or B, shown in figure 74. In the current view, these structures (even supposing the waterproofing is perfectly laid) are considered *incomplete because they do not assure any protection against condensation* in the spring/summer period. It is known that this form of moisture comes from the air, and not from the ground, which in this case acts a cold storage. In type A traditional structures, the subfloor of cellars and basements is the twin brother of highway formations, constructed within formworks and filled with chunks of tuff, stone, or large pebbles, almost as if we expected tanks to drive through our homes. This structure dissipates a great deal of winter heat.

It is commonly believed that the type B subfloor, with short sleeper walls and air spaces (on the Roman model) represents real progress over gravel and tuff. As far as condensation is concerned, this is an illusion. Many builders discover this when magnificent cellars (in reinforced concrete buildings) made with sleeper walls and no stinting on asphalt depreciate after the first rentals because condensation makes them damp and unwholesome from spring to summer. The sleeper wall and air-space system (type B) is heat dispersive as well, and should be abandoned nowadays when cellars are intended to store antique furniture and books along with wine casks.

While we are in the cellar (even without wine casks), another traditional construction detail seems a serious thermal error: in subfloors of tuff or stone, the asphalt layer (as protection against rising capillary damp) is placed directly beneath the bedding layer of the floor. This location is sensible in terraces because it rains on the roof and the water must be quickly blocked. With respect to cellar floors, however, it is irrational because the moisture comes from below and there is no reason to let it soak the subfloor and rise by capillarity to within a few centimeters of the inhabitants' feet. It is more logical to put the asphalt entirely beneath the subfloor because that is the only way to be sure the subfloor is dry, wholesome, thermally non-conductive and capable of arresting, or notably reducing, condensation.

Figures 75-77 show the three types of subfloor that we advise for two-pronged defense against both capillary moisture rising from the subsoil and condensation of atmospheric origin. Naturally, these types are not compulsory, but can be varied in

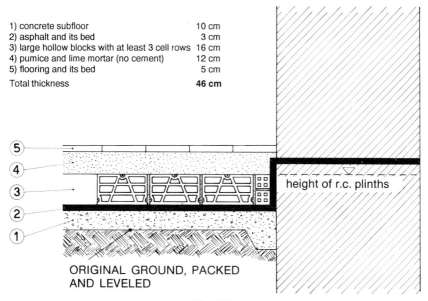

1) concrete subfloor	10 cm
2) asphalt and its bed	3 cm
3) large hollow blocks with at least 3 cell rows	16 cm
4) pumice and lime mortar (no cement)	12 cm
5) flooring and its bed	5 cm
Total thickness	**46 cm**

height of r.c. plinths

ORIGINAL GROUND, PACKED AND LEVELED

Fig. 75.

First type for homes and public places. The subfloor of dry-worked hollow brick floor blocks, kept dry by the underlying asphalt layer, is valid against both rising damp and condensation. The thermal resistance of this floor system is R = 1.

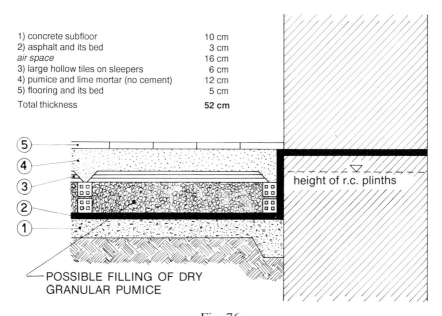

1) concrete subfloor	10 cm
2) asphalt and its bed	3 cm
air space	16 cm
3) large hollow tiles on sleepers	6 cm
4) pumice and lime mortar (no cement)	12 cm
5) flooring and its bed	5 cm
Total thickness	**52 cm**

height of r.c. plinths

POSSIBLE FILLING OF DRY GRANULAR PUMICE

Fig. 76.

Second type for homes and public places. A subfloor of sleeper walls and air spaces can also be kept dry if the asphalt is laid underneath. The floor system thus becomes effective against both types of humidity. With empty air spaces, its thermal resistance is R = 1.05; a filling of dry granulate increases the resistance to R = 1.80.

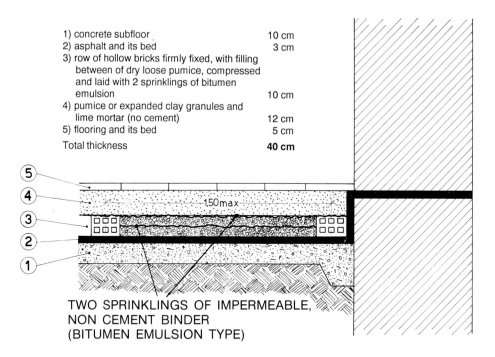

1) concrete subfloor	10 cm
2) asphalt and its bed	3 cm
3) row of hollow bricks firmly fixed, with filling between of dry loose pumice, compressed and laid with 2 sprinklings of bitumen emulsion	10 cm
4) pumice or expanded clay granules and lime mortar (no cement)	12 cm
5) flooring and its bed	5 cm
Total thickness	**40 cm**

1,50 max

TWO SPRINKLINGS OF IMPERMEABLE, NON CEMENT BINDER (BITUMEN EMULSION TYPE)

Fig. 77.

Third type for garages or storerooms. The subfloor with short sleeper walls can be strengthened and simplified by eliminating the large, flat tiles. Like the preceding examples, this system is also effective against both types of moisture. Its thermal resistance is R = 1.30.

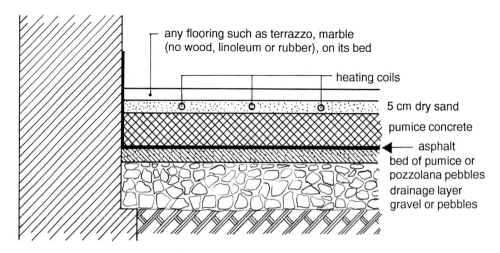

any flooring such as terrazzo, marble (no wood, linoleum or rubber), on its bed

heating coils

5 cm dry sand

pumice concrete

asphalt
bed of pumice or pozzolana pebbles
drainage layer
gravel or pebbles

Fig. 78.

Radiant floor with heating coils embedded in a layer of dry sand (wood, linoleum and rubber are excluded).

accordance with local materials and work-site needs, so long as the following general rules are observed:

- Use well-dried material of low specific gravity – absolutely **no** sand, gravel, tuff, sandstone or calcareous stones.

- Place the asphalt *beneath the subfloor*, not beneath the flooring, so that the entire subfloor system remains dry.

- Do not lay the floor directly on *reinforced concrete slab*, even for short distances, because every such contact can give rise to condensation stains; interpose a non-conductor – a hollow brick at least, if nothing better is available.

- As a rule, the overall thermal resistance of a good subfloor system, from the ground up, should not be lower than 1 $\dfrac{m^2 h \,°C}{kcal}$ or [0.9] $\dfrac{m^2 \,°C}{W}$ and preferably higher, as in the types suggested here.

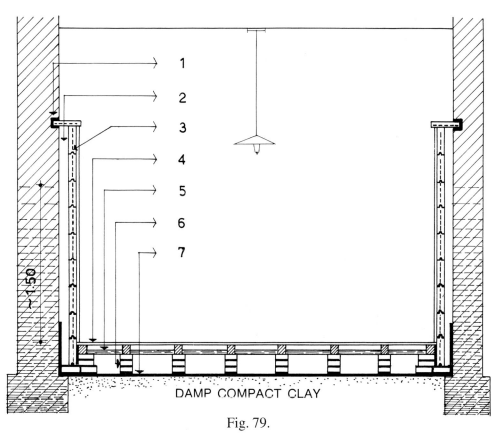

Fig. 79.

"Dry" restoration of a very damp breakfast room in a country house, using a thin counterwall: 1) mastic; 2) 3 cm air; 3) hollow tile; 4) larch wood 2.5 cm; 5) rock wool; 6) sleeper walls laid with mastic; 7) damp-proof membrane.

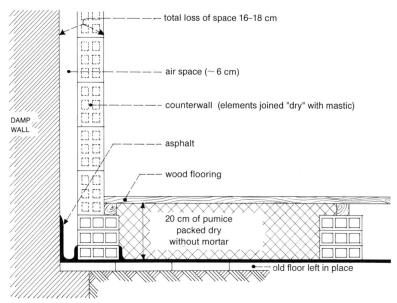

Fig. 80.

Restoration of semi-basements with the 'dry' method. The space can be occupied immediately.

Pumice and expanded clay granulate are suitable for subfloor construction, so long as they are not mixed with cement. Use a cement-lime mortar or, better, leave it dry, when possible.

Other types of subfloors, for special, more complex requirements, are indicated in Figures 78-80.

Figure 78 shows a modern subfloor system with an imbedded serpentine of heating coils – the so-called 'radiant floor' with which any room can be made habitable. The coils must extend over at least ¾ of the floor surface.

See also the 'dry' execution of the subfloors in figures 79 and 80, done without a drop of water so the premises can be occupied immediately.

The three rules, to repeat, of sensible subfloors as protection against both ground moisture and condensation are:

- *Place the asphalt beneath and not above the subfloor system.*
- *Use dry filler, specific gravity not above 0.8.*
- *Never rest the floor on reinforced concrete,* but interpose at least a tile of flat hollow brick to avoid localized condensation stains due to the specific gravity of the concrete.

Should subfloors be ventilated?

Ventilation through air vents on opposite walls is indispensable in the traditional, moisture-laden subfloors of old buildings. Otherwise, mold and rot develop. On the other hand, this type of ventilation may excessively cool the subfloor mass by evaporation as well as lower the temperature of the overlying flooring. Then follows the unwelcome surprise of finding that the premises one intended to restore are still cold and unpleasant. Heating can be used as a last resort.

Air vents are superfluous, however, if the above-mentioned rules are followed in reconstructing the subfloor, and the work is done with new, sound, light and dry materials. Above all, the asphalt or other damp-proof course must be positioned beneath the subfloor proper (as shown in figs. 75 and 76). The only case where air holes might be useful is when flooding from specific causes is expected; here, the air vents must also act as drains and be placed low.

To summarize: We do not recommend ventilation in new, sensibly constructed subfloors, but we feel it is indispensable in damp, traditionally constructed ones that cannot be modified. A subfloor that is damp at the outset, however, will remain so for the building's life span, even if it is ventilated. If one doesn't have a good pair of dry shoes, one must go on walking in wet ones.

How to improve rooms below street level

In reinforced-concrete framed buildings, the basement is sometimes planned to be subdivided by partitions (of brick, wood, glass, etc.) into separate, closed rooms.

With this type of arrangement, one can surely predict static, stale-smelling air, due to lack of circulation and air exchange. One can also predict an insurgence of mold in the corners and along the baseboards, even though the walls are dry. The most serious economic damage will strike any organic materials in storage, e.g. fruit, paper, books, leather, wood, etc. To keep the air from stagnating, one must arrange for it to circulate automatically by leaving vents and passages along the tops and bottoms and in the corners of all the partitions, and by building all the doors with grills, as shown in figure 81.

Figure 81 shows the solution devised for the new headquarters of the Labor Office in Via de Lollis in Rome. The basement rooms were intended for storage of archives in separate, locked rooms. The aim was to provide fresh air and light through horizontal grills in the sidewalk. At the same time, a perimeter trench on the street side, tightly sealed off from the building, keeps cold, condensation and traffic vibrations away from the underground rooms. Previously, the mass of damp earth from the street bed had transmitted all three conditions to the building. The results have proven to be excellent, and there is no need, given the Roman climate, to add ventilation or heating plants.

¶38.   Small freestanding houses without cellars.

— Where, for economic reasons, there is little or no elevation of the ground floor above the soil, the humidity of small houses will be closely linked to the nature of the ground. Two extreme cases are due to clayey soil, which holds rainwater, and to sandy soil, which favors so-called 'reverse condensation' beneath the floor.

In the former case, repairs must be aimed at collecting and carrying off dispersed water, while also *using drainage to offset the clayey nature* of the soil, which tends to

Fig. 81.

a. Grills on partitions and doors help to secure maximum air circulation in underground premises that have been partitioned into separate, closed storerooms.

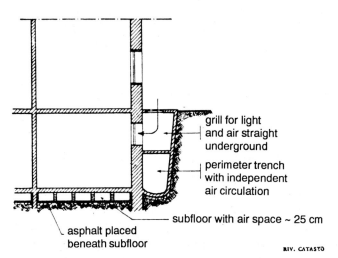

grill for light
and air straight
underground

perimeter trench
with independent
air circulation

subfloor with air space ~ 25 cm

asphalt placed
beneath subfloor

RIV. CATASTO

81b. Transverse section of the masonry beneath the sidewalk, with separate air circuits for the trench and the storerooms.

81c. Perspective view of the longitudinal section of the structure in the preceding figure. The small sidewalk grill on the right helps to ventilate the perimeter trench. The two large grills on the left bring air into two underground storerooms.

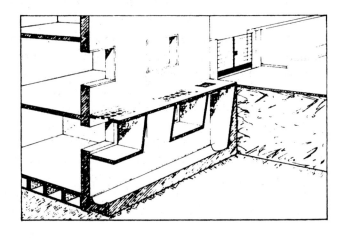

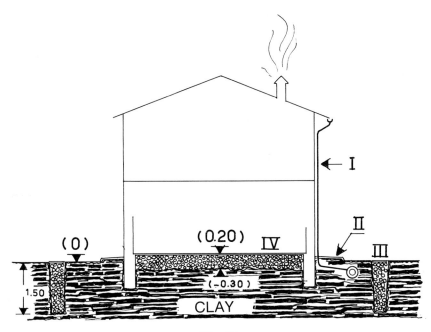

Fig. 82.

Restoration of a small house that suffered from diffused dampness due to the clayey nature of the soil.

hold water excessively, rainwater in particular. Figure 82 schematically indicates the overall plan used in the successful repair of the freestanding house. Items I, II, and III (guttering, sidewalks, and drainage) serve to collect and carry away dispersed surface water originating from rainfall. Item IV, which consists of the construction of an anti-capillary subfloor of large pebbles, is an optimum precaution against the possible residual moisture of the ground covered by the building. A subfloor system with air chambers would have been even better, but the owner could not afford one. The drainage (III) is set away from the house to avoid structural damage to the small, lightly founded building.

Damage of a different sort is found in small seaside constructions on sand (houses, cottages, cabins for beach camps, etc.), where the ground floor is set only two or three steps up from the outside level. It is a common construction error, in some places, to consider that the moisture from the sand has been neutralized by installing a complete asphalt layer prior to paving, and that either a greater elevation or a true air chamber would be useless and expensive (fig. 83). Technical attention and expenditure are entirely dedicated to this insulating layer, and the builder is confident that he has provided good protection against any kind of humidity attack. Instead, the very frequent presence of high moisture contents (such as the 22% found by the author beneath the subfloor asphalt in a damp house in Rome Lido) provokes such a high and unexpected *dispersion of heat through the floor* that the entire ground floor is made uninhabitable by the cooling of the

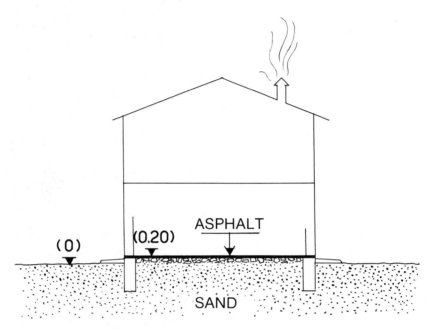

Fig. 83.

Small house affected by spring/summer condensation because it is too close to the damp ground. The asphalt is of no help in preventing excess heat dispersion through the floor.

air, which consequently tends to become saturated. This environmental change in the state of the air is produced continuously from early spring to about midsummer, and occasionally in winter, especially on warm, humid days.

Raising the height of the floor the 50 cm necessary to create a good air space is almost always unthinkable, but the house can still be made habitable with two makeshift remedies, so long as they are applied together: superimposed wood flooring (on sleepers, even inexpensive ones), covering the entire cold floor area, and winter heating prolonged into late spring. If the house is inhabited in winter, it should be heated for at least a week before it is occupied, and kept heated as long as seems necessary, far into the spring. If liquid gas heaters are used, the water vapor produced must be carefully vented, for according to a colorful American saying, a gas heater steams like a pair of oxen in a stall.

Chapter Eight

THE CHARACTERISTICS OF CONDENSATION

¶39.   Condensation due to cold. Dispersive walls.

— Condensation is due exclusively to cooling of the air, and is linked to momentary and seasonal changes in the weather that cause the temperature to fall. There are two principal forms of condensation: winter and summer.

Winter condensation is produced in buildings that are inadequately insulated against the cold of the outside air. Summer condensation, which is caused by cold that has remained imprisoned underground, occurs only in the stories in contact with the ground, as there is a contrast between the warm summer air and the walls that are still cold due to thermal inertia. It is known that daily fluctuations in temperature do not penetrate more than a meter into the ground, but that annual fluctuations go deeper, with a time lag. The delay in annual temperature extremes (winter minimum and summer maximum) is roughly six days for every 25 cm of depth. Thus in the plains of central and Mediterranean Europe – such as the Po Valley, central France, or the Hungarian plains, where the average temperature in January is about 2°C – the lowest temperature would presumably be reached underground after three months, or around mid-April, at a depth of 3-3.30 m. From this we must infer that in cellars with floors 3 or 4 m below street level, true cold arrives in April when the outside air is already warm and loaded with moisture, which easily condenses. In July, when the outside temperature is 30°C, the temperature in the cellar will still be the 20-22°C of April and will seem cold compared to midsummer heat (fig. 84). Finally, the dog days of August will be felt underground three months later, in November, when the outside air has already begun to get cold. Then, however, the cold air contains little water vapor and is innocuous as far as condensation is concerned.

Condensation, as opposed to rising damp, is thus an intermittent phenomenon. Yet, it is as damaging as rising damp and equally capable of making affected premises uninhabitable.

It is not easy to diagnose condensation unless the phenomenon occurs while the investigation is being made, and one rarely catches condensation in action in structures above ground. The practical rule suggested by the authors has been discussed in relation to assessment of habitability (see ¶21), and consists of experimentally locating the 'cold wall' by means of optical scanning thermometers. An immediate measurement of the surface temperatures of the walls, floor, and ceiling of the premises is thereby obtained. The surrounding ground temperatures can also be measured when a damaging external micro-climate is suspected. The surface having the lowest temperature is the culprit because it subtracts heat from the air and brings the air to saturation, or close to it,

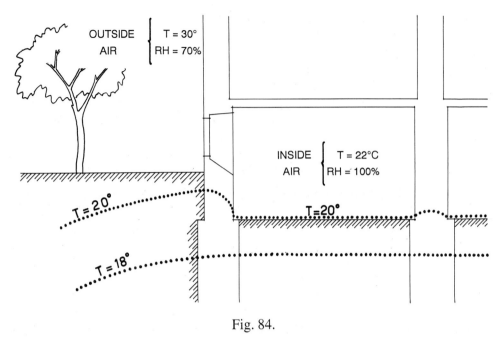

Fig. 84.

In temperate climates, spring/summer condensation typically occurs in basements without winter heating (thermal inertia of low winter temperatures in the ground and wall fabric).

depending on how often the air is replenished from outside. The surface having the lowest thermal value draws condensation to itself just as the lowest point in the ground collects rainwater.

There is only one means to combat condensation: heat. The air must be kept from cooling in one of the two following ways: either the insulation of the locale is increased (which increases resistance to heat dispersion), or additional calories are supplied to compensate for heat loss. Heating is the generic remedy in both winter and summer (yes, also in summer) but is not to be recommended when static air can draw moisture from the environment itself, as happens when there are evaporating surfaces (laundries, damp walls, etc.). In fact, static air tends to become saturated *at a constant temperature whenever there is water to evaporate and heat* to cause evaporation. This situation is sometimes found in ground floors and basements where the floors and walls are already invaded by that other fearsome kind of humidity: rising damp. In cellars, even those without winter heating, the moisture of the warm floor passes into the air; when the air becomes saturated, condensation is then deposited on the upper parts of the walls, on the vaulting, on the window panes and on all the coldest parts of the structure. In winter the air acts as a vehicle for the continuous passage of water from the parts that are warm (being in contact with the ground) to the surfaces of the parts that are cold (being in the air). The whole environment becomes extremely damp, due to the ground in the lower area and to the air in the upper area.

When only surface condensation is involved, moisture manifests itself in two different ways, depending on the external structure of the bodies it touches. It *wets* impermeable surfaces such as metal, marble, ceramic, cement rendering, paint, and it *stains* (to a slightly darker color tone) when the surface is absorbent, as in plaster, lime rendering, brick or tile. It is very abundant on the surfaces of bodies that are good heat conductors and thus do not store, but immediately disperse, the heat liberated by the condensation, remaining cold themselves. Thus, in winter when there is a warm, damp wind, it is easier to find a film of condensed water on metals than on stone. Among stones, more condensation is found on those with high specific gravity such as basalt, sienite, granite and Carrara marble, and on the treads and risers of stairways. Over the years, such a veil of condensation causes the ruin of the marble facings in cold churches.

When condensation is present, it is necessary to verify, by a simple calculation, which part of the masonry structure has insufficient thermal protection and provokes the phenomenon by excessive heat dispersion. The most exposed structures are:

- roofs and outer walls, for winter condensation
- floors of stories over open, cold cellars, for all condensation
- floors directly over ground, and all embanked walls, for spring and summer condensation

For reasons of health, the total thermal resistance per m of dispersive surface should not go below that limit of 1 [0.9] or 0.8 [0.7] which we have indicated in ¶21 on *Practical assessment of habitability* as the minimum protection necessary in the two typical climates of zone A and zone B. The total thermal resistance of a wall, usually indicated as R, is the inverse of the total coefficient of transmission K used in heating technology, i.e., the inverse of the number of calories that escape ($R = 1/K$).

To verify the total thermal resistance per m of a wall, roof, or floor, after ascertaining the type of structure (brick, sandstone, blocks, reinforced concrete, etc.) and the exact thickness expressed in meters, one applies the well-known formula:

$$[1] \qquad R = \frac{1}{\alpha_1} + \frac{D_1}{\lambda_1} + \frac{D_2}{\lambda_2} \ldots \ldots + \frac{1}{\alpha_2}$$

in which the symbols stand for the following:

R = total thermal resistance expressed in $\dfrac{m^2 h\,°C}{kcal}$ or $\dfrac{m^2\,°C}{W}$

α_1 = coefficient of admission of the heat of internal air to the inside wall; usually this is made to equal 7 [8.1] for the horizontal or upward passage of heat and to equal 5 [5.8] for the downward passage of heat, e.g., from the air in a room to the floor

α_2 = coefficient of emission from the outer wall face to the outside air; usually this is made to equal 20 [23.2] under normal ventilation, but can reach 50 [58.0] if the outer wall is exposed to exceptionally high winds, over 40 km/h

$\lambda_1 \lambda_2 ... =$ coefficients of the internal thermal conductivity of the successive layers of different materials that make up the wall, if it is not homogeneous

$D_1 D_2$ = thicknesses (expressed in meters) of the various successive layers

For example, the resistance of a wall of common brick ($\lambda = 0.7$), 0.55 m thick, including plaster, will be:

$$R = \frac{1}{7} + \frac{0.55}{0.7} + \frac{1}{20}$$

$$= 0.14 + 0.79 + 0.05$$

$$= 0.98 \text{ or, in round figures, } 1 \frac{m^2 h \,°C}{kcal} \text{ or } [0.86] \frac{m^2 \,°C}{W}$$

To apply formula [1] correctly, one must think of the wall as separated into different, homogeneous, vertical layers (plaster, brick, air, etc.). In such a case, the thermal resistance of each layer increases with its thickness. The air layer is an exception, however, for its resistance reaches a maximum ($R = 0.18$) at a thickness of 4-6 cm; beyond this, air currents impede a further increase in resistance. Thus, air spaces more than 5-6 cm thick are a waste of space (fig. 104, p. 160).

The technology of thermo-insulating construction materials is based entirely on careful incorporation of air spaces, large or small (fig. 85). Notable progress in the production of bricks was made first by the introduction of hollow bricks with horizontal air cells, and later of blocks with vertical cavities, followed by perforated bricks (common bricks lightened with a number of vertical holes). These perforated bricks, made with special clay and put in place with a thin bed of cement mortar, now bear heavy loads

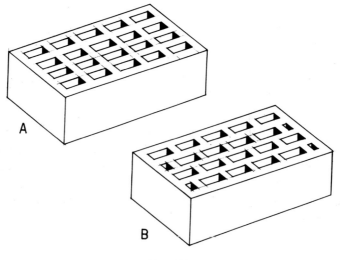

Fig. 85.

The reciprocal position of air spaces should be carefully studied. If the holes are offset, the route of the heat flow is lengthened and thermal protection grows in any given weight of block. Block B offers about 22% more resistance than block A.

(on the order of 25 kg/cm) while offering thermal resistance equal to that of the old hollow brick with horizontal cells. In Basel, Switzerland, a twelve-story building (without reinforced concrete frame!) was constructed with an exterior wall entirely of perforated brick, uniformly 38 cm thick (three bricks) from ground floor to roof. Having uniform thickness makes sense because the thermal protection must also be uniform. This construction was a triumph for perforated brick.

Although the production of bricks of high compressive strength from heavy vitrified or ceramic paste may represent an undoubtedly brilliant technical achievement, from the health viewpoint it is not unlike the production of vibrated cement. Such compact, non-porous materials, which can be used in ever thinner sizes, are hygienically questionable because they have no insulating properties.

Fig. 86.

Given equal volume and weight, a solid, light block provides more insulation than a pressed block with large air spaces.

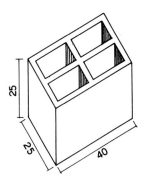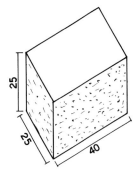

As a general criterion for selecting materials, it should be borne in mind that, *given the same basic material and apparent specific gravity of a construction element*, a solid, light, multi-cellular block provides better insulation than a block that has been pressed or vibrated and in which thermal resistance is obtained with large holes (fig. 86). As regards vibrated or steam-treated cement, the indiscriminate use of blocks made from a mixture with a high, effective specific gravity (i.e., related to the volume of the conglomerate and not to the apparent specific gravity of the block) for construction of public housing and rural homes is to be condemned from the viewpoint of occupants' health.

In effect, as can be seen from the formula [1], the thermal protection of any layer is directly proportional to its thickness and inversely proportional to its coefficient of internal thermal conductivity. The higher a material's conductivity, the less effective it is at protecting against heat and cold. Internal conductivity, usually indicated by the Greek letter λ (lambda), increases as the specific gravity and moisture content increase. In practice, all materials in place contain a percentage of water which increases their thermal conductivity with respect to the theoretical condition of the dry state.

Exterior walls, for instance, even though nominally dry, contain more water than interior walls and have a higher λ.

In Table IV below, where we have grouped the coefficients of thermal conductivity, we indicate first the specific gravity of each material and then the two λ values that every

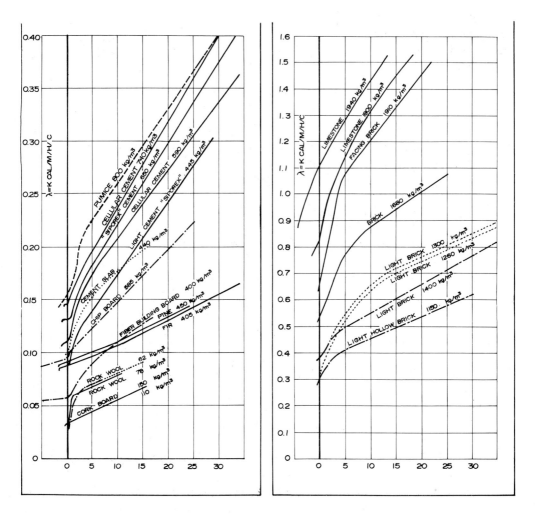

Fig. 87.

Jesperson's graphs: influence of moisture content on the thermal conductivity of construction materials.

porous material can assume as a result of the moisture it inevitably acquires when used in normally dry interior or exterior walls (in a healthy atmosphere, that is).[1]

When walls and materials are impregnated with water (rising damp, leaking roofs, winter condensation, driving rain), the λ value no longer has any significance as far as health is concerned because the premises become uninhabitable. Thus the thermal conductivity of saturated materials is important in industry (notably refrigeration), but not in construction.

---

1   The table, for the most part, gives the values indicated by Cadiergues.

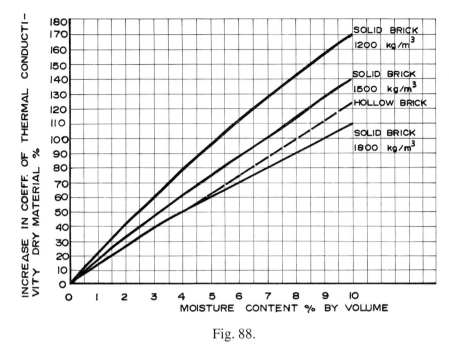

Fig. 88.

The influence of moisture on the thermal conductivity of brick. (From Industria Italiana dei Laterizi, 1956.)

The reader should also note that the theoretical λ value of any building material, as measured and certified by university or industrial laboratories, applies to *completely oven-dried material*, in conformity with laboratory standards. It is important to remember this point so that the figures can be adjusted to reflect the practical λ value of the material in place. In Table IV, for example, cellular concrete with a specific gravity of 800 kg/m^3 has values of 0.36 [0.42] and 0.42 [0.49] respectively, depending on whether it is situated in an interior or exterior wall; its theoretical λ in the dry state is much lower: 0.23 [0.27]. An official laboratory certificate would have indicated this theoretical value, which is of little practical use.

To convert theoretical λ values, given by analysis of totally dry materials, to the practical (and for our purposes, essential) values for materials in place, see the chart below on *Percentages of increase of thermal conductivity with respect to the dry state*, taken from Cadiergues. This chart may be useful, although the figures are quite approximate and entire categories of widely used materials are not covered. Figure 87 gives two well-known graphs by H.B. Jesperson of Denmark, which are more complete. For brick, the graph in fig. 88 is proposed by the European Association of Brick Manufacturers.

Finally, since we have advised the use of various types of panels and linings in restoration of premises suffering from condensation (Table III, ¶23), the following pedestrian advice should be remembered in order to avoid disappointment: mineral wool (rock or glass) is made into magnificent insulating products in semi-rigid panels, but it absorbs water in quantity if put into contact with damp walls. In such a case, they need only be protected with bituminized paper or polyethylene sheathing so that their extraordinary thermal protection is not lost. Similarly, panels of wood strips and binder are, in practice, permeable by air, sometimes greatly so, but the λ values indicated in Table IV do not envisage a corresponding heat loss. Therefore, such panels must be protected by applying a sheet or plaster or whatever is at hand, if there is any likelihood of a difference of air pressure between the two faces which would cause heat loss through air movement.

CHART OF PERCENTAGE INCREASE IN THERMAL CONDUCTIVITY AS COMPARED TO THE DRY STATE (from Cadiergues).

Material	% of increase in wall	
	inner	outer
Bricks	20	45
Stones	55	80
Cement mortar	30	60
Plaster	30	60
Concrete	40	70
Wood and fiber panels with organic binder	16	19
Particle board with magnesic binder	19	25
Peat	25	40
Cork	3	5

¶40. Principles of defense against condensation.

— Four general principles to combat condensation may be followed. The first is to reduce the production of water vapor; this applies if the vapor originates inside the premises. The second is to eliminate (if possible) heavy materials that conduct heat (marble, cement, vitrified brick) and to remedy excess heat dispersion by adding thermal resistance (insulation). The third may seem paradoxical, for it goes against common usage; it involves using artificial summer heating instead of the damaging ventilating fans that are so frequently and unwisely advised. The fourth and last also goes against common practice; it involves occasionally going without winter heating (which increases evaporation from damp walls when rising damp is also present) and using moderate natural ventilation with dry, cold air (an excellent vehicle for vapor) instead.

Winter condensation. Overcrowding. Cement-block buildings.

To avoid the possibility of condensation in homes, well-constructed walls should guarantee a minimum thermal resistance of $R = 1$ $m^2h°C/kcal$ [0.9 $m^2°C/W$] in cold climates and 0.8 [0.7] in warmer climates. These minimums are fixed in relation to sensible use of the premises; abnormal use that can strain the thermal protection of well-built walls in winter are overcrowding and excessive gas combustion (see fig. 158, p. 233).

TABLE IV – COEFFICIENTS OF THE INTERNAL THERMAL CONDUCTIVITY OF WALLS AND VARIOUS MATERIALS
(at normal temperatures and moisture conditions in buildings)

STRUCTURE OR MATERIAL	Specific gravity kg/m³	Coeffic. λ = (kcal/mh°C) wall		Coeffic. λ = (W/m°C) wall	
		inner	outer	inner	outer
Brick walls:					
– solid brick	1600	0.54	0.65	0.63	0.75
	1800	0.62	0.75	0.72	0.87
	2000	0.74	0.90	0.86	1.04
– light brick, hollow brick (with air cells parallel to the wall)	800	0.24	0.29	0.28	0.34
	1000	0.29	0.35	0.34	0.40
	1200	0.35	0.42	0.40	0.48
	1400	0.43	0.52	0.50	0.60
Tuff walls (large chips, chunks or squared blocks):	1300	0.31	0.37	0.36	0.43
	1400	0.36	0.44	0.41	0.51
	1500	0.45	0.54	0.52	0.62
	1600	0.52	0.64	0.60	0.74
Walls of calcareous stone, sandstone or light schists:	1600	0.68	0.79	0.79	0.92
	1800	0.68	0.95	0.79	1.10
	2000	1.01	1.17	1.17	1.36
	2200	1.18	1.37	1.37	1.59
Renderings:					
– normal lime/sand	1600	0.45	0.56	0.52	0.65
	1800	0.58	0.72	0.67	0.84
– normal lime/pozzolana	1200	0.32	0.37	0.37	0.43
	1400	0.40	0.47	0.47	0.55
– light, of lime/pozzolana	600	0.13	0.15	0.15	0.17
	800	0.19	0.22	0.22	0.26
– plaster (gypsum)	1000	0.38	0.46	0.44	0.53
	1200	0.48	0.60	0.56	0.70
– porous plaster, applied in slabs	600	0.25	0.30	0.29	0.35
– cement and sand	2000	0.73	0.90	0.85	1.05
	2200	0.94	1.20	1.09	1.40
Heavy natural stone, alone:					
– gneiss and granite	from 2400 to 3000		2.8		3.3
			2.9		3.4

STRUCTURE OR MATERIAL	Specific gravity kg/m^3	Coeffic. λ = (kcal/mh°C) wall		Coeffic. λ = (W/m°C) wall	
		inner	outer	inner	outer
– marble	from 2500 to 2850		2.7 3.0		3.1 3.5
– basalt	from 2800 to 3000		3.0 3.2		3.5 3.7
– slate: across lamination parallel to lamination	2700 "		1.5 2.4		1.7 2.8
Walls of heavy stone: For an average composition of 70% stone and 30% lime/sand mortar, one takes an average λ equal to ¾ the above values.					
Various concretes:					
– with ground brick, or lean, or cellular	1600 1800	0.54 0.68	0.63 0.80	0.63 0.79	0.73 0.93
– with regular proportion of cement (not reinforced): not vibrated	2000	0.85	1.00	0.99	1.12
vibrated	2200 2400	1.00 1.20	1.20 1.40	1.12 1.40	1.40 1.63
– normal for reinforced concrete	2300 2400	1.20	1.40	1.40	1.63
– non-cellular concrete of light aggregates (slag, pumice, pozzolana pebbles, vermiculite, obsidian, etc.)	600 800 1000 1200 1400	0.13 0.19 0.24 0.32 0.40	0.15 0.22 0.28 0.37 0.47	0.15 0.22 0.28 0.37 0.47	0.17 0.26 0.33 0.43 0.55
Normal cellular concretes	600 800 1000 1200 1400	0.25 0.36 0.50 0.65 0.81	0.29 0.42 0.58 0.76 0.94	0.29 0.42 0.58 0.76 0.94	0.34 0.49 0.67 0.88 1.09
Fillers of loose materials (that do not draw water by absorption):					
– mineral powders, fossil powder type	200 400 600 800 1000 1200 1400	0.06 0.09 0.12 0.16 0.20 0.25 0.30	0.07 0.10 0.14 0.18 0.23 0.29 0.34	0.07 0.10 0.14 0.19 0.23 0.29 0.35	0.08 0.12 0.16 0.21 0.27 0.34 0.40

STRUCTURE OR MATERIAL	Specific gravity kg/m^3	Coeffic. λ = (kcal/mh°C) wall		Coeffic. λ = (W/m°C) wall	
		inner	outer	inner	outer
– granular, such as pumice and cinders	400	0.12	0.15	0.14	0.17
	600	0.14	0.18	0.16	0.21
	800	0.17	0.21	0.20	0.24
	1000	0.21	0.25	0.24	0.29
– vermiculite (expanded mica)	100	0.05	0.06	0.06	0.07
– sand	1600	0.36	0.42	0.42	0.49
– crushed brick	1000	0.29	0.35	0.34	0.41
– gravel	1800	0.43	0.50	0.50	0.58
	2000	0.51	0.59	0.59	0.69
	2200	0.60	0.70	0.70	0.81
– wood shavings, sawdust, cork chips	200	0.057	0.059	0.066	0.068
	250	0.059	0.061	0.068	0.070
	300	0.061	0.063	0.070	0.073

Wood (as blocks, planks or plywood, always cross-grain and not exposed to rain):

STRUCTURE OR MATERIAL	Specific gravity kg/m^3	inner	outer	inner	outer
– softwood (fir, poplar, pine, etc.)	500	0.110	0.115	0.13	0.13
	600	0.130	0.135	0.15	0.16
– hardwood (chestnut, beech, oak)	700	0.145	0.150	0.17	0.17
	900	0.185	0.190	0.22	0.22

Boards of vegetable material (not exposed to rain):

STRUCTURE OR MATERIAL	Specific gravity kg/m^3	inner	outer	inner	outer
–shredded wood cemented in slabs (e.g., with magnesite binder)	200	0.052	0.055	0.06	0.06
N.B. – The indicated λ values presume	300	0.057	0.060	0.07	0.07
that permeability to air has been inhibited,	400	0.070	0.074	0.08	0.09
if necessary, with renderings or other	500	0.087	0.091	0.10	0.11
facings.	600	0.105	0.110	0.12	0.13
– hardboard or fiberboard with synthetic or glue binder (e.g., 'Masonite')	200	0.037	0.038	0.04	0.04
	400	0.044	0.045	0.05	0.05
	600	0.060	0.061	0.07	0.07
	900	0.100	0.105	0.12	0.12
	1000	0.120	0.125	0.14	0.14
– cork board:					
expanded	120	0.033	0.034	0.04	0.04
with casein binder	200	0.040	0.041	0.05	0.05
with bituminous binder	300	0.049	0.050	0.06	0.06
	400	0.056	0.057	0.07	0.07
	500	0.063	0.064	0.07	0.07

VARIOUS MATERIALS IN PLACE UNDER NORMAL CONDITIONS OF TEMPERATURE AND HUMIDITY	specific gravity kg/m³	Coefficient λ = kcal/m h°C	Coefficient λ = W/m°C
Mineral fibers (which do not draw water by absorption):			
– *asbestos felt,* mats, molded with binder, pipe, insulation, slabs	200	0.048	0.06
	300	0.056	0.07
	500	0.072	0.08
	800	0.130	0.15
	1000	0.150	0.17
	1200	0.180	0.21
– *mineral wool* (rock or glass)			
a) in mats or blankets between bituminized sheets or (better for construction) in standard semi-rigid felts, 1-0.50 m, organic bonded	from 30 to 150	from 0.030 to 0.045	0.03 0.05
b) in rigid slabs, as above	from 150 to 300	0.05	0.06
c) *idem,* in slabs compressed between floors	from 150 to 300	0.075	0.09
Asbestos cement:			
– in light slabs	1000 1200	0.25	0.29
– in compressed slabs and shingles	1800 2000	0.65	0.76
Magnesia cement:	800	0.14	0.16
Waterproofing:			
– asphalt	2150	0.80	0.93
– bitumen	1050	0.14	0.16
– tarred cardboard	1100	0.12	0.14
Expanded synthetic resins (e.g., polyvinylchloride, polystyrene, polyurethane, etc.):	from 15 to 60	from 0.027 to 0.040	0.03 0.05
Linoleum:	1180	0.16	0.19
Compressed straw:	400	0.07	0.08
Paper and cardboard:	700	0.12	0.14
Glass (windowpanes):		0.70	0.81
Ceramic (tiles):	1900	0.60	0.70
Porcelain (tiles):	2300	0.90	1.05
Rubber:			
– natural	1150	0.20	0.23

VARIOUS MATERIALS IN PLACE UNDER NORMAL CONDITIONS OF TEMPERATURE AND HUMIDITY	specific gravity kg/m³	Coefficient λ = kcal/m h°C	Coefficient λ = W/m°C
– spongy	200	0.04	0.05
	400	0.06	0.07
– synthetic	1250	0.40	0.47
Air - Water - Earth:			
– snow (light or compressed)	200	0.13	0.15
	400	0.29	0.34
	800	1.07	1.24
– water	1000	0.52	0.60
– perfectly still air		0.02	0.02
– soils:			
dry gravelly or sandy		0.40	0.46
dry clayey		0.50	0.58
common, with normal moisture		1.00	1.16
arable, with about 15% water		2.00	2.33

For hollow blocks of cement with pumice or volcanic ash or other light granules, the calculation of thermal resistance is made case by case on the basis of the specific gravity of the concrete and on the number of air cells traversed by the heat flow. In the wall shown in figure 163 (p. 242), each block has two air cells, but the heat flow crosses only one. Thus the wall's total thermal resistance has the value $R = 0.60$ [0.52], which is insufficient for any climate. When the heat flow crosses two air cells, one has $R = 0.70 \div 0.72$ [0.60÷0.62], which is still insufficient. With three air cells, one finally reaches the value $R = 0.84$ [0.72], which is acceptable for warm climates, provided that light concrete is used, i.e., specific gravity not above 1200 kg/m³. The above values are indicative only.

To put these words into figures, we cite some data measured in France[2] in a small, four-room house containing 170 m³ of air. It was found that the occupants generated 25-30 kg of water vapor in 24 hours, corresponding to an average of 6.1-7.3 g per m³ per hour.

Human evaporation and breathing produce 50 to 80 g of water vapor an hour per adult. Gas combustion produces 800 g of vapor per m³ of gas consumed. A family commonly uses around 4 m³ of gas a day.

---

2   "L'eau dans les murs," *Cahiers du centre scientifique et technique du bâtiment*, No.28, 2nd trimester 1958, Paris.

The average hourly vapor production figures found in the French study were as follows:

- 8 g/m^{3}h – in overcrowded housing
- 5 g/m^{3}h – in uncrowded public housing
- 2 g/m^{3}h – in middle-class housing

As a remedy for winter dampness in homes, French health experts now favor more active ventilation, regulated so the efficiency of the heating is not reduced. This involves at least *two changes of air* per hour for the entire house (heating calculations are usually based on only one change). Rather than intermittently opening the windows, which is damaging, the air change is effected with window vents or exhaust fans that have an acceptable and continuous action.

Reclamation of housing that is damp in winter, using intensified heating and ventilation, could thus be obtained with a running cost equivalent to a third more than the normal heating expense, assuming that work to improve the thermal protection of the outer walls and roof is not contemplated.

Let us consider the wall of solid brick in figure 89. It is an exterior wall of good thickness (0.60 m), and has a thermal resistance of $1/K = R = 1$ [0.9] which, as we have seen, guarantees complete health protection, even in cold climates. In fact, when the outdoor temperature is -1°C and the indoor temperature is 18°C with 60% RH, there is certainly condensation (so-called 'interstitial') at that given depth where the water vapor (which fills the pores of the wall along with air) is cooled enough to reach dewpoint. This phenomenon produces a negligible amount of condensation which has no effect on the inner wall face and does not cause the slightest damage to health. All goes well *because the RH of the inside air is 60%, a normal amount* for homes in winter.

However, if overcrowding (many people sleeping in a small room) or an unventilated gas stove cause the RH to rise to 83-85%, the zone of interstitial condensation moves toward the inner wall face and afflicts the wall surface with an abundant, continuous deposition of liquid water. This happens because condensation is produced at around 15°C when the RH is 83-85% – precisely the surface temperature of the inner wall when the inside air is 18°C and the outside air is -1°C. Therefore, the environment becomes damp, the wall's initial thermal resistance decreases rapidly; a vicious circle begins, with moisture in the walls causing cooling and cooling causing more moisture to form on the wall surface.

It is an error to believe that intensified heating always compensates for possible inadequacy in thermal protection. This generic remedy is only effective within given limits. For instance, when a structure is decidedly inferior in resistance (a skylight of concrete and glass, or a two-brick thick wall constructed of solid, heavy brick – $R = 0.5$), it would be unwise to raise the heat alone, as might be requested to meet user requirements (in a laboratory, an operating room, etc.). With the usual outdoor temperature at -1°C and RH of the inside air at 65%, condensation would form even if the temperature were forced up to 22°C.

In conclusion, good construction must always assure, as a general rule, the minimum thermal protection specified in ¶21. If condensation forms from excess vapor

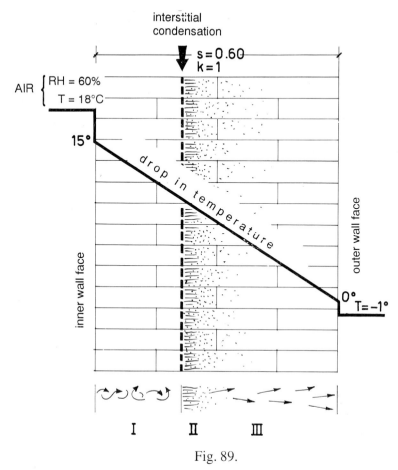

Fig. 89.

Diagram of water movement due to winter condensation (vertical section): I) zone of water vapor passage by diffusion II) condensation zone (formation of liquid water) III) zone of capillary advance from wet to dry.

produced by special user requirements, the following general rule should be kept in mind: *Excess water vapor should be combatted with ventilation in combination with an adequate rise in heat.*

When condensation occurs at night (bedrooms, dormitories), it is expedient to keep the heating on all night. Indeed, the fact that many systems are turned off at night often limits the effectiveness of intensified heating. In cold places, winter condensation is often a nocturnal phenomenon that arises after the heat goes off. At this point, the inner face of the wall begins to cool down while the RH of the air increases, especially in sleeping quarters.

One way to protect oneself is to delay the cooling of the wall. The lower the wall's thermal inertia, the faster it will cool; this thermal inertia is directly related to the weight

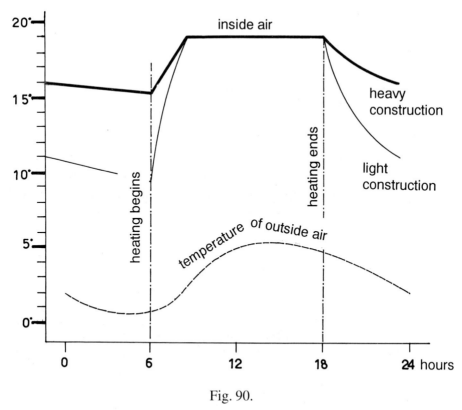

Fig. 90.

Behavior of air temperature with intermittent heating, depending on the building's thermal inertia.

per square meter of wall. Figure 90 shows the effect of light or heavy walls on the air temperature when the furnace is on from 6 a.m. to 6 p.m. daily.

There are two different ways to slow nocturnal cooling and prevent condensation:

- Increase the wall's *thermal inertia* (i.e., its thickness and weight) so much that its stored heat warms the air when the furnace is off.
- Increase the wall's *thermal resistance* (with light insulation) so much that it keeps the inside air warm when the heating is off.

In our view, the problem of wall thickness must be judged by health standards and must not be reduced to a mere question of winter fuel savings. The German regulation DIN No.4108, for example, is compiled exclusively for the use of heating engineers. Its requirements for normal-weight walls could often lead to rather insufficient wall thicknesses. In fact, if one starts with the minimum thermal protection values prescribed by the German guidelines for normal walls, from one face to the other, and adds the additional thermal resistances of immission and emission (0.19 for walls and roof, and 0.25 for floors), one gets the results below. The figures refer to the three climate zones into which Germany is divided for the purposes of these regulations.

CHART OF MINIMUM PROTECTION REQUIRED
BY GERMAN HEATING STANDARDS

Specific Masonry Structure	Total thermal protection, including resistances of immission and emission $R = m^2h°C/kcal$		
	Zone 1	Zone 2	Zone 3
Exteriorr walls	0.64	0.74	0.84
Stairwells	0.49	0.49	0.59
Cellar ceilings	1.00	1.00	1.00
Roofing over open passages	1.75	2.00	2.25
Roofs and terraces	0.84	0.84	0.84

It is interesting to note that in Germany, according to the unified standard, the minimum protection requirements seem rather low, at least for outer walls, roofs and terraces, perhaps because the major heat losses are offset by the generalized adoption of double glazing. It must also be clarified that these rather low protection figures have been fixed and accepted by heating engineers, who must be able to plan heating systems even for old homes with very little protection. The problem is thus treated from a technical standpoint, not a health one.

Quite different values of minimum protection were officially suggested in England by the famous Eggerton Committee which set the standards for post-war reconstruction at the request of the Ministry of Labour. The minimum thermal protection advised for the exterior walls of living areas and roofs was $R = 1.33$ [1.14], whereas $R = 1.03$ [0.89] was considered adequate for other rooms. As one can see, values for new public housing in England are considerably higher than those accepted by German heating engineers, which shows that *the hygienic problem of the protection needed in a new, well-built house is entirely different from the technical problem of how to heat an old, badly built house in winter.* The engineers who manage to install such heating may be very good, but the inhabitants will still suffer in transitional seasons and with every vicissitude of winter and summer climate.

In Italy, maximum damage from winter condensation occurs in buildings constructed with cement blocks. As stated, light concrete offers thermal resistance of $R = 0.60, 0.72, 0.84$ [0.52, 0.62, 0.72], depending on whether the air flow crosses one, two or three air cells. All of these values are insufficient for the climate in the Po valley or the Alps, and the first two are also inadequate for maritime zones. Beware of cement blocks!

In houses, the first condensation stains appear where the thermal protection is least adequate: windowsills and areas adjacent to corner columns. The corner is the weakest thermal point in reinforced framed buildings. Hans Knodel describes an original experiment in *Gesundheits.* A pomade of wheat flour and skim milk was brushed in a horizontal

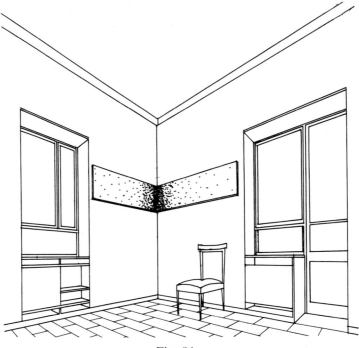

Fig. 91.

In framed constructions, the wall area most exposed to condensation is the part adjacent to the corner column (experiment by H. Knodel).

strip along both corner walls and left to dry, as indicated in figure 91. The experiment was conducted in January-February 1954, when the outside temperature ranged between -10°C and -20°C. After four to six weeks, an abundant growth of mold developed in the corner area because condensation immediately activated the implantation of spores on the pomade strip. Near the center of the walls, the spores did not take hold because the pomade remained dry, having little condensation.

Starting from 18°C, which is the usual temperature required in centrally heated premises, we indicate below in round numbers the temperature decrease that will provoke condensation.

TEMPERATURE DECREASES BELOW 18°C THAT CAUSE CONDENSATION

RH of air at 18°C	95%	90%	85%	80%	75%	70%	65%	60%
Decrease provoking condensation (°C)	0.5	1.5	2.5	3.5	4.5	5.5	6.5	7.5
Dew-point temperature (°C)	17.5	16.5	15.5	14.5	13.5	12.5	11.5	10.5

Put roughly, at 95% RH (i.e., a saturation deficit of 5%) only a half-degree decrease in *any inside temperature* (between 20°C and 5°C) nears dew point. With each further 5% of saturation deficit, one further degree of temperature decrease will bring condensation. The following practical formula expresses the relationship of the temperature of the inside air (T_i), its relative humidity (RH%) and the temperature at which condensation is likely to occur (T_c):

$$[2] \qquad T_c = T_i - (0.5 + \frac{95 - RH\%}{5})$$

For example, take a closed room in winter, where the central mass of air is 15°C and the RH is 70%. The air layer in contact with the exterior wall will be cooled somewhat and will reach dewpoint when the wall temperature is equal to or less than:

$$[2] \qquad T = 15 - (0.5 + \frac{95 - 70}{5})$$

$$= 15 - 5.5$$

$$= 9.5°C$$

Therefore, condensation forms and wets the wall only when the wall temperature falls to 9.5°C or below. Formula [2] is applicable for RH figures rounded off by 5% and for internal temperatures between 20°C and 5°C. The formula, however, is only a rough guide which can be useful for a first opinion. If a totally accurate determination is necessary, one must use the tables in air-conditioning manuals which provide the water vapor pressure and saturated weight at any given air temperature.

Intermittent heating provokes winter condensation primarily in bedrooms, where the sleepers' breathing produces water vapor. Indeed, good central heating causes mold to develop in the most elegant of modern homes, complete with every comfort, where such a vulgar flaw would seem technically improbable. For instance, two banal defects are sometimes tolerated in reinforced concrete buildings, leading to disputes when the premises are occupied. Both defects are due to insignificant, minor construction economies. The first consists of planning stairwells in thin, reinforced concrete (for fire protection) without improving their thermal resistance with a lining of hollow brick or some other material. Condensation thus appears on the apartment walls bordering the stairwell. The second defect occurs where an intensive building project is going on next to a vacant lot. The end walls of one building are built thinly because they are meant eventually to be partition walls once an adjacent building is erected. Sometimes, though, it takes years for the next building to rise, and meanwhile the end rooms fill with mold. When mold appears and the unpleasant odor of the spores spreads through a room, it means that *water is present in the plaster* of the inner wall face and that evaporation is unable to eliminate it. This is a serious situation.

In walls built of capillary material (brick, tuff, soft sandstone), limited condensation is not damaging if the moisture, passing through the wall to the outer surface, can evaporate in the open air. Although analysis of the inner part of the wall might indicate modest amounts of moisture, one finds that the water is carried from the inside to the outside, so long as the inexcusable error of applying cement or waterproof renderings is not committed. When the inner wall face is lined with cement, rivulets of condensation run down it and collect on the floor; when the outer wall face is so lined, water accumulates in the wall, which becomes damp throughout. Both cases create unhealthy conditions.

When moisture can pass freely, its movement is affected by two factors: capillarity and evaporation. Capillary material absorbs condensation and spreads it toward the driest area, the outer face. There, evaporation eliminates the water, impedes saturation and keeps capillary power active (figs. 89 and 92).

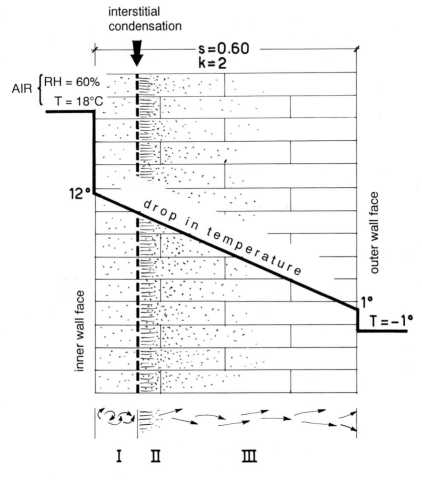

Fig. 92.

In the same wall as shown in fig. 89, the heat loss (coefficient K) increases if the fabric is already invaded by rising damp. The surface of interstitial condensation moves toward the inner wall face and may even reach it.

If a wall is built of heavy, anti-capillary stone, such as compact limestone, gneiss or basalt, or with cement blocks, the material impedes the transverse passage of moisture and causes it to accumulate on the inner side of the wall. Disastrous consequences ensue from a health standpoint. Reinforced concrete (fig. 93) causes the same unfortunate situation. In Italy, given the prevalence of masonry over wood construction, there is always a remedy at hand against condensation: a counterwall of hollow bricks with an airtight cavity between.

According to I.S. Cammerer, when one speaks of a wall's 'breathing,' one conceives of it as a passage of air. In reality, due to its striking nature, the passage of water constitutes the real 'breathing' of house walls in winter. The phenomenon becomes dramatic in stable walls. The graph in figure 94 summarizes an analysis of wall samples taken at various depths in a sandstone stable wall, 47 cm thick. One sees how the absorption of water reaches the enormous value of 20.4% by weight on the inner face, and then the moisture content gradually declines within the wall, reaching a minimum of 5.24% on the face exposed to the open air.

From Cammerer's experiments one can draw the following practical conclusions:

- In order for condensation to be carried away from the inside to the outside of a wall, *two conditions are necessary:* One is that the temperature of the outside air must not fall below -1°C; the other is that the wall, rendering included, must have good capillary properties.

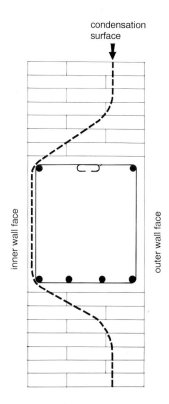

Fig. 93.

When the wall structure is not uniform as regards heat flow (as in r.c. buildings), the surface of interstitial condensation curves and nears the inner wall face in areas of greater thermal dispersion. Moisture stains appear, tracing the outline of the r.c. structure.

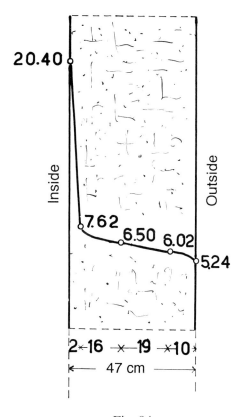

Fig. 94.

Passage of condensation moisture through a sandstone stable wall (from K. Stietenroth).

- *Common brick* walls eliminate condensation best.
- Walls of average thickness for buildings and of good capillarity (brick, tuff, sandstone) allow a passage of 300 g of water a day per m^3 of wall, in relation to a temperature gap of 16°C between indoors and out.

In a normal 4 x 5 m room with an outer wall surface of 10 m^2, excepting the window, there would be a passage of 3 kg of water in 24 hours. The renderings most suitable for water passage are highly absorbent plaster on the inner face and normally absorbent lime mortar on the outer face.

Defense against winter condensation of inside air is a problem in cold climates. Nocturnal condensation is also sometimes a problem in warm climate zones where the temperature drops sharply at night.

According to Rowley and Lund of the United States, the true, serious and consistent winter condensation that will ultimately soak a wall is produced only in those regions of the globe where the average January temperature is below 1.7°C. Therefore, in Europe the problem should not arise in France, England or the Mediterranean Basin; it is certainly important, however, in Scandinavia, Germany, Austria, the Danube Plain and, finally, the Po Valley.

In the United States, the problem has caught the attention of experts in relation to the increasing spread of air conditioning along with artificial humidification of heating air. During severe weather, the moist air produces intense localized condensation, stains, deterioration, etc. Waterproofing the outside of walls is usually considered a serious mistake. Instead, one is advised to line the inner face, varying the thickness and materials of the lining until condensation of ambient water vapor is blocked even when *the outside temperature is at its lowest*. Other experts have accepted internal condensation as a lesser evil; they use a light rendering to absorb the condensation while the wall itself is kept from becoming damp and losing its insulating properties by placing a 'vapor barrier' directly beneath the absorbent rendering (fig. 95). To summarize, in serious cases (when the January isotherm goes below 2°C, in round numbers), defense against winter conden-sation can follow one of two rules:

- Improve the thermal resistance of the inner wall.
- Impede moisture from penetrating beyond the internal rendering.

In our view, the first solution is preferable.

Panels made of wood fiber or other organic materials were once the most common types of insulation applied to inner walls. Today, there is more emphasis on expanded resin sheets (polystyrene, polyurethane, etc.), glass wool or rock wool (see Table III). It is wise to take the manufacturer's thermal resistance figures with a grain of salt, if only to allow for joints, nails, inevitable damage during installation and deterioration over time. In order to calculate thermal resistance, one must start from the actual coefficient of internal conductivity in relation to the moisture content percentage, rather than the coefficient in relation to the totally dry state. When the insulation is being installed, one must make sure that *the air layers intentionally created between the lining and the wall are airtight* and do not communicate with either the inside or the outside.

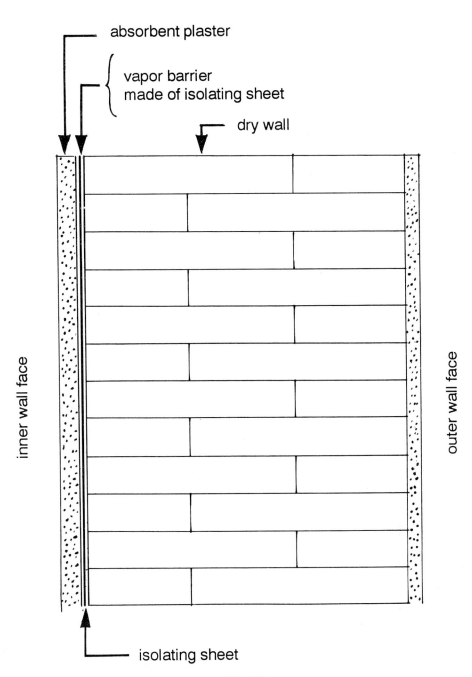

Fig. 95.

An absorbent internal rendering is currently suggested for extreme cases of winter condensation. The rendering is superimposed over a "vapor barrier" of absolutely waterproof bituminized paper or aluminum foil. Such barriers must have no rips or breaks of any kind.

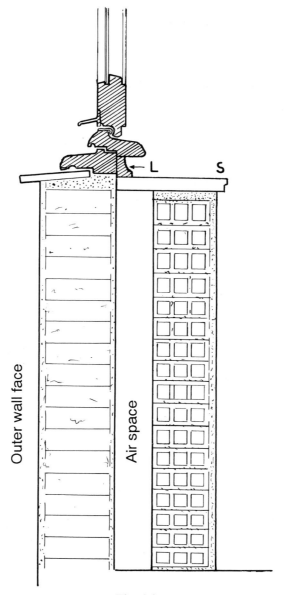

Fig. 96.

Windowsills are well protected against condensation with a brick counterwall (a sill S and a listel L connect with the old windowsill).

Windowsills are the spot most subject to condensation, even in mild climates, and consequently show repeated staining and erosion. The best remedy in this case is a counterwall of hollow bricks laid flat, with a new sill on top connected to the old one and a listel to seal off the air (fig. 96). When condensation stains appear only around the window frame, the work must be aimed at improving the air seal with a joint covering that blocks the influx of cold air. The best remedy of all is still double glazing, by which we mean true double glazing and not simply doubling the glass on an old window frame. In Sweden, double windows have become obligatory in order to save fuel; in many warmer countries this solution could even make heating superfluous. Apart from reducing noise and dust, double glazing reclaims an area of almost a square meter from the window that is normally unusable due to drafts.

W. Schüle has demonstrated that in small, freestanding, one-story buildings, the maximum savings on heating fuel is obtained by applying double-glazed windows and outer doors, not by adding insulation to the walls (Table V).

TABLE V. HEAT SAVINGS REALIZED THROUGH INSULATION OF WALLS VERSUS DOUBLE GLAZING (from W. Schüle)

TYPE OF WALL		HEAT DISPERSION				Savings compared to type 1
		Walls 97 m^2	Windows 22 m^2	Outer doors 6.6 m^2	Roof and floor 174 m^2	
1.	Non-insulated walls (K = 1.34); plain glazing; hourly calorie requirement 18,700	29.9%	34.8%	9.1%	26.2%	0
2.	Insulated walls (K = 1); plain glazing; hourly calorie req. 17,300	24.3%	37.6%	9.8%	28.3%	7.5%
3	Non-insulated walls (K = 1.34); *double glazing*; hourly calorie requirement 14,950	37.5%	21.7%	8.0%	32.8%	20%

¶41. Sirocco beading.

— This is a transitory winter phenomenon, *linked to the entry of sultry outside air into cold premises.* Beads of water are deposited on floors and all the walls, regardless of their position; it often occurs in the entries of churches and apartment buildings. *It is most frequently produced in the open areas of ground floors, especially when they are protected by thick or embanked walls, i.e., in premises that remain cold because of their high thermal inertia.*

Three conditions help to create this phenomenon in winter (the last is unpredictable and temporary):

- lack of heating
- very thick walls that are particularly cold due to their situation and structure – northern exposures, courtyards, cloisters, narrow streets, etc.
- a sudden change in the weather, with barometric depression and warmer temperatures after a period of intense cold

When this winter phenomenon occurs, it usually lasts for two or three days. It is more common in coastal and Mediterranean zones exposed to the sirocco or warm sea winds. In Rome, for example, it produces heavy condensation which supplies a considerable amount of water to plastered walls. On marble, paint and waterproof facings, the condensation appears as heavy dew which eventually runs down the wall in rivulets and collects at the base. This is the so-called 'sirocco beading' which is characteristic of lobbies, stairways, porticos and, in general, any area open to the outside sir.

Because winter periods of moist, mild weather occur only occasionally, the water supply produced in such periods is also occasional and does not change the healthfulness of an environment. Nevertheless, it can damage perishable goods, furniture, wall decorations and works of art.

The generic remedy is to keep out such warm, moist air as soon as it is noticed.

¶42.   Tendency to spring and summer condensation.

— Take a fine May day with the air temperature at 20°C and an RH of 70%. If this air enters a basement where it is cooled to 16°C, its RH will climb to 90%, going from a perfectly tolerable to a damaging level. This change in RH is due entirely to the decrease in air temperature; the absolute humidity (actual weight of water vapor per m^3 of air) remains exactly the same – 12 g in this case – whether the air is outside or inside, warm or cool.

In other words, even when the walls are perfectly dry and contribute no moisture, one finds a serious state of atmospheric humidity which *would not have happened in a warmer environment.*

This is a fairly common situation. The air is close to saturation for long, specific periods of the year although there is no source of moisture in the damp premises. Neither evaporating wall surfaces (wall analysis has proven negative) nor overcrowding of people or animals, nor gas combustion nor poor air exchange are present. Indeed, ventilation is executed precisely in order to combat the unhealthy state of the premises. In this particular case, the humidity *comes in with the outside air* and does not reach condensation.

To clarify our terms, we call this state of atmospheric humidity '**tendency to spring and summer saturation.**' As the phrase indicates, this tendency is produced especially in spring and summer, and in premises that are dry, cold, sunless or exposed to the north and that have a high thermal inertia due to very thick walls or underground location. Every spring the same scene is repeated. Mold flourishes, rheumatics complain, curators, librarians and archivists worry about their collections stored in rooms that were dry for the rest of the year.

This humidity is transitory and does not affect the inner wall fabric because it usually does not condense. Nevertheless, it is more than sufficient to make a space unhealthy for several months. This situation is common and often gives rise to disagreement between tenant and landlord, as the tenant supposes the walls are seriously damp when, in fact, they are not. Pseudo-condensation is easily diagnosed from three symptoms

- state of the air close to saturation (above 80% RH)
- state of the walls: normal at depth
- seasonal repetition of the phenomenon for a fixed period each year, from early spring to late summer, while the premises appear healthy the rest of the year:

The following six environmental conditions favor the appearance of this phenomenon:

- situation in lower stories, ground floors, basements
- absence or premature cessation of winter heating
- sunless situations or northern exposures
- little air exchange
- very thick walls, thus having notable thermal inertia
- floor laid directly on the ground

All six conditions need not be present to affect the tendency to spring/summer saturation; three or four will suffice and sometimes only two. Increased ventilation is not effective against this problem because if every mass of air that enters has time to cool, it simply adds more moisture. *The air introduced would have to be dry enough to bear the temperature decrease caused by cold walls and basement floors.* For example, returning to the case given at the beginning of this section, if outside air entering the basement at 20°C had an RH of 50% instead of 70%, it could withstand a temperature decrease to 16°C without damaging the environment's healthfulness. The RH would rise to only 65%, which is optimum for health. In such a case, ventilation would be useful because it would clear and progressively warm the environment.

In practice, it is very difficult to tell when the air is dry enough in relation to its own temperature and that of the premises in need of improvement. As a result, it is better *not to use fans at all* unless one has trained staff and instruments to check whether the fans are useful or damaging.

In particularly important cases, or where the commercial yield of the premises warrants the expense, a drying and ventilating plant can be installed. The market offers various types of these plants, which are based on the hygroscopic properties of silica gel, lithium chloride or other salts. For several hours a day, a fan draws the damp air through the hygroscopic material, where a part of the moisture is left behind. There are also electric *dehumidifiers* with localized action for storerooms.

Such installations are definitely inadvisable for homes and low-yield premises. Simple, inexpensive remedies for such cases are given in the following section on summer condensation, to which we refer the reader.

For basement quarters and small workshops, a *sure, fast and relatively inexpensive remedy for transitory seasonal atmospheric humidity* is to maintain good winter heating well into late spring, and to apply a simple wooden over-floor.

Another quick remedy is to use electric heaters temporarily during the seasonal humidity period . About five calories per hour are needed for each cubic meter of space, i.e., in round figures, 1 kW installed every 170 m^3 of the environment. The heaters should be used only when people are present.

Summer Condensation

This phenomenon is the same as that described above but in accentuated form. Here there is the added problem of liquid water condensing from the air onto the walls and floor and wetting the masonry surfaces.

The environmental conditions favorable to condensation are the same as those listed above. Condensation is often aided by the presence of *cold* walls that are also afflicted with rising damp. These walls ultimately have two distinct water supplies: the first a permanent supply from the ground, the second, only in summer, from the air. If one measures the moisture content of surface samples from the inner wall face, one finds it is much higher than the constant moisture content of depth samples. This measurement confirms the presence of two contemporaneous moisture sources which must be treated separately. The rising damp must be countered with the measures indicated in Chapter Seven, and the condensation, as a general rule, countered by measures that *impede the cooling of warm air* as it gradually enters from outside.

Common pavings of cast stone, hard or vitrified fire clay, cement (not to mention marble!) have a devilish cooling power which is much more serious than is commonly believed. When the summer air that enters by the windows strikes a cold floor and raises its temperature by 1°C, each paving square (usual size 20 x 20 cm) absorbs enough calories to cool, in turn, three cubic meters of air by 1°C. Thus, the first and most effective suggestion is to remove ruthlessly any sort of heavy material from the floor. If parquet flooring proves too expensive, one can apply simple tight planking of boards at least 2 cm thick and 4 m long, such as those used in reinforced concrete formworks. The boards are joined tongue-and-groove, planed only on the upper side and superimposed directly on the old floor. This immediately brings about a remarkable improvement.

Similarly, it is necessary to eliminate any marble or ceramic facing and harmful cement renderings. Even common renderings of lime and sand have cooling power (although inferior to that of cement) and should be replaced, assuming there is no rising damp, by some lighter rendering with a specific gravity below 800 kg/m^3, if possible.

In cellars or basements having very thick walls and floors either on the ground or over a compact mass, definitive restoration is obtained by increasing thermal resistance with two well-known structures: an anti-condensation subfloor beneath the flooring and counterwalls on the main walls. In every case, new renderings should be of light material and new flooring should be of wood.

If one must limit expenditure to the most useful work – walls or floor – it is always best to build the subfloor. If there is no space for a counterwall, a very light rendering can be used instead, once it has been ascertained that there is no rising damp. If rising damp is also present, a counterwall is indispensable.

There may also be situations where haste is required or some other factor limits the time and desire to carry out major work. So long as there is no rising damp, two quick measures against summer condensation can be used. *Either line the walls with insulating sheets or heat the premises.* As stated in ¶23, there are insulating slabs and sheets on the market to suit every case and pocket book. If insulation is used against summer condensation alone (i.e., when analysis has ruled out rising damp) the face in contact with the wall must first be spread with bitumen or a similar product to counteract mold.

The second type of quick remedy for condensation is to *have the environment warm when air enters from outside*. Heating well into late spring will suffice, or else portable electric heaters can be used during the condensation period.

Strange as it may seem, moderate summer heating in damp basements feels pleasant to those who enter or stay there; indeed, the higher the temperature and the more ruinous the sunshine outdoors, the more pleasant the heated basement seems. Some of our readers cannot fail to be astonished at the success of this measure. Precise guidelines are given in ¶56, which is specifically about summer heating to combat condensation. The use of ventilating fans in damp cellars and basements is damaging and should be avoided; this simply causes badly advised landlords and tenants to waste money and lose patience.

¶43. Moisture from subterranean air. Knapen's critical zone.

— Contrary to the old theory that groundwater comes from downward filtration of rainwater, some authors have hypothesized that it originates from condensation of the water vapor contained in subterranean air. This hypothesis is strongly contested, although it is a good explanation of the existence of springs on some mountain tops where the ground's geological configuration would make it impossible for water to be supplied through strata connected with higher-placed basins.

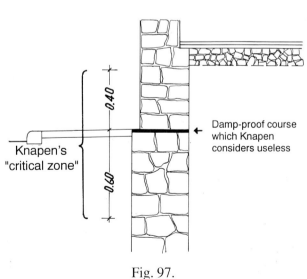

Fig. 97.

According to Kanpen, the base of a wall is subject to condensation of subterranean air for about 60 cm underground and 40 cm above ground; this would be the "critical zone."

Similarly, as regards wall moisture, Knapen has not given any weight to the idea of rising damp as supplied by capillary water. Instead, he has advanced the daring theory that moisture in the lower stories of buildings is due to condensation of the water vapor contained in the warm saturated air that escapes from the subsoil whenever there is a barometric depression.

Knapen's theories are audacious and we mention them for the sake of objectivity without endorsing them. For example, he undervalues the capillary power of walls which could not, in his view, raise water up to 3-4 m above ground; consequently the

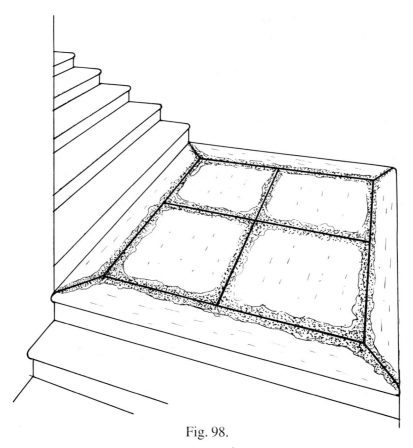

Fig. 98.

On some days of barometric depression, condensation of telluric air (which is rising through the joints) is visible around the edges of paving stones.

presence of moisture at such heights can only be explained as condensation. This leads to Knapen's truly unpalatable statement that a damp-proof course through a wall is of no use (fig. 97).

Knapen has been particularly concerned with the humidity that one finds along the wall base in almost every house; he speaks of a critical zone which he first identified in posts fixed in the ground and then noticed in walls as well. This zone is the most directly subject to condensation when dewpoint is reached, notable during barometric depressions. The warm, foul air, which leaves the city soil at a temperature of 12°C finds its way blocked by cement, asphalt and paving, so it infiltrates along the walls. In winter, as it contacts the base area of the walls, it cools to dewpoint; the phenomenon might also occur in summer, due to nocturnal cooling, but would not be as intense. The critical zone is about a meter high, exceeds 60 cm below grade and 40 cm above, and is found in all buildings.

Certainly, there is no doubt that condensation from telluric air exists. Knapen is quite right in his observation that such condensation is even visible on the marble slabs and paving stones of courtyards, gardens, open vestibules and porches. This phenomenon is especially evident early in the morning, when the central areas of the slabs and stones often seem dry and the edges along the joints appear wet (fig. 98). Air fills the pores of the ground between the ground surface and the top of the water table for a height that may vary from an average of 1-2 m up to 20 m or more. It should be borne in mind, however, that almost all cities are built alongside rivers or on the sea coast and, therefore, the groundwater table is never very far beneath the surface. Since the porosity of loose soil is around 50% on average, every cubic meter of soil can contain half a cubic meter of telluric air. Many factors can cause this air to rise; those that have an important quantitative effect are barometric depression, differing temperature with respect to the outside, and excesses of temperature in the air contained in houses. Telluric air, especially in cities, is noted for being unwholesome due to the presence of gas seepage from the mains and noxious sewer gas; some authors describe it as 'urban malaria.' Closed basements that are well heated in winter exert a drawing action on the air in the ground below. Still, it is impossible to explain how condensation could occur when the temperature of the overlying air is higher than that of the air in the ground.

Fig. 99.

Unexpected moisture in houses situated on high, dry ground can only be explained as condensation of air in the ground.

On the other hand, condensation is evident when air leaves the subsoil during barometric depressions and enters a cold environment (fig. 98). This phenomenon sheds light on some otherwise inexplicable cases of masonry dampness, such as are found in buildings on hilltops over dry soil; it also seems the only convincing explanation for the mountain-top springs mentioned earlier (fig. 99).

In our view, Knapen's emphasis on this cause of humidity is exaggerated and must be rejected. Rather, telluric condensation should be seen as rare in comparison to the multiplicity of wall moisture cases due to damp rising from the subsoil. Objective observation of the plinths of buildings shows that the humidity of the so-called 'critical zone' (leaving aside telluric air) can also be imputed to quite banal causes: rainwater

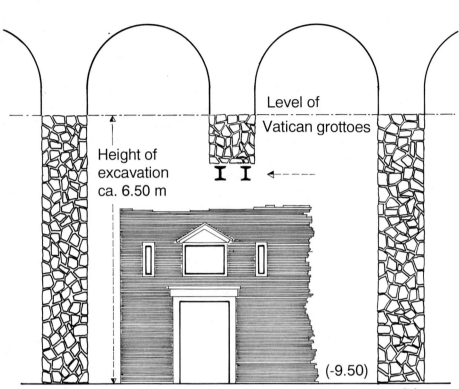

Basilica floor   (0.00)

Level of
Vatican grottoes

Height of
excavation
ca. 6.50 m

(-9.50)

Level of Roman sepulchre

Fig. 100.

An impressive example of condensation of telluric air, due to barometric depression, in the underground area of St. Peter's in Rome. Considerable moisture drips from the iron beams indicated by the arrow.

rebound or absorption. In fact, where rainwater does not strike (under balconies, jutties, overhangs in general) the plinth appears dry.

   An unusual example of telluric air condensation is often visible in the immense hall beneath the central nave of St. Peter's in Rome (fig. 100). We happened to encounter it in full winter, during a sirocco phase with very low barometric pressure. The condensation began forming after the excavations that brought to light the necropolis surrounding the tomb of the First Apostle. Two aspects of the phenomenon are typical: first the moisture deposited on the walls does not show because it is uniformly absorbed. Second, the moisture is easily seen on massive metal elements such as the large iron beams supporting a suspended pillar, as indicated in the figure. With every fall in the barometer, there is a great deal of weeping from these beams – so much so, in fact, that it seems like rain. This case is unique because of the vast extent of evaporating surface and the mass of air involved in a closed, subterranean space.

In ordinary buildings, barometric depressions probably mobilize rather small volumes of air. Therefore, the amount of moisture affecting the walls of the bottom story should be considered quantitatively negligible.

Nevertheless, for those rare occasions where condensation of telluric air must be studied, the following diagnostic elements should be kept in mind:

Characteristics of condensation of subterranean air:

- It is produced during barometric depressions and is, hence, an intermittent source of moisture.
- It is specific to underground rooms and basements.
- It is uniform throughout a building or group of buildings in the same zone.
- It is produced only where the composition of the ground permits, i.e., where filtration of telluric air through the foundation planes is possible. Sandy, gravelly, pozzolanic, detrital or embanked soils are favorable. Rocky or compact clay soils are unfavorable.
- It is greater the more extensive the layer of subterranean air that feeds it, i.e., the deeper the groundwater table, as happens in hilltop and mountaintop houses.
- In temperate climates, it tends to disappear in summer, unlike normal condensation of outdoor air. It is accentuated at night in hot zones.

As for remedies, see the approach indicated for intermittent sirocco condensation. The phenomenon can occur either in winter or in summer, but in the latter case it is exclusively nocturnal. To avoid being confused as to the true origin of condensation, remember that telluric air condensation *always coincides with accentuated barometric depression,* which also causes the foul odor of escaping sewer air.

¶44. Variable stains from individual materials and reinforced concrete.

— Under this heading we empirically group those highly visible manifestations of *alternating humidity* (well-defined zones of rounded stains or parallel stripes) that always appear and disappear in *precisely the same location*. They disappear, or at least fade, during dry weather; they return when the air is damp.

It is better, for practical purposes, to consider the case of massive, traditionally constructed walls apart from that of light, modern structures with reinforced concrete frames.

Massive traditional-type walls

Isolated, rounded stains are usually attributed to the presence of hygroscopic salts that have spread throughout bricks and stone taken from previous buildings. Presumably, these materials had been part of structures that were impregnated with organic refuse, so when they are reused, salts pass from them into the plaster and cause variable stains. Masons in central Italy speak of 'saltpetered' bricks or tuff. Still, it seems strange that there should always be saltpeter or other hygroscopic salts in recycled materials, so that we find Bianchini's hypothesis more likely in many cases. His idea is that such recycled materials, notably blocks of stone, have undergone a sort of surface cementing with mortar that has left them virtually enveloped in an impermeable coating. Thus, when they are reused in a *slightly damp structure*, they evaporate moisture much more slowly than the rest of the wall. A joint factor would then be necessary, i.e., a state of diffused general dampness and light general dampness in the wall where they are placed. Under these conditions, a rise of RH during sultry weather would be enough to slow evaporation in these blocks, which would then accumulate a high percentage of water compared to the surrounding wall.

This explanation, at least for old walls where the whole mass is slightly damp, would account for the frequency of variable staining when it is known that demolition materials have been used. It seems doubtful that such materials would always have been soaked in foul water.

Yet, variable stains are also produced by new stone blocks, fresh from the quarry, in recently built, but perfectly dry walls. In our view, one of the following factors will be at the root of the problem:

- the presence of isolated deposits of hygroscopic salts
- the presence of metal, stone, cement or elements of high specific gravity and thermal conductivity with respect to the rest of the wall mass
- the presence, in a slightly damp wall, of single bricks or stones that have been used before and have undergone the above-mentioned surface cementing

The humidity stain that appears during sultry or rainy days is due, in the first instance, to *dissolution of hygroscopic salts.* In the second case, it is due to actual *condensation,* because the heavy element reaches dewpoint long before the rest of the wall. In the third case, it is due to the *greater difficulty of evaporation* in cemented pieces compared to the rest of a slightly damp wall.

Whatever their origin, variable stains from isolated materials involve only a small amount of water; their humidity is more unsightly than damaging. Often these stains are a sign, as has been stated, that light humidity of some other origin is diffused throughout the wall, and has been attracted by the hygroscopic salts. It is necessary to diagnose this other source of moisture, rather than to seek the cause of variable humidity.

The presence of blocks or single elements of high specific gravity compared to the rest of the mass is the second cause of variable staining, and produces true condensation. Given two different building materials in a wall, condensation occurs whenever only one reaches dewpoint. This phenomenon occurs even within one kind of material when it has components of differing density, e.g., certain kinds of breccia marble. The recurring preference of humidity stains for tombstones and the decorative elements on some churches and historic buildings can thus be explained when rising damp or other water infiltration has been ruled out. In these cases, a variation in specific gravity gives rise to condensation.

The phenomenon manifests itself in a picturesque fashion in some cases where the wall fabric is constructed with strips of heavy material (compact limestone, basalt, gneiss, etc.) alternating with strips of brick; humidity then appears on the plaster in alternate dark and light horizontal stripes, or pattern staining. We can also see this feature on the ceilings of some urban kitchens when pots are boiling on gas burners and producing abundant water vapor. Condensation darkens the plaster where there are steel or reinforced concrete beams (heavy and therefore condensation-producing materials). Where there are planks or bricks between the beams, the plaster remains dry and light-colored.

The only way to avoid pattern staining in ceilings is to apply shaped insulating tiles over steel beams during construction or to lay hollow brick beneath reinforced concrete beams, so that there will be a uniform anti-condensation surface when the plaster is spread. For ceilings in old buildings, already disfigured by condensation, it is useless to change colors, use impermeable paint, or replaster so long as the basic cause remains. The only efficacious remedy is to apply a false ceiling or a simple adherent lining of insulating board. Metal sheets or other metallic elements, even if masked by stucco, must be eliminated from the lower surface. Expanded resins are also excellent as linings.

To combat variable stains on inner walls, one must first make sure that the wall, apart from the areas specifically betrayed by external staining, is dry in the mass. Samples must be taken in areas *where the wall is not stained,* and their moisture content measured. It is utterly pointless to take samples within the perimeter of the stains themselves, as they would obviously be wet.

If one finds a general state of dampness outside the stained areas, such humidity – although not apparent – can be more important than the variable sort and should be treated separately. The most frequent cases are caused by general, diffused moisture, coming from the subsoil or deposited by condensation. Often when this overall dampness is eliminated the variable stains disappear as well.

The most vigorous remedy for true variable stains in old, thick-walled buildings is to remove the isolated elements that are causing the trouble, but this is easier said than done. More prosaically, one can try the operation prescribed in the Bible,[3] for this ailment has always accompanied human habitation and good masons have been dealing with it for centuries. The operation is as follows: First strip the plaster and scrape the wall fabric, digging out all the mortar joints 5-6 cm deep. If any elements, stone or brick, seem visibly at fault or if there are any heavy stones, they must be extracted. Wash the exposed wall thoroughly and repeatedly, if possible with distilled water or rainwater, or at least with clean water, and leave it to dry for more than a month. Then refill the joints with good, normal mortar, not too rich, making sure that no rubble from the previous mortar is included. Finally, spread *a good, simple plaster* that is rather porous and *resist the temptation to mix in cement or hydrofuges.*

This treatment generally works well, but a few stains may crop up after four or five years, either on the new plaster itself or at the edges where the new plaster joins the old.

Structures in reinforced concrete

In modern, reinforced-concrete framed structures, the pattern staining traces the concrete elements very clearly. Where there is winter heating, the stains tend to become permanent after a while, because (as has been demonstrated) the *atmospheric dust is carried by condensation selectively to cold cement* strips rather than to other areas.

---

3   Leviticus XIV:34 ff.

Clearly, this phenomenon involves true condensation due to the uneven composition of the wall, which allows more heat flow where there is cement and less where there is brick. This is shown in figure 93 on the behavior of interstitial condensation. The stains are more pronounced over radiators where the heat flow is greatest.

Old convection-type heating systems seem to produce more staining than modern radiant floor heating systems, perhaps because they set up localized currents of rising air that carry fine dust continuously along the same route. The dust is slowly deposited, producing the same effect that smoke could have in a few minutes.

When the stains become persistent, it is pointless to repaint or replaster as mentioned above for ceilings. The only remedy is to increase thermal resistance where the dispersive reinforced concrete structure is close beneath the plaster. One needs insulated linings or new, light renderings as thick as their adhesive power will allow. As seen in Table II, ¶23, a 40 cm thick reinforced concrete column has very low thermal resistance ($R = 0.50 \, m^2h°C/kcal$) which must be improved to at least 0.90-0.80, depending on the local climate. Table III lists additional structures that can be chosen to fit each case. One of the most practical is a counterwall of hollow bricks, set on edge, and resting against the column. Simple, corrugated cardboard interposed between the column and counterwall forms at least a minimum of air space and, thus, the whole provides additional resistance of $R = 0.40$. If a dry procedure is preferred, a lining of good insulating panels will also attain the same result, so long as it is set slightly away from the wall. Results are less certain with anti-condensation renderings; in any event, a rendering must add real thickness – not less than 5-4 cm – and be done, for instance, with pumice and lime mortar. The rendering's specific gravity in the dry state must not exceed 0.8. This kind of rendering can supply additional resistance of $R = 0.12$-0.15.

For ceilings, light panels are advisable, preferably installed dry with light fixing trim. Renderings and plastic stuccos should be avoided so as to prevent later disillusionment when the joints come apart.

Chapter Nine

WHEN CONDENSATION IS DUE TO THE IGNORANCE OF VARIOUS SPECIALISTS

¶45.   When the gardener cuts off the sunlight.

—Lack of forethought can often backfire when numerous trees are planted around single houses, large public buildings, schools and/or hospitals. When first planted, the saplings are slender and innocuous, if not downright scrawny. If the improvident planter could come back after thirty years, he would be taken aback to find how the graceful little deodar cedar and the small magnolia grandiflora have gotten out of hand, pushing their branches against the very windows of the house and making the ground beneath them damp and gloomy, right up to the doorstep. A bothersome tree can always be cut down, but it hardly ever is, being protected by a certain conservative, aesthetic and sentimental inertia. Moreover, in a city, everyone protests (starting with the mayor) when one dares to touch a large tree *that has always been there.*

It is better never to plant tall trees, especially evergreens, near a house. The error is a common one, brought about by a snobbish sense of false luxury played upon by nurserymen who usually suggest cedars, magnolias and pines, full-grown and very expensive (principally because they are heavy). We do not live in the midst of forests and among the wolves. Small, deciduous trees should surround our homes, shading them from the heat of summer and allowing precious sunshine to reach them in autumn and winter.

Evergreens frequently cause humidity problems. Once one makes the initial error of lightheartedly planting small trees to the south of a house, one finds fifteen years later that the heating plant is insufficient (yet it was properly calculated!) and the rooms in the lower floors are gradually becoming inhospitable and infected with mold. To assess whether the damage is due to the old evergreen's proximity to the house, the temperature of the ground must be measured prior to the spring equinox, *half a meter deep* in the open strip of soil surrounding the house. The measurements must be taken outside the rooms considered unwholesome, three or four meters away from the house, both in the cone of shade under the tree and in the sunny areas nearby. If the internal ground temperatures in the shade are 3°C or more below those of the sunlit area, the house's humidity is surely due to the thermal drop created by the tree; the only remedy at this point is to cut it down.

When planting new gardens, a prudent health rule (if one must insist on tall trees in the southern arc) is to maintain the minimum distances indicated in figure 101, so as to *exploit the sun during the worst period,* around the winter solstice. The average heights reached by different types of trees after a few decades are indicated in the figure, but the

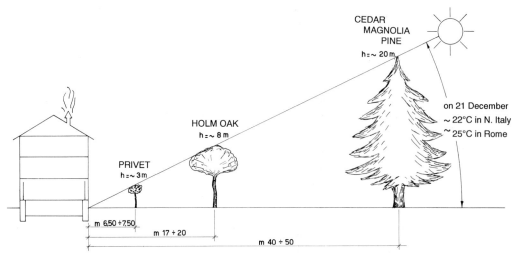

Fig. 101.

Tall trees (especially evergreens) situated to the south of a house cool the ground and bring winter moisture. Planting should be planned to maximize winter sunshine by placing the trees a sufficient distance from the house, as shown here in an illustration for Rome. The distances should be even greater where the altitude of the sun is lower in winter, e.g., 22° in northern Italy, 15° in London.

reader may wish to adjust these figures in view of local botanical data. Still, unless one wants rheumatism at home, the wisest and most natural approach is to plant only deciduous trees.

¶46.   When fantastic traditional ideas about local climate hold sway.

— In many long-settled zones, strange and mythical beliefs are perpetuated about the malign recurring power of some local climatic factor. Intermittent or seasonal humidity in temples and houses is also often blamed on this factor, although there is actually an entirely different reason which can now be verified with instruments. In Egypt, the interior dampness of peasant homes, as well as that of rock-carved temples or pyramid burial cells, is still attributed to the Nile's periodical flooding, which presumably causes moisture to rise from the water table. This is wrong, because the farmer's small houses and the pyramids are built on sand, and water cannot ascend by capillary action in sand. Remember figure 7. Condensation is involved here, but the ignorant find it incomprehensible.

In Trieste, every misfortune is blamed on the violent 'bora' wind, which knocks people down and breaks their legs when it is dry, and passes through walls when it is wet. Yet here again, condensation is at fault because rainwater penetrates no more than 2 or 3 cm into a wall, barring special cases.

The 'mistral' in Provence has terrible and mysterious powers: it makes nanny-goats miscarry, disrupts women's menstral cycles, drives men to folly and causes small rural buildings to fall into the swamp with a loud cracking of their crude bricks. Suicides, landslides and collapses in Germany and Switzerland are attributed to the 'foehn,' which is a dry wind that falls vertically and overheats the air by compression, even in winter.

On the slopes of the Italian Alps and in the high Apennines overlying the Gulf of Genoa, every manifestation of spring condensation is falsely attributed to 'the melting snow,' which is a spring phenomenon that swells all the brooks and streams descending to the gulf. We were asked to consult on the crypt of the old church of San Colombano in Bobbio, which is in the high Apennines north of Genoa. Every spring the crypt filled with water because, it was said, of the melting snow farther uphill. According to local

CRYPT OF SAN COLOMBANO IN BOBBIO: STRUCTURES THAT PRODUCE CONDENSATION OF AMBIENT WATER VAPOR BY COOLING DUE TO THERMAL INERTIA:

(a) Floor of high specific gravity with subfloor of cement concrete laid on damp ground – no air space.

(b) Counterwall insufficient to protect the air in the crypt from coldness of wall.

(c) Massive concrete dike added outside to combat dampness – damaging due to thermal inertia.

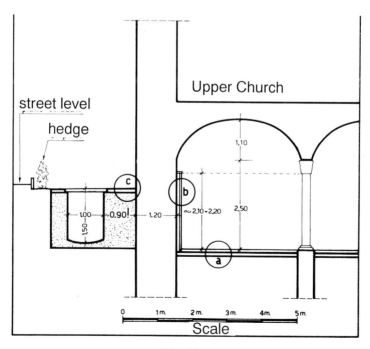

Fig. 102.

The true, prevailing cause of seasonal spring/summer moisture is condensation due to the thermal inertia of "cold" wall masses.

technicians, this water impregnated the ground in spring 2 to 3 m deep around the crypt, and finally traversed the crypt's thick outer wall itself, flooding the pavement every spring (and only then), always just when the snow was melting. The technical office in charge carried out two expensive repair projects (fig. 102):

- A thick, heavy floor of cement and asphalt was constructed (without an air chamber) inside the crypt; it was conceived as a watertight seal against flooding from the surrounding ground.

- A one-meter wide ditch was built around the outside of the crypt. Reinforced concrete was used so that the water in the surrounding ground could not reach the wall. The side of the ditch touching the crypt was conceived as a dike of cement concrete, 90 cm thick.

An enormous amount of money was spent, but the sole result was to double the crypt's thermal inertia and thereby double the amount of cold stored in winter, which consequently doubled the condensation of warm spring air. A few years later, the abbot of San Colombano finally lost patience, as he saw that the diligently executed work was reducing the crypt to a pond, and called on the Italian National Research Council's committee for study of damp masonry. Careful measurements and analysis established that an accentuated, and indeed serious, case of spring condensation was involved; it called for entirely different work than had been done. In fact, the prescription was to throw out the heavy sealing pavement of the crypt and construct another with light materials and an underlying air chamber. Moreover, a network of electric wires was installed just beneath the floor surface in order to create a continuous, light amount of radiant heat from late February through March: just 4-5 calories per m^3 of air. The windows were kept slightly ajar to provide some air exchange.

Chapter Ten

OUTER WALLS WITH HOLLOW BRICK OR CAVITIES BENEFIT THE BUILDER, NOT THE TENANT

¶47. Cavity walls in framed buildings.

— The infill wall normally used in reinforced framed buildings is a double one, the so-called 'cavity' wall, formed by an exterior single leaf of solid brick and an interior leaf of hollow brick, separated by an air space. Contrary to popular belief, a cavity wall does not assure better thermal protection than the old solid, three-brick wall, because the thermal resistance of the central brick row (which has been eliminated) is roughly equal to that of the air space that replaces it. The real advantage lies in the wall's lower weight and the reduced space it occupies because the cavity takes up only 5 cm. Therefore, the adoption of cavity walls in reinforced concrete structures has *not brought about any improvement in health terms;* indeed, as brick sizes have been reduced, or when bricks are used on edge, health protection has often declined.

Figure 103 indicates the comparative thermal resistance (or protection, in health terms) of various popular types of cavity walls. Only the first two and the last (which have thermal resistance around 1 [0.9]) guarantee the health protection needed against condensation in cold climates. One solution would be to use hollow bricks in the outer leaf, but this must be ruled out because they are more vulnerable to bad weather, and because mortar cannot be used on the open ends. As a consequence, the external rendering would be the only seal for the air space. The overall thermal protection of the wall actually decreases more than it seems to increase when hollow brick is used in the outer leaf.

People often ask whether it is worthwhile to increase the thermal protection of a cavity wall by filling the air space with a foam or some kind of loose insulating material. In order to offset the practical difficulties and expense involved, this procedure is only worthwhile when it at least doubles the thermal resistance of the unfilled space (fig. 104), i.e., if the filling provides at least $R = 0.36$ versus the $R - 0.18$ of a cavity. The following chart shows the thickness of various fillers that would provide $R = 0.36$.

with wide bricks (14 cm):

$$R = \frac{0.14}{0.75} + 0.18 + \frac{0.14}{0.35} + 0.19 = 0.96 \ [0.82]$$

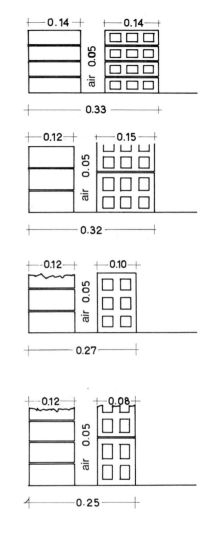

with standard bricks (one solid, one hollow):

$$R = \frac{0.12}{0.75} + 0.18 + \frac{0.15}{0.35} + 0.19 = 0.96 \ [0.82]$$

with standard bricks (one solid outside, one 6-cell hollow inside, laid on edge):

$$R = \frac{0.12}{0.75} + 0.18 + \frac{0.10}{0.35} + 0.19 = 0.82 \ [0.70]$$

with standard bricks (one solid outside, one 4-cell hollow inside, laid on edge):

$$R = \frac{0.12}{0.75} + 0.18 + \frac{0.08}{0.35} + 0.19 = 0.76 \ [0.65]$$

mixed: light tuff and hollow brick laid flat:

$$R = \frac{0.12}{0.44} + 0.18 + \frac{0.15}{0.35} + 0.19 = 1.07 \ [1.00]$$

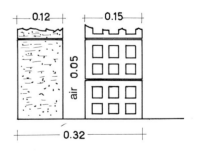

Fig. 103.

Thermal resistance of current types of cavity infill walls, valid only if the air space is truly sealed (see fig. 111) and if the outer leaf is not beaten by rain.

CHART SHOWING THE UTILITY OF FILLERS FOR VERTICAL CAVITIES

FILLER			Minimum thickness (cm) needed to reach $R \geq 0.36 \dfrac{m^2 h°C}{kcal}$
Material	Volumetric weight kg/m³	$\lambda \dfrac{kcal}{m^2 h°C}$	
Loose materials:			
dry sand	1600	0.42	15
crushed brick/tile	1000	0.35	13
pozzolana pebbles (light and dry) or volcanic ash	1000	0.25	9
cinders or dry pumice	600	0.18	6.5
diatomaceous earth	300	0.10	4
expanded mica rock wool glass wool	50÷100	0.05	2
Compact but not compressed materials:			+
cellular cement	800	0.42	15
lightweight aggregate concrete of lime, cinders or pumice	800	0.22	8
foamed synthetic resin	30	0.04÷0.05	2

Nowadays, what might be called 'modified' cavity walls are used to improve air-space protection without causing practical difficulties. Thermal resistance is usually increased by two relatively simple techniques: insertion of aluminum foil in the cavity as a lining on either the inner or outer leaf or insertion of a layer of mineral wool (glass or rock) which has very high thermal resistance and does not rot. In the former case, the protection of the cavity rises to ca. 0.45; in the latter it rises to ca. 0.58 – a significant increase.

We shall describe these two systems separately.

Aluminum (even if opaque) is known for its exceptionally low emission coefficient (0.35) as compared to a brick wall (4.6). If a brick wall is tightly lined with aluminum foil, it will disperse stored heat at an emission rate 13 times slower than if it were bare. As aluminum does not emit heat by radiation, it also reflects the heat radiations that strike it. Therefore, it is equally useful to line either side of the cavity, so long as a spatterdash coat has first been applied. If the aluminum lining is on the warm side, the heat will be conserved; if it is on the cold side, the heat will be repelled. In both cases, radiant heat will be kept from passing through the cavity, and the thermal resistance will be increased

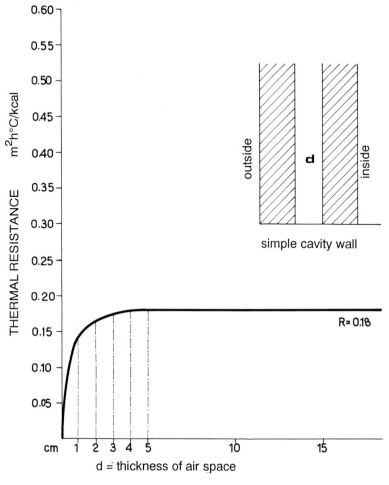

Fig. 104.

Thermal resistance of a simple air space.

about one and a half times (fig. 105). This impressive result is due to the fact that the greater the temperature drop between the two sides of the cavity, the more heat passes by radiation, as opposed to conduction and convection (the two other ways heat travels) (fig. 106).

As has been said, only one side of the cavity need be lined. Indeed, the advantage of a double lining would not compensate for the extra expense involved. For practical reasons, it is usually preferable to line the inner side of the outer leaf.

The other system of improving cavity walls – lining with mineral wool – is easier to apply. This system is within the possibilities of every builder, and the author has further simplified the installation technique: wood frameworks, washers, nails, etc., have been eliminated, and we have shown that the fastest and least expensive method on construction

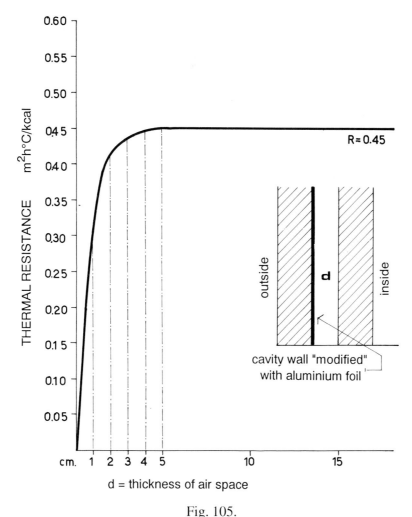

Fig. 105.

Thermal resistance of the air space in cavity walling modified with aluminum lining.

sites is to use good, adhesive mastic *once the wall surface has been given a coat of spatterdash* (fig. 107).

The spatterdash is indispensable because it assures that the cavity is well sealed (guaranteeing the theoretical basic resistance $R = 0.18$, plus that of rock wool to obtain $R = 0.58$) and because it favors good adhesion of the mineral wool panels with the minimum amount of mastic and labor. The author supervised the first, large-scale use of rock wool for thermal improvement of cavity walls in June, 1956, in Rome; the afore-mentioned technique was used in a housing project on Via Anapo (figs. 108, 109, 110).

The lining was applied on the sides of the building facing NE and NW and on the entire perimeter of the top story, including windowsills (thus, even on the south side). In our view, for cavity walls to represent *technical progress* in health terms, they must meet both of the following thermal protection requirements:

Fig. 106.

Heat passage across a vertical air space,
5 cm thick, when the temperature differen-
tial between the two faces of the chamber is
8°C. Three-quarters of the heat passes by
radiation.

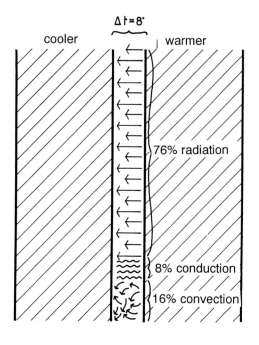

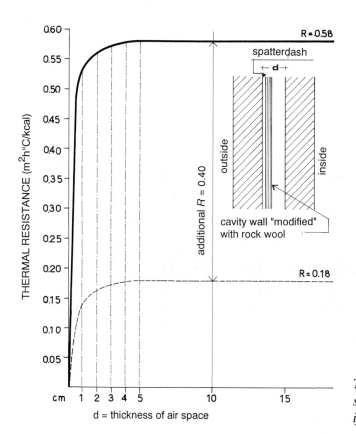

Fig. 107.

Thermal resistance of the air
space in cavity walling mod-
ified with rock wool panels.

Fig. 108.

Simplified application of rock wool in cavity infill walls, using the Massari system. Step one: mastic is spread on the panels.

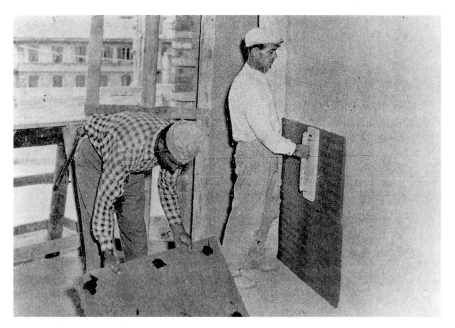

Fig. 109.

Step two: the panels are applied to the outer leaf of the cavity wall, previously given a spatterdash coat and now thoroughly dry.

Fig. 110.

Step three: the inner leaf of the cavity wall is constructed with hollow brick laid either flat or on edge. Every square meter or so, place a hollow brick across the cavity to the rock wool panels (with cells parallel to the lining).

VERTICAL SECTION

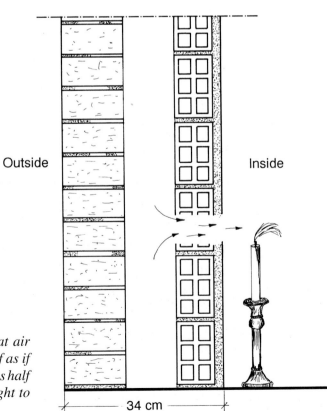

Outside   Inside

Fig. 111.

The candle test confirms that air passes through the outer leaf as if through a sieve; the cavity has half the thermal resistance it ought to have.

34 cm

Fig. 112.

Another oversight in infill wall con-
struction may be leaving the shutter
housing open to the air space; the warm
air inside the wall escapes outdoors.

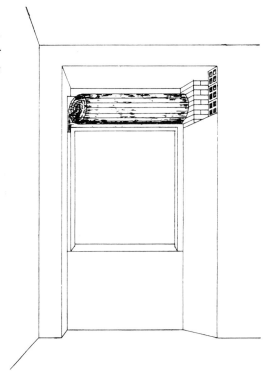

- *In winter* they must impede condensation in northern-exposure bedrooms at the peak time of nocturnal cooling (dawn) when the heating has been turned off.
- *In summer* they must prevent overheating of the inner leaf on the sunny side (SW).

These are the requirements of a properly built cavity wall from a health standpoint. They can only be met by adopting what we call 'modified' cavity walls.

This section has dealt exclusively with infill walls in framed buildings. It must be remembered that reinforced concrete structures cause the greatest heat dispersion and therefore, all beams and columns must be adequately insulated, as discussed in ¶44.

¶48.   Errors in constructing the air space.

— Two qualities are essential to this structure: the enclosed air must be truly still and the empty space must be truly empty. If joints in the outer leaf are not properly sealed, outside air can penetrate and circulate, cooling the whole structure. As indicated in figure 111, a candle test can be used to check for air currents. To avoid this serious defect, many Italian agencies that construct public housing now require that the outer leaf be given a spatterdash coat on the side facing the cavity. This is a very wise precaution.

If the candle test is positive, figure 112 indicates the second test to check whether the cavity communicates with the housings for rolling shutters.

Finally, during construction, the cavity may fill with mortar, dropped by a hasty or careless mason (fig. 113). The space may become completely filled with porous, solidified mortar from the floor level up to 40-50 cm high. In this case, an unpleasant strip of

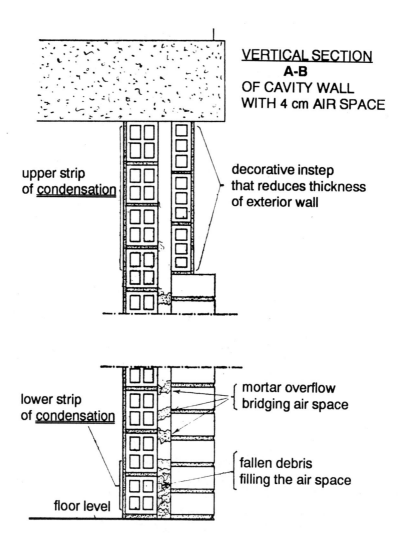

Fig. 113.

Vertical section of one of the two defective infill walls: note the mortar bridges which annull the air space's role as thermal protection.

condensation will appear in winter along the base of the walls in the newly occupied rooms. One must then patiently drill holes in the baseboards at floor level, about every 80 cm, and extract all the mortar concretions with thin curved tools.

Careless workmanship can certainly cause a great deal of trouble!

Fig. 114.

In Iglesias (Sardinia) in January, tests confirmed that the surface temperature of the NW wall, pelted by rain for several days before the measurements were taken, was lower than that of the dry NE wall.

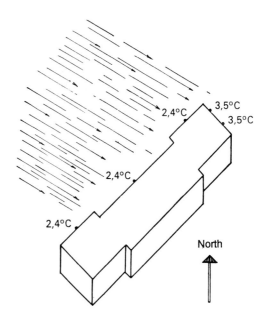

Fig. 115.

The damp houses of the Valverde quarter in Iglesias are constructed of hollow pumice blocks and have no cornices. Rooms of the sides to NE (blind wall in photo) and NW (window wall) are stained by condensation due to insufficient thermal protection. The outer wall, especially on the NW side which is pelted by driving rain and dried by wind, undergoes a temperature drop that has repercussions inside.

¶49.   Filling the cavity when the wall proves ineffective against humidity.

— In outer walls made with hollow blocks or having a single cavity stretching from one vertical column to another, the condensation that forms on the inner wall face (notably in bedrooms and on sides beaten by driving rain) is an indisputable sign of hygienic uninhabitability. Something must be done. The quickest and least expensive remedy consists of filling the cavities with a light insulating material offering high thermal protection.

Nowadays, there are specialized firms throughout western Europe that do this work with equipment suited to the kind of insulation employed, e.g., loose, expanded clay granules, loose vermiculite (never used with mortar or other binders) or various semi-fluid resin foams of the polyurethane type. The problem is more economic than technical. Loose, simple, local materials such as charcoal and pumice can also be used, so long as they are dust-free and thoroughly dry. Any master mason can do this work.

Pumice was used at Iglesias, Sardinia, because it comes at low cost from the nearby Lipari islands. The work is illustrated in figs. 116-118.

Fig. 116.

In the first phase of the work, the outer sides of the blocks are perforated with an 8 cm core drill just at ceiling level.

Fig. 117.

In the second phase, granular pumice is fed by gravity through a hopper. The pumice is first dusted and sifted to remove fine grains less than 5 mm in diameter.

Fig. 118.

One workman pours the granules into the holes above, while another tests results at the base of the wall, where an iron bar inserted into a hole vibrates as the granules fall.

The houses were two stories high (ground floor and upper floor) with outer bearing walls of two-cell pumice block, 30 cm thick. The heat flow traversed only one air cell.

This low-cost housing had no heating and was very damp, particularly in the northwestern exposures (figs. 114-115). Measurement of the external surface temperatures of the walls, taken on a cold January morning, confirmed the tenants' statements that the rooms exposed to driving rain on the northwest were colder than those on the northeast which were not so exposed. The interior dampness was due to insufficient thermal protection, with consequent condensation due to cooling on the northwest side beaten by rain. There was no trace of liquid water inside the wall; rather, there was saturated air.

The walls of one very damp, two-story house were successfully filled in September 1963, using the method described in the captions and photos in figs. 116-118. The tenants did not have to move out during the work. During the following winter, comparative measurements were taken of both the surface temperature of the inner walls and the RH in two corner rooms in the same position and with the same number of occupants; the outer walls of one room had been filled with pumice, the others had been left hollow as before. The filled walls consistently registered at least one degree higher in temperature than the others: psychrometer measurements of the RH read 75% in the room with filled walls and 81% in the other. The differences may seem small, but the constant, slight improvement meant that condensation was completely eliminated.

REPAIR COSTS. — The cost of the work per square meter of outer wall was about one-quarter that of an overall outer lining with a one-brick wall of solid brick. This latter solution, as regards increasing thermal protection, is one of the mildest of the possible treatments for cases of condensation. The 'stuffing' operation calls for just two tools: a common mono-phase electric drill (0.5 kW) with a hollow core drill to make the holes (fig. 116), and a metal hopper with its base slanted 40° to assist the gravitational flow of the granules into the hole, as shown in fig. 117.

Specialized labor is not necessary; a pair of workmen will do. The operation can be accelerated with a small electric hoist to carry up the granules and a tilted vibrating table for prior removal of dust from the pumice or whatever light granules are being used. For the pilot project at Iglesias, the dust removal was done by hand. This type of rehabilitation is inexpensive and easy to organize and can be used for any damp house exposed to driving rain, if it has outer walls of hollow blocks or cavity construction. The only precaution needed is to be sure the mass of the filler has a roughly uniform grain size, is thoroughly dry and loose, and is put into the holes without mortar. Preventive dust removal is always needed to remove fine grains or dust and to deprive the mass of any capillarity.

Chapter Eleven

DRIVING RAIN NEVER PASSES
THROUGH A WELL-CONSTRUCTED WALL

¶50. Wetting of the outer facade and cooling of the inner wall face.

— Local climate determines which side of a building will be exposed to driving rain. In Rome it is the southeastern side; in England, the southwestern; in Athens, the northern; in Vienna, the northwestern.

The amount of water involved in this form of humidity – i.e., the part retained by the wall – is not great. Driving rain supplies intermittent moisture, yet such moisture can become intense in periods of frequent rainstorms when evaporation between one absorption and another is no longer able to prevent a cumulative effect.

Horizontal penetration of water into a compact wall is due to a combination of two different forces: *wind pressure and the material's capillarity.*

Normal wind pressure on a surface varies between a few kilograms up to a maximum of 150 kg/m^2 during hurricanes. Usually, except for rare peaks at the height of violent winds, the pressure does not exceed 12 kg/m^2, corresponding to a wind speed of 45 km/h. This is the pressure of a column of water 12 mm high, i.e., little more than 0.001 atmosphere, or very little. This means that the wind can really only be blamed for bringing the rain into contact with the wall, whereas *penetration into the wall is principally due to capillary absorption and thus, to the material's own properties.*

The capillary absorption power of a facing or rendering can be checked easily with a hydrostatic test, using a watertight box to supply the wall with water. See the model in figure 119, taken from an article by Mamillan[1]; the amount of water in the box must be kept constant by means of a graduated drip tube. Actually, this test exerts a much higher pressure than natural wind. Mamillan's careful experiments, both with this box and with artificial rain, following a technique used by Croiset, have established the following data for fired clay facings:

- Water penetration occurs principally through the joints, which absorb four to five times more than the brick.
- If the joints have not been thoroughly filled with mortar and shaped, the amount of water absorbed ranges between 2 and 9 liters/m^2 per minute.

---

1   M. Mamillan, "Le mouvement de l'eau dans les murs," *Annales de l'Institut technique du bâtiment et des travaux publics,* No. 217, January 1966, p. 132, Paris.

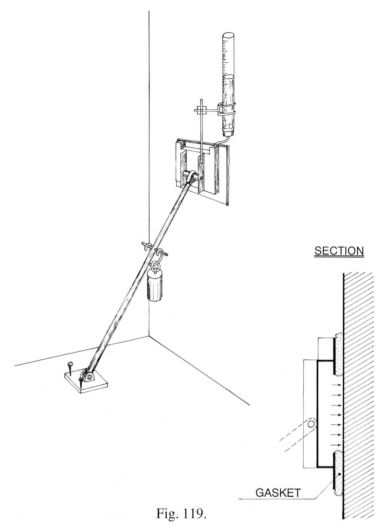

SECTION

GASKET

Fig. 119.

Hydrostatic box to test the capillary absorption of a wall.

- If the joints are properly filled and shaped, the water absorbed fluctuates between 0.5 and 0.8 liters/m^2, again per minute.

- When the bricks have not been dampened at all prior to placement in the facing, they withdraw water from the mortar on which they are laid. Contraction of the mortar bed leads to surface cracking between the mortar and brick, and rainwater penetrates mainly through these cracks. Bricks should first be immersed at least two minutes.

- To reduce the absorption of a brick facing, the joints must be compressed or pointed, using mortar cement and not-too-fine sand.

- As to renderings, the most surprising fact is that *minimum absorption occurs with a normal rendering* of lime and sand, perfectly executed and not subject to fine cracking over the course of time: 0.1 liters/m^2/min. We might add that more fine cracking is likely when more cement is added under the illusion of making the rendering waterproof.

- If the rendering cracks, absorption rises to 2 or 3 liters/m^2/min, which is still less than that of a brick facing with poor joints.

A good picture of the action of driving rain on the sides of a building can be obtained by superimposing a wind rose over a rough ground plan. Figure 120 shows Kieslinger's example of the Votivkirche of Vienna. The various percentages of hours of driving rain, with respect to the annual total, are given below for the different compass points.

Exposure	N	NE	E	SE	S	SW	W	NW
% hrs of driving rain	6.8	1.1	2.2	9.2	2.9	6.4	30	41.4

Water penetration is not very deep in a uniformly constructed wall of brick and rendering: no more than 6-7 cm beneath the rendering.

W. Schüle's graphs in figures 121-122 give penetration measurements for two types of walls: normal brick with rendering, and Rhenish brick, which is a mixture of pumice and hydraulic binder, similar to pumice blocks but solid. The quantitatively damaging penetration of driving rain *does not exceed 4-5 cm* (6-7 cm, including rendering) in a brick wall.

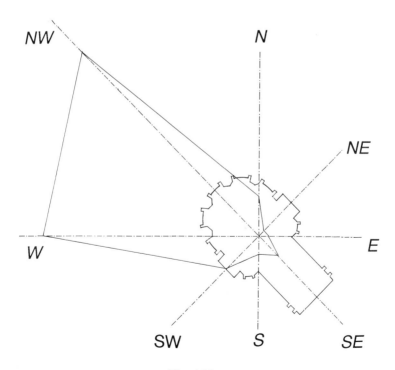

Fig. 120.

A wind rose showing the direction of rainy winds can illustrate the variable intensity of driving rain on the walls of a building (from Kieslinger).

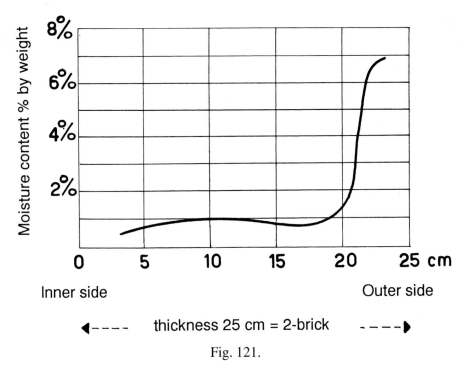

◀ - - - -   thickness 25 cm = 2-brick   - - - - ▶

Fig. 121.

In a normal two-brick wall with rendering on both sides, rainwater penetrates only a few cm: not beyond 6-7 cm, rendering included (W. Schüle's experiments).

Rhenish brick behaves differently, probably because of the inferior materials used in the mix; in fact, moisture penetrates through the entire thickness (which is actually not very great: 14 cm, i.e., one brick) to the inner wall face, and is still present, at a high percentage of 17%, within the wall after 11 days.

From Schüle's graphs one can deduce that:

- Humidity from driving rain penetrates only 6-7 cm beneath the rendering in a brick wall.
- Drying occurs in a few days.
- The behavior of other materials is completely unlike that of brick; moisture penetration can be quite different, and evaporation speed can be slower or faster depending on the material's characteristics.

If rainwater penetration is so slight in solid brick walls, how can we explain the moisture that sometimes appears on the inner wall face? There are two possible causes: Either the wall was poorly built, leaving some opening, or there is condensation on the inner wall face, produced by the cooling of an insufficiently thick wall.

We shall leave aside poor construction of the outer wall and worksite carelessness, such as hasty closure of the scaffolding holes on a facade; all of these are accidental factors, producing rather localized moisture that is persistent and annoying, but not really serious.

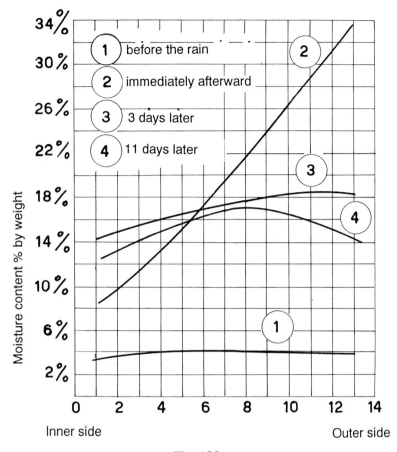

Fig. 122.

A one-brick wall of unbaked Rhenish brick tends to hold a high moisture content (W. Schüle's experiments). The mix of pumice and cement for Rhenish bricks is the same as for 'blocks.' The result is very poor with respect to rain.

The truly worrisome cases are those of general dampness, which not only makes a few rooms uninhabitable but also affects whole blocks and even entire neighborhoods. This situation no longer involves minor, accidental causes, but *systematic construction defects* or, strange to say, defects due to improper climatization of the building with respect to local conditions. The latter sometimes happen when housing agencies rely on centralized planning.

There are three of these systematic defects:

- the use of hollow materials in the infill walls of reinforced concrete frames on the exposures beaten by driving rain
- the use of walls that are insufficiently thick for the local climate
- the use, in prefabricated structures, of joints that give rise to capillary aspiration of driving rain

In localities exposed to driving rain, it is prudent to exclude any type of building material with horizontal cells from the outer wall, whether brick or cement. In fact, the mason spreads the mortar only on the flat beds, never putting it on the ends where it would simply disappear in the holes. As a result, protection of vertical joints in the finished wall depends entirely on the outer rendering, which will be easily traversed by driving rain as soon as it cracks.

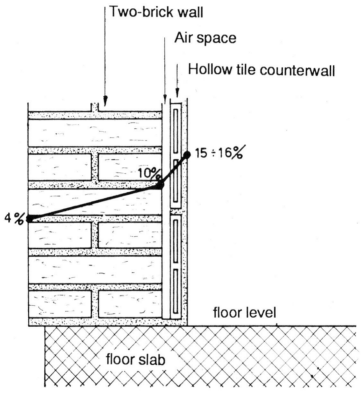

Fig. 123.

Rainwater never traverses a wall: diagram of the percentage moisture content in a damp wall in public housing in Mestre, Italy. The maximum (15-16%) indicates that the water itself originates on the inner wall face. It spreads by capillarity toward dryer areas, i.e. from inside out, where the brick facing favors capillary migration as soon as it dries out after the rain.

From 1957 to 1964 the author had occasion to examine some twenty newly built, low-cost housing projects affected by humidity under the most diverse environmental and climatic conditions – from Trieste to Palermo, from Rapallo to Rome, from Mantua to Avellino. This work was initiated by the Italian National Research Council study group on masonry dampness, which was concerned with the effect of rain on buildings. The results are given below.

Cooling, not water penetration

We ascertained that, in Italy, about 90% of the cases of humidity in new houses are linked to periodical driving rain, and are limited to the building sides exposed to the rain and wind. Measurements of the water distribution within the damp wall have clearly shown that the maximum amount of moisture is always found on the inner face. Even if the inspection is made shortly after a heavy, driving rainstorm (as we fortunately were able to do in Mestre and Trieste), there is only a slight amount of water in the wall core and outside, while it abounds in high percentages on the wall of the room, as shown in figures 123-124, revealing that its origin is mainly on the inner wall itself. Even if there

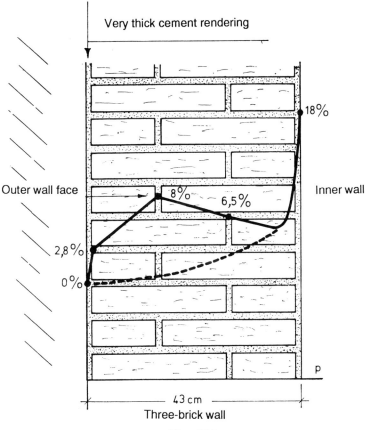

Fig. 124.

Wall exposed to strong, rainy bora winds, in public housing at Chiadino in Monte above Trieste. Two separate water supplies can be identified: condensation in action (as in the preceding case in Mestre), with a very high, 18% moisture content on the surface of the inner wall face; and rainwater infiltration where the vertical mortar joints had not been filled. There is an 8% residual accumulation of rainwater near the outer wall face, where it is blocked because a thick cement rendering slows its evaporation. The dotted line represents the situation that would probably occur (similar to fig.123) if the outer wall face had a rendering of normal mortar instead of cement.

are systematic construction deficiencies, as in the wall in figure 124 where the vertical joints between bricks were poorly mortared or not mortared at all, the rainwater can only penetrate about 12-15 cm into the wall. Except for absolutely exceptional cases, we can state that, in Italy, *water never passes through the wall of a house,* no matter how clamorous the manifestation appears to be or how high the measurement of humidity on the inner wall. This finding is in complete contrast to the basic hypothesis derived from laboratory experiments conducted in France.

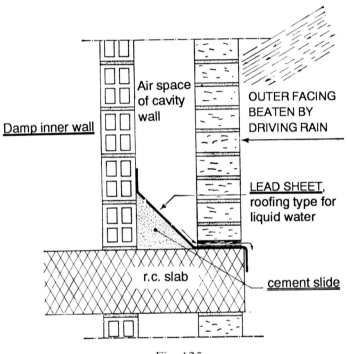

Fig. 125.

An original counter-proof that rain does not traverse walls: The lead sheet inserted into the air space of a cavity wall to intercept rainwater in a damp house in Avellino did not work; the inner wall remained as damp as ever because this was actually a case of condensation due to the combined effect of cold and overcrowding.

An original counter-proof that water does not traverse walls is shown in the experiment carried out by the worthy Public Housing Institute of Avellino, a city subject to heavy driving rain from the west and the Gulf of Naples. Having noted the frequency in winter of water on the floors, exclusively along the line where they joined the walls on the western side, the local technicians started from the *logical* hypothesis that the rainwater was able to traverse the solid one-brick outer leaf of the cavity infill wall and collect on the reinforced concrete floor slab. From there it supposedly passed under the inner, hollow-brick leaf of the cavity wall and flowed onto the floor in the rooms. To block this water penetration, the experimental measure shown in figure 125 was applied to the entire side of a house; a lead sheet was inserted in the cavity in order to intercept the rainwater and expel it through the holes predisposed in the outer facing. After two years of observations, the technicians admitted that no results had been obtained because the water continued to appear as before, on the floor along the walls exposed to the west and the driving rain. Measurements taken by the author in Avellino again confirmed that the water on the floors was decidedly not due to rain, but rather to condensation of excess water vapor produced by overcrowding; the condensation coincided with the period right after the rain when the outer leaf was dried by evaporation, undergoing intense cooling which reached the internal wall where the air was already close to saturation from human breathing.

Contrary to what builders commonly believe, it has been found that the cavity wall is a very poor structure as far as condensation is concerned; aside from intermittent cooling due to rain, this kind of wall is also subject to constant cooling in winter due to circulation of air from the outside into the cavity – although theoretically such circulation should never occur. The thermal resistance calculation for the cavity should give

$$R = 0.18 \frac{m^2 h\,°C}{kcal} \quad [0.15 \frac{m^2\,°C}{W}]$$

when the air is still; if there are currents, the calculation can sink to

$$R = 0.10 \frac{m^2 h\,°C}{kcal} \quad [0.09 \frac{m^2\,°C}{W}],$$

i.e., about half the theoretical value, as we have often discovered in practice.

Recent research in France has indicated that the major part of the water absorbed by a wall surface evaporates during the course of the following day, if the weather is clear. This observation applies either to cavity walls, which are easily cooled for lack of proper sealing, or to other, solid walls of any kind. Yet, if the rain continues for a long period, each day's evaporation is immediately replaced by new rainwater contributions. During experiments conducted by the C.S.T.B. at Champs-sur-Marne near Paris, in a zone exposed to westerly driving rain, a sample wall progressively accumulated 10-20 liters of water per meter (ascertained by variations in weight) between September and April. Unfortunately the experimental program did not include study of variations in surface temperature and therefore the cooling produced by the rain was not measured.[2]

Psychrometric cooling

How much is a house cooled by driving rain? For houses that have one side affected by condensation following cooling of a rain-beaten outer wall, the cooling of the wall can be considered to be transferred to the outside air, giving us a hypothetical *equivalent driving rain temperature*. The driving rain temperature is none other than the actual air temperature reduced a certain amount due to the cooling of the wall. This decrease is linked to RH and air speed, which affect the air's drying capacity, and is *independent of the latitude of the place*. In other words, the decrease is equal to the difference between

---

2   M. Croiset, "L'eau dans les murs," *Cahiers du C.S.T.B.,* No. 28, Paris.

the air temperature registered by a dry bulb thermometer and that registered by a wet bulb thermometer; this difference can be measured with any psychrometer (see ¶15). The dryer and more windy the air following a rainy period (e.g., the 'tramontana' in Ancona or Rome, or the bora in Trieste), the greater the decrease and thus the lower the equivalent temperature of the air on the wet side of the building.

Our reason for suggesting an equivalent driving rain temperature as a working hypothesis is to give a numerical picture of the damage done by driving rain, in any climate, by expressing it as a drop in air temperature. Let us take the case of Genoa, a city highly exposed to rain humidity, as one can see from its buildings, which are all lined with slate on the same side. In January, the average RH in Genoa is 58%, one of the lowest in Italy; this RH is roughly equivalent to a temperature gap of 3°C between the dry and wet bulb thermometers of a psychrometer. These three degrees can be seen as the decrease in temperature of outdoor air in relation to a wall that has been dampened by rain and then cooled by evaporation. This means, starting conventionally from the average January temperature of 8.4°C, that the air on the three dry sides of a house in Genoa would have the above-mentioned temperature of 8.4°C. On the wet side, the damage to the building from rainfall could be expressed as a reduction in the air temperature to 5.4°C (8.4 - 3). This would be the equivalent driving rain temperature on that side. This equivalent temperature is *also applicable to the heating plant* (fig. 126).

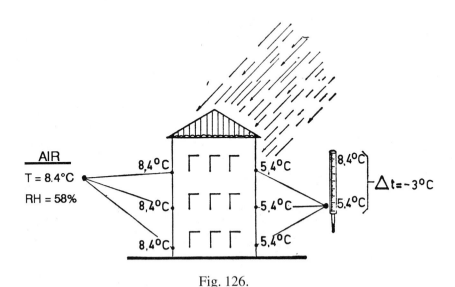

Fig. 126.

The air in winter in Genoa is quite dry, but the city is also one of the most exposed to driving rain. In fact, moisture arises from rapid evaporation from wet walls, due to the generally dry air. On the rain-beaten side, it is as if the temperature of the outside air drops from 8.4°C to 5.4°C.

EXTERIOR WALL STRUCTURE

DECREASE

in temperature on the
rain-beaten wall (in °C)

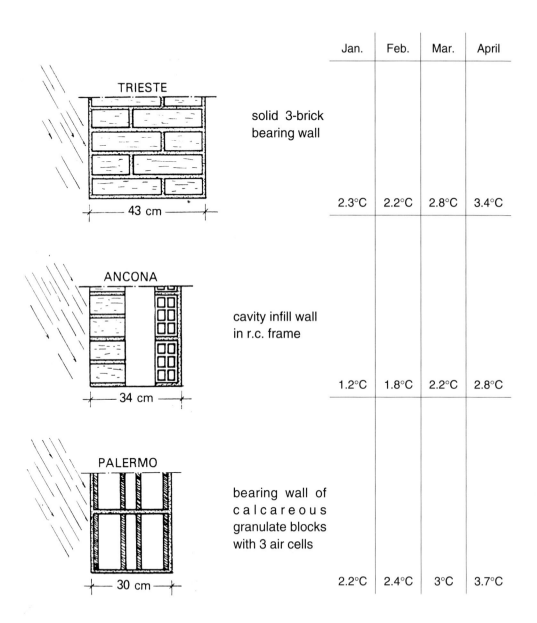

	Jan.	Feb.	Mar.	April
TRIESTE — solid 3-brick bearing wall — 43 cm	2.3°C	2.2°C	2.8°C	3.4°C
ANCONA — cavity infill wall in r.c. frame — 34 cm	1.2°C	1.8°C	2.2°C	2.8°C
PALERMO — bearing wall of calcareous granulate blocks with 3 air cells — 30 cm	2.2°C	2.4°C	3°C	3.7°C

Fig. 127.

Cooling from driving rain is independent of latitude, but correlated to wind speed and low RH; each type of public housing is constructed with its own type of excellent outer wall, but is equally subject to condensation on one side in such different climates as those of Trieste, Ancona and Palermo.

The extent of rainwater cooling

On the basis of the climatic conditions of various Italian cities, taken as random geographical samples, the calculated decrease in air temperature on the rain-beaten side of a building would range between 0.4°C and 3.7°C during the winter/ spring period. As a rule, the temperature gap becomes greater from winter to spring, more markedly on the southern coasts as in Palermo, where it goes from 2.2°C in January to 3.7°C in April. In general, greater decreases are noted in coastal cities because the RH in winter is lower there, with correspondingly faster evaporation, than in the interior plains which have more continental climates. One could say there is a slight climatic compensation for the cities in cold and foggy zones such as the Po Valley, as they suffer slightly less from extra rainwater cooling than do the maritime cities.

With regard to buildings, and taking values roughly deduced from the average, the winter/spring decrease can be assumed as a base value of 3°C, the same for the three cities shown in figure 127. Given this base value, what remedy is there? Some builders cling to the perennial hope of combating driving rain with waterproof cement renderings, but this is a vain hope indeed. Apart from the well-known need to let the wall 'breathe,' that is, to let it evaporate normal internal condensation (here, brick facings are always preferable), no cement rendering on the *outside* can withstand seasonal thermal alterations and remain free of fine cracking. Water can then penetrate rapidly into the capillary network and accumulates in the liquid state at a slight depth in the wall, being kept from vaporizing by the rendering, or evaporating very slowly at best. In short, water enters the wall easily but exits with great difficulty. See the graph in figure 124, which shows the percentage distribution of water measured in a solid brick wall that had a formidable cement rendering, applied under the illusion that it would withstand the rainy bora wind (public housing in Chiadino di Monte, above Trieste). Nonetheless, even if absolutely long-lasting and waterproof renderings existed, it must be remembered that some degree of cooling would still occur, as happens on a metallic surface when rainwater alternately wets it and evaporates. The extent of cooling depends on the rhythm and speed of the rain/wind succession and the RH of the wind.

Builders so far have shown very imprecise thinking when it comes to critical understanding of the 'humidity' phenomenon, or rational development of solutions. The working hypothesis of an *equivalent temperature* of the outdoor air, as a result of the wall's heat loss through evaporation from the wet surface, allows us to reexamine the whole phenomenon of wall dampness with new insight.

How to prevent rain humidity in new buildings

In calculating heat loss for the planning of heating systems, one usually applies some increases for the needs of certain rooms that have poor exposures or are subject to wind. The most common increases are as follows:

In Italy

    northern exposure 15%
    corner position 10-15%
    very high ceilings, max. 20%

In France

    northern exposure 10%
    corner position or high winds   . . 5%
    damp climate 10%
    very high ceilings, max 20%

In centrally heated buildings, driving rain moisture can be prevented by correcting the base temperature or, better, by *increasing calorie requirements specifically for the rooms exposed to driving rain; the increase is added to the normal base figures.*

As all traditional increment coefficients are rounded off for practical reasons, one can propose similarly rounded figures for the driving rain increment, as follows:

- 15% for central/northern localities where the temperature gap between indoors and outdoors is equal to, or greater than 18°C (at 18°C indoors)

- 20% for southern and insular localities where the anticipated temperature gap is less than 18°C

Up to this point we have spoken of heated buildings. For constructions in zones where heating is considered superfluous, prevention of rain humidity must be obtained by modifying the outer wall structure to increase thermal resistance, but *only on the one or two sides exposed to driving rain.* A similar modification is needed for the roof. The increase in thermal resistance must range from 50% minimum to 100% maximum with respect to that of the dry sides, however built. This increase must be foreseen in the planning stage, either by allowing for thicker walls or, better, structural variations using insulating materials. The planner's discretion in varying the protective increase between 50-100% must be related to the wall's capacity to absorb water and to the presence or absence of a cornice and jutties on the building.

SUMMARY

The practical results of the observations and studies made over seven years in twenty neighborhoods throughout Italy can be summarized in the following points:

- In Italy, driving rain is the preponderant cause of humidity in new houses – about 90% of all cases.

- The humidity is limited to one (or at most two) exposed side of a building; buildings in coastal cities are more vulnerable.

- In the plains where a continental climate prevails (Po Valley), efficient and prolonged central heating eliminates the humidity; autonomous, one-family heating plants do not assure the same benefit because they are often at variance in timing and management.

- In Italy, it has never been found that rainwater completely traverses a wall.

- In Italy, moisture on the inner walls and water that collects at the wall base are always due to condensation, given the combined effect of cold and overcrowding.

- Cooling does not depend on the latitude of the place but on RH and wind speed.

- For the calculation of heating plants, we advance the hypothesis of an *equivalent outdoor air temperature,* valid only for the rain-beaten side of a building; this temperature is the same as that of the wet bulb thermometer of a psychrometer.

- The decrease in air temperature on the wet side of a building is given an average base value of 3°C for the winter/spring period; in Italy, the manifestations of humidity intensify in the spring.

- The structures that are very sensitive to cooling are pumice blocks with two or four air cells and cavity infill walls where the internal air space communicates to some extent with the outside air (if the outer leaf facing the cavity is not plastered).

- Cooling of any type of wall is reduced if its surface is equipped against water absorption, for instance with ship-lapped ceramic tiles or periodic silicone treatments. Cooling is thus reduced but not completely eliminated.

- No cement-type rendering, no matter how waterproof it seems, can protect a wall from cooling. Even a metal wall, although completely waterproof, is cooled when it is alternately dampened by rain and dried by evaporation.

- Immunization of new buildings must be foreseen in the planning stage. Two different thermal rules are applied, depending on whether or not there is a heating plant. If there is a furnace, the heat requirements for rooms exposed to rain must be increased by 15-20%; if local climate obviates the need for heating, the thermal resistance of the rain-beaten wall(s) must be increased 50-100% with respect to the others, whatever conventional structure they may have.

- For programmed humidity protection in new public housing, a prerequisite is for the planner to be informed beforehand of the local phenomenon of driving rain, just as he or she is informed of the zone's seismic potential.

¶51.   Terrace waterproofing.

— The kind of structure needed to make a terrace completely watertight varies greatly from place to place because it depends upon the amount of rainfall. It also depends upon summer sunshine, which causes the structure to expand in the heat and then, with nocturnal cooling, to crack around the edges where the waterproofing layers are not elastic enough. In any case, we shall limit ourselves to speaking of temperate climates. The technique of terrace protection has evolved in the wake of the excellent industrial products that have appeared in recent years. Formerly, one of the following practical systems was used as a defense against rainfall:

- a 16 mm thick layer of asphalt, applied hot
- a layer of so-called 'paper felts or bituminized cardboard.' These paper felts had to be made of long, organic fibers, such as cotton, jute or wool, and mixed only with bitumen, never tar

Both systems involved a considerable addition of inert powders – so-called 'mineral filler' – which is of dubious value. In fact, a first improvement in the hot asphalt system was the complete elimination of sand filler from the mix. Let us compare the two mixtures.

Old mixture, 16 mm thick	New mixture, 10 mm thick
asphalt mastic, 60 parts by weight	asphalt mastic, 92 parts by weight
natural bitumen, 4 parts	natural bitumen, 8 parts
sifted sand, 36 parts	sifted sand, none

The terraces of many old buildings in Europe and America are still protected by one of the two techniques mentioned above. Even today, these systems continue to be used for country homes or in remote places because they are inexpensive and can be applied by any competent workman. When carefully executed, they last for 30 years. In urban areas, however, they are universally considered to be outdated and technically disqualified. What innovation has replaced them?

Nowadays, the main emphasis is on elastic sheets derived from the so-called 'elastomers,' i.e., totally artificial types of rubber that no longer bear any resemblance to the old latex from rubber trees. With special treatments, such as vulcanization, the different elastomers become imbued with a wide variety of properties by stressing one quality or another (many of which are mutually contradictory), such as impermeability to water but not to water vapor, or elasticity or plasticity. But, perhaps the greatest merit of vulcanization is that it gives *long life* to various chosen qualities in artificial rubber. For example, if elasticity is wanted, vulcanization will impede hardening for an average of 30 years. The rubber stays young. Too bad it's not yet possible to vulcanize people.

We give below the qualities required of elastic sheets for terraces today. The sheets are often formed of two superimposed layers, each having its own characteristics:

- excellent behavior under cold or heat
- little residual deformation after compression and tension
- absolute impermeability to water and good permeability to vapor
- resistance to ozone and ultraviolet (UV) radiation
- resistance to smog, especially to saltiness and sulfur dioxide
- long-term conservation of the above qualities

As indicated above, commercially available elastic sheets (sold in 10 m rolls) are often composed of two bonded layers; for instance, DuPont's Hypalon has a lower layer of neoprene, protected from the sunlight, and an upper layer of polyethylene chlorosulfon-ate, which is resistant to UV radiation and ozone. Often the elastic sheets are thinly lined with copper or aluminum foil on one side, or the foil is imbedded between the two layers. The latter is the best solution for terraces meant to be walked on, when a paving such as stoneware tiles or cement squares is laid over the waterproofing. If no paving is laid, as on domes, for instance, the metal foil goes on the outside … in the hope that it will withstand UV radiation, ozone and, above all, sulfur dioxide. From the commercial viewpoint, elastic sheets for building can be listed in groups according to the elastomer from which they are derived:

"WARM" FLAT ROOF COVERING

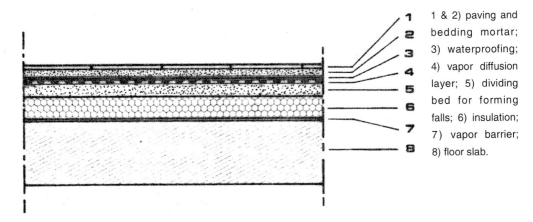

1 & 2) paving and bedding mortar; 3) waterproofing; 4) vapor diffusion layer; 5) dividing bed for forming falls; 6) insulation; 7) vapor barrier; 8) floor slab.

"COLD" FLAT ROOF COVERING, i.e. with air space

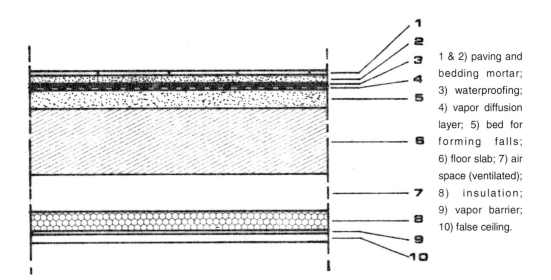

1 & 2) paving and bedding mortar; 3) waterproofing; 4) vapor diffusion layer; 5) bed for forming falls; 6) floor slab; 7) air space (ventilated); 8) insulation; 9) vapor barrier; 10) false ceiling.

Fig. 128.

The two stratigraphic compositions of terraces according to the most recent ideas of specialists. The waterproof layer can be either above or below the thermal protection.

- DuPont's NEOPRENE and Bayer's BAYPREN are derived from *polychloroprene*
- Esso's ESSO BUTYL is derived from *copolymers isobutylene-isoprene*
- DuPont's HYPALON is derived from *polyethylene chlorosulfonate*
- Montedison's DUTRAL and DSM's KELTAN are derived from *copolymers ethylene-propylene.*

This is merely an indicative list, partly because some of the major manufacturers of waterproof sheeting have preferred to stress plasticity over elasticity. Again, as an indication, we give two products *not* derived from elastomers, but from equally worthwhile thermoplastic materials:

- Schidkroet's RHEPANOL is derived from *polyisobutylene*
- Montedison's PLYPAC is derived from *polyvinylchloride*

The weak point in waterproofing with elastic or plastic sheets, of whatever type or brand, is the bonding of the overlapping edges; this bonding must be executed with great care, with a suitable adhesive, and often with heat and adequate pressure as well. Special, easy-to-handle equipment now exists for this purpose.

Finally, it must be remembered that all terraces must be adequately protected against winter cold and summer heat, notably direct insolation. Thermal protection can range from the traditional Italian bed of pozzolana and crushed tiles to new compositions of pumice, expanded clay granules, cellular cement, vermiculite, cork, etc., or to layers of rock or glass wool, expanded resins, and so forth. It is essential for such thermal protection to be applied above the terrace floor, not beneath, to save the floor from excess dimensional change due to thermal expansion. It is also necessary for the insulating material not to contain water that can vaporize, and to be rigid enough to be walked on if the terrace is used. The stratigraphic composition of a modern terrace, starting from the top, should follow one of the two schemes in figure 128, depending on the case.

A means of dispersing or blocking vapor from below is needed for terraces over large rooms, crowded or steamy premises, or, again, where there is no terrace paving. In the last case, blistering in the bituminous layer of the surface waterproofing is much to be feared. The blistering (apart from small bubbles due to gasification of the light hydrocarbons in the bitumen) is due principally to small amounts of water underneath the waterproofing. The water can be a construction residue (such as the water remaining in concrete containing vermiculite or pumice), or it can come from the small amounts that are absorbed day by day from below due to condensation on the ceiling or diffusion caused by the porosity of the ceiling itself. In any case, the problem is quite serious in flat terrace coverings or in curved roofs that are not trafficked and are thus not furnished with true paving and mortared elements. There are special roof ventilators on the market which are fairly effective in relieving evaporation pressure; these are positioned evenly over the terrace, one every so many square meters.

Chapter Twelve

ARE HEATING AND VENTILATION USEFUL AGAINST HUMIDITY?

¶52. The efficacy and limitations of ventilation and heating.

— We should not endow heating and ventilation with powers they do not have; heating may be useful for people, but even when accompanied by ventilation it does not stop rising damp. *We must avoid the pitfall of believing that walls can be dried out when rising damp is present.*

Even when accelerated with fans, air exchange acts to dry a wall (by exhausting its water reserves) only in new buildings; in old buildings with serious cases of moisture rising from the subsoil, *ventilation has no practical effect on the drying of the walls* because the water supply is inexhaustible. In our own experience, analysis of wall samples has confirmed that the moisture content remains the same, no matter how active the ventilation. Figures 129 and 130 illustrate a thorough ventilation system installed by the author during the Second World War to combat mold in the collection of the Library of Archaeology and Art History; the books were being temporarily stored in the underground room of the Auditorium in Via della Lungara in Rome. The graph shows a decrease of RH from about 80% to about 65% each day from 10 a.m. to 6 p.m., during the time the exhaust fan was working. As soon as the fan was turned off, the RH climbed back up to maximum.

The true benefit of ventilation is simply that it keeps the environmental air from becoming overloaded with vapor. Since people and objects are immersed in the air, and through it are subjected to humidity from the walls, improvement of the air has the same practical effect as drying the walls – but *only as long as the ventilation lasts.*

Heating, apart from its physiological benefits, also has a strong improving effect on the air for two reasons: it lowers the RH and it speeds up natural air exchange through wall apertures. Yet, if the environment is so tightly closed that air exchange is hindered, heating cannot prevent the air from becoming saturated from its contact with damp walls; moreover, a new danger arises in that optimum conditions for the growth of microorganisms and mold are created. Moisture, high temperature and stagnant air favor a virulent development of microscopic flora which rapidly attack any organic substance present: paper, leather, wood, glue and foodstuffs. Therefore, winter heating to counteract the effects of rising damp is advisable only where there is active ventilation as well, but paradoxical as it may seem, heating is always advisable against seasonal dampness in spring and summer.

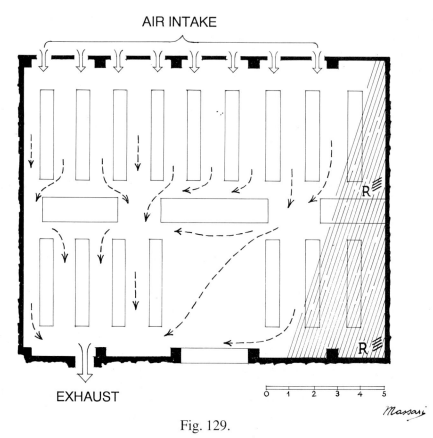

Fig. 129.

Plan of the underground storeroom of the Archaeology Library, and scheme of forced ventilation between the stacks; in dead corners (shaded areas) electric heaters (R) supplement the ventilation where it is insufficient.

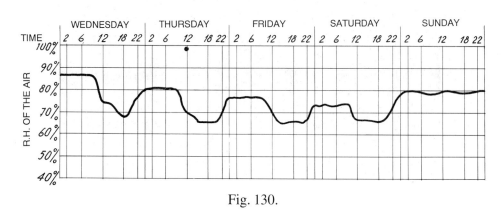

Fig. 130.

The effect of daytime ventilation on the air in the room shown in the preceding figure. The exchange was 9-10 volumes of air per hour (violent).

We have said elsewhere that ventilation is similar to what a doctor would call a 'symptomatic' cure, in that it does not remove the cause, but only relieves the symptoms, the manifestations of the ailment. Heating, however, does actively combat seasonal and meteorological condensation.

Despite their limitations, **both increased ventilation and heating are the most immediately effective means of bringing about temporary hygienic improvement of damp premises. They are also generally the most economical**, as they permit us to regulate expenditure on the basis of results obtained.

Ventilation can be: *natural,* when obtained through doors, windows or air vents set into the walls; *accelerated,* when one tries to increase it with thermal (old draft chimneys) or mechanical means (modern exhaust fans).

¶53. Natural ventilation.

— Air exchange is due to temperature differences between indoor and outdoor air and to wind action. There are but two elementary ways to increase natural ventilation: increase the openings through which the exchange can take place and reduce resistance to internal circulation. Often such resistance is considerable; an empty room may not seem likely to suffer from humidity, but once congested with furniture, crates or shelves, it can become damp – given only a slight moisture content in some wall – because air circulation is hindered. Stagnation of saturated air is usually found up to about 40 cm above the entire floor, as well as behind pictures and furniture against the wall.

To eliminate stagnation and pockets of saturated air, a modest but efficacious remedy is to open air vents at floor level in the bearing wall; it is also worthwhile to

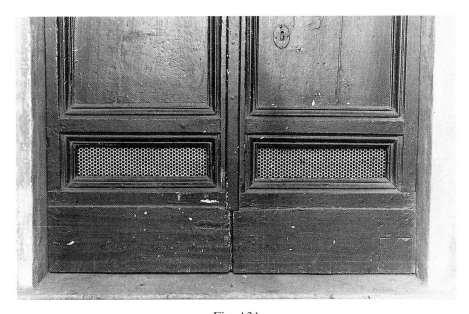

Fig. 131.

The substitution of air grills for lower panels on doors increases natural ventilation, even when the doors are closed.

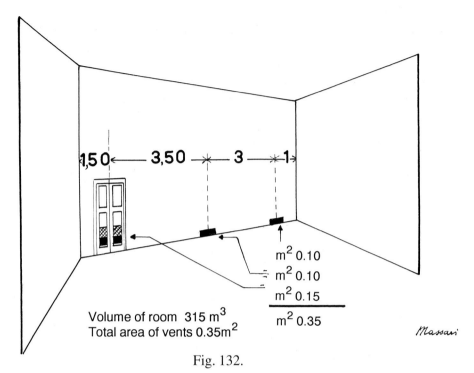

Fig. 132.

The total area of ventilation apertures must be proportional to the volume of the room being rehabilitated.

Fig. 133.

Type of air vent with adjustable grill.

substitute grills for the lower sections on doors so that air flow is maintained even when the doors are closed (fig. 131).

The size and number of air vents through the walls must be proportional to the volume of air in the premises; from our own practical experience, we suggest that *the total area of the apertures should be not less than 0.1 m^2 per every 100 m^3 of the environment.* There is no need for pedantic rules on the size and shape of individual air vents (fig. 132), but if the wall is over 60 cm thick, it is advisable for each vent to measure

Fig. 134.

Window fixture with adjustable louvers for natural ventilation.

at least 25 x 25 cm; otherwise, friction resistance to air flow in the passage reduces effectiveness. Placement of the vents must be subordinated to the room's decor so that they will not be covered by furniture: on average, one vent is needed per every 3-4 m of wall, and the vents should be spaced so that some occur in the corners where they are most useful. It is a good idea to cover the vents with grills so they do not collect debris, and if greater precision is desired one can select adjustable louvered grills. Better still, one can have the grills made to order; unfortunately, the technique of humidity defense is still so little known that few ready-made products are found on the market (fig. 133).

Opposite the openings located in the bearing wall, one must allow sufficient air to enter through the windows, either by keeping them slightly ajar or having open louvers in the upper sections. The area of the openings must at least equal that of the holes in the wall. Still, this elementary prescription is easier said than done; rarely does one find service personnel sufficiently trained in regulating outer window and door fittings, whether in large warehouses, archives or library stacks, or even in private homes. Therefore it is safer to modify the glazing, resolving the problem case by case so enough air is allowed to pass even when the windows are closed, and one thus avoids overdependence on manual control. One excellent solution is the *louvered window* (fig. 134); another is the window with *incomplete double glazing* (fig. 135), which has the advantage of not producing annoying drafts and which any good carpenter can adapt to existing windows, following the rules given above. If the premises are unoccupied, one can even resort to the drastic solution of removing an upper pane in each window and replacing it with a fine metal screen, like mosquito netting, except on facades exposed to driving rain.

Generally, in cases of rising damp, the *opening of air vents in the bearing wall and a corresponding alteration of the opposing window fixtures are sufficient to obtain a decided improvement in premises where visible humidity damage is high but the wall moisture content analysis is low;* the improvement is sometimes quite miraculous. We recommend this system even if exact calculation of the apertures is not possible.

Knapen, who has elegantly standardized this type of natural ventilation under the name of 'differential horizontal aeration,' does not attempt to calculate how many changes of air can be obtained in a given room. He proposes opening low, medium and high vents (fig. 136), and recommends the vent shape shown in fig. 137; his justification is that the passage opened in the wall would contain two counterpoised gaseous wedges (ADGFBC and ADGFEH), which would penetrate as easily as solid wedges do, "since a tiny pressure differential would allow one to prevail over the other, and thus the air would flow in both directions." This explanation is superfluous, and the shape of the vent is justified by the need to keep

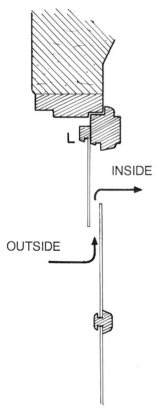

Fig. 135.

Incomplete double glazing is a simple way to assure ventilation with closed windows. It can be applied to any fixture already in place, without any special or patented pieces.

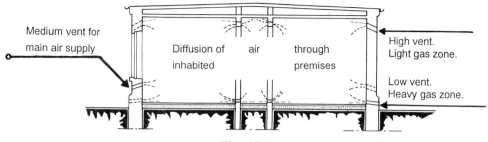

Fig. 136.

Knapen's placement of air vents to assure natural ventilation.

out snow and rain without looking for further reasons. Basically, what is involved is the activation of *continuous* air exchange, independent of the windows, by utilizing the slight temperature differences that are found in the opposite walls of a building due to their different exposures; Knapen says that a difference of only 2°C will attract horizontal ventilation. His method is undoubtedly excellent and particularly advisable for new constructions and public gathering places – schools, conference halls, barracks, etc. – all environments in which it is necessary to carry off light gaseous products and stale air which tend to accumulate near the ceiling; high vents deal with this problem efficiently but occasionally cool the environment.

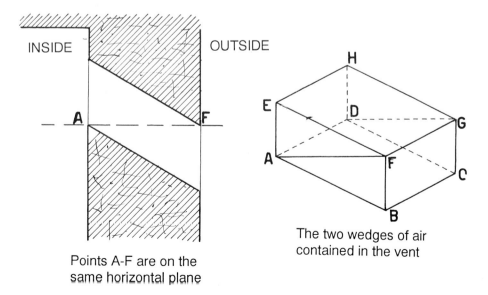

Fig. 137.

Vertical section of an air vent for an outer wall, according to Knapen.

Air vents are more effective in the direction of the prevailing wind. As Pagliani has shown, wind action is much more energetic than action due to temperature; in fact, the pressure generated by the ordinary temperature difference between indoors and outdoors does not exceed 2 kg per m^2 of wall, whereas even a moderate wind gives three or four times that pressure. Windy days are frequent in central-peninsular Italy, and in maritime climates in general; on the average, for 4-5 days per month, the wind exceeds a speed of 7 m/s and activates an energetic air exchange.

¶54. Air exchange with natural draft chimneys.

— Natural ventilation of damp premises, semi-basements and perimeter trenches can be sharply increased by linking them to specially built chimneys or to old, disused pipes. Natural draft chimneys function either thermally or dynamically; the former type works on temperature differences and is valid for places where there is little wind and where there are notable temperature gaps between indoors and outdoors; the latter type works in windy locations and is completely independent of temperature.

On the principle of Pitot's tube, horizontal wind, *whatever its direction,* exercises a drawing action on the upper mouth of a chimney. Wind action should be considered as prevailing over thermal action. A possible vertical wind component, even one which moves downwards, is not harmful as it would be in a fireplace chimney, and is still useful for purposes of air exchange; the flow would move in the opposite direction but the air would still be changed.

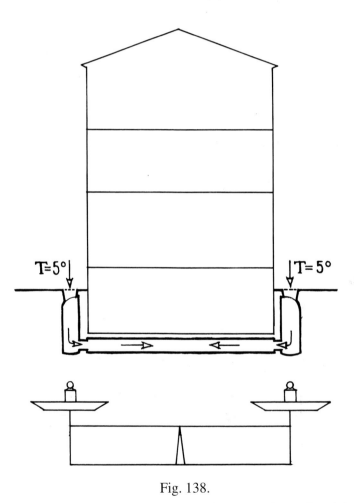

Fig. 138.

The weights of the two columns of air over the grills of the trench counterbalance each other. There is no ventilation inside the trench.

Suppose one wanted to ventilate a perimeter trench around a

building, as well as the air chamber constructed under the floor, as in fig. 138. The weights of the two air columns counterbalance each other and the air does not move. Instead, if the perimeter trench is mostly covered and then connected to the vertical pipe of an old, abandoned chimney (fig. 139), the air column contained in the chimney pipe takes on the temperature of the heated building, reaching 15°C for instance, and becomes much lighter than the outside air. The weight drop produces active ventilation in the trench. The trench must be narrow, however – no wider than 25-30 cm – because otherwise the air mass it contains, and which the chimney must draw up, becomes too much for the chimney's limited opening.

Figure 140 gives a comparison between the draft of a smoke stack and the functioning of a perimeter trench ventilation shaft. When the fireplace is too large, the hot air is unable to go up the chimney, which is usually blamed for the problem. We say it 'doesn't draw.' If the lower opening is reduced by substituting a stove for the fireplace, the same chimney pipe 'draws.'

It is also important for the perimeter trench to be narrow because the evaporation of a damp surface is proportional to air speed and therefore, given equal volumes of air exchange, it is beneficial for the air speed to increase. The opposite is the case for a chimney, however. To have maximum drawing power, it should be as large as possible in section, even if air speed is reduced, because the chimney certainly does not need to be dried, and an increase in air speed would only increase friction without providing any counter benefit.

For the restoration of the church of San Marco in Rome, which was seriously affected by

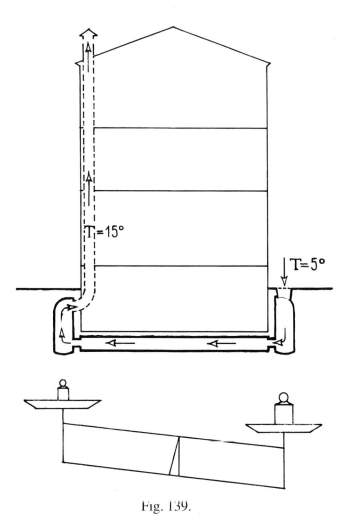

Fig. 139.

The weights of the two columns, no longer in balance, activate ventilation.

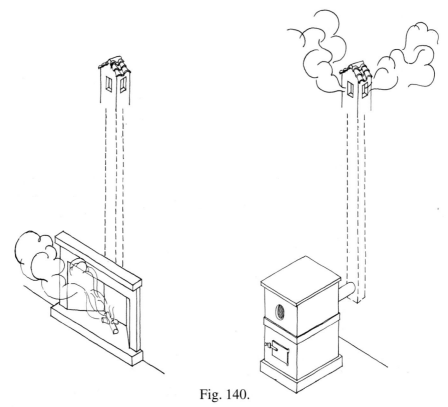

Fig. 140.

The same chimney "does not draw" for a large, open fireplace, but "draws" for a stove.

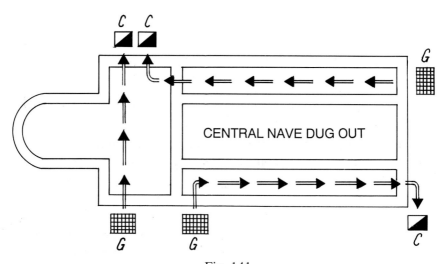

Fig. 141.

The three natural ventilation circuits of the subterranean area in the church of San Marco in Rome: G) air grills in the pavement outside C) chimneys at least 12 m high.

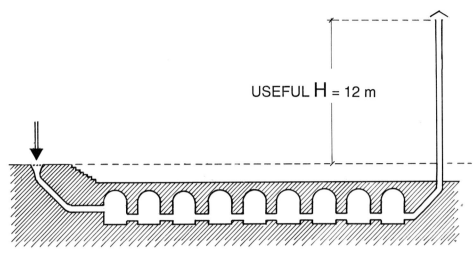

Fig. 142.

Typical subterranean ventilation circuit of the right aisle. Vertical scheme.

rising damp, our project called for dividing the basement into three completely independent ventilation circuits (fig. 141). Two vertical chimneys were constructed: the larger
one, which served two circuits, could not be taller than 12 m for architectural reasons; the
other, which served the third circuit, was 18 m high. Figure 142 shows the rough plan of
the typical circuit under the right nave. The available load, i.e., the pressure or depression
given by the 12 m high chimney, was figured on the basis of a hypothetical winter
temperature gap of only 10°C, with absolutely no wind.

	T°C	Relative humidity	Air weight kg/m^3
Cold external air	5	60%	1.2671
Warm subterranean air	15	100%	1.2178

Usable difference in weight: 0.0493 kg.

In winter, the temperature difference provokes upward air movement with a direct
draft, while in full summer a similar, inverse weight difference produces suction above
the grill and a movement in the opposite direction, with air entering the chimney and
exiting by the external grill.

Naturally, in these chimney ventilation circuits the available load is so small
(0.6 mm of water in the case shown) that one must exploit every possible aspect. Use
large-section chimneys; carefully reduce leaks; round off corners; avoid changes in
section size; use smooth pipes of fiber cement or Eternit™, and so forth.

As shown by capacity checks in the chimneys of San Marco, the system works well, but it is more active under wind action than the action of temperature.

When the wind is irregular, the direction of the draft constantly changes and air exchange is always effective. Under wind action, the load quite often reaches 6-7 mm of a water column and the chimney's draft is at least ten times more active than under the simple action of temperature.

One recommendation in conclusion: beware of thinking one can use the commercial-sized chimney pipes that are used in cities for wood or gas stoves (i.e., 10 x 10 cm on the sides or at most 14 x 14 cm). Here, sections of about 0.10-0.40 m^2 are needed and thus chimneys with sides or diameters on the order of 30-60 cm, which is quite an encumbrance. As a rule, *chimneys with sides less than 30 cm will never work as exhaust chimneys.*

To improve drawing power in winter, one can put a heat source in the chimney (radiators, electric resistors, gas fires, etc.). The heating apparatus must be placed in the base of the chimney without creating resistance to the air flow.

¶55. Forced ventilation.

— One uses either a propeller fan applied directly to an external window or wall grill for the simplest installations, or a centrifugal fan which channels and collects the air, and serves for installations with many openings.

The performance of each type is characterized by two figures: its cubic meter capacity per minute, and its static pressure, given in millimeters of a column of water. The static pressure must be in proportion to the resistance the moving air has to overcome.

We advise that the following conventional average data be stipulated:

* It should be sufficient for the rehabilitation of any damp premises to reduce the RH of the air *below 65% in winter and 75% in summer.*
* Prima facie, two changes of air per hour can be presumed to be sufficient, depending on the condition of the walls, on the obstacles to circulation caused by furniture or the shape of the room, and on the occasional or constant presence of people.

The limits indicated for RH – 65% in winter and 75% in summer – are high if judged by the criteria of air conditioning, but the problem (which is modest in our view) is to make damp premises tolerably usable at little expense, when otherwise they are not.

Since we limit ourselves to introducing natural air, forced ventilation will always be subordinate to the RH of the outdoor air, in the sense that one turns the ventilation on or off, rather arbitrarily, depending on whether the outdoor air is suitable or unsuitable for carrying off internal humidity.

Indeed, it would be quite pointless to force ventilation with air that does not have the capacity to remove moisture, and it would become downright damaging if the air (as happens in summer) were likely to cause condensation.

Therefore, the ventilation timetable becomes very important in relation to daily variations in outdoor RH, and the seasonal opportuneness becomes important in relation to annual variations in RH.

As is known, maximum humidity occurs at night in our climate between midnight and 6 a.m., and the minimum occurs during the day, fairly constantly between 11 a.m. and 4 p.m. A sharp increase occurs after 6 p.m. In summer, 50% RH is common during the day at 2 p.m., and 90 or 95% after midnight. Therefore, when using natural air, the first rule is never ventilate at night to improve damp conditions, especially in summer when one is most tempted to turn on the fan.

On the whole, rehabilitating ventilation must be restricted to a daytime schedule.

The two seasonal dangers to avoid are excessive cooling of the environment in winter due to over-violent ventilation, and condensation in summer due to the introduction of very damp, albeit warm air. The latter danger greatly limits the possibilities of forced ventilation in summer, for it requires such supervision and control that *it becomes inadvisable on the whole.*

One must also bear in mind that forced ventilation provokes evaporation from damp wall surfaces; the dryer the air introduced from outside, the greater the lowering of wall temperature by evaporation. We give below a table of the wall cooling caused by outside air introduced at 10°C, 18°C and 30°C and for diverse RH conditions of the air itself:

TABLE VI – COOLING OF DAMP WALL SURFACES EXPOSED TO FORCED VENTILATION

I.						
For air introduced at 10°C with *RH of* ..	95%	87%	74%	62%	50%	39%
Cooling of the wall from 10°C to	9.6	9	8	7	6	5
II.						
For air introduced at 18°C with *RH of* ..	96%	90%	80%	71%	62%	53%
Cooling of the wall from 18°C to	17.6	17	16	15	14	13
III.						
For air introduced at 30°C with *RH of* ..	97%	93%	85%	78%	72%	65%
Cooling of the wall from 30°C to	29.6	29	28	27	26	25

To summarize, the criteria we suggest for efficacious forced ventilation with *natural air*, for the purpose of improving damp premises, are given below.

- The capacity of the electric fans should be adequate for at least two air changes an hour; usually the smallest fans on the market will suffice. Do not overdo the power installed, except when fighting an invasion of mold by creating violent air exchange in unfrequented storerooms.
- In winter, be satisfied if the air introduced increases its absolute humidity and at the same time reduces the RH to at least 65%; in summer, be satisfied if the air introduced does not increase in RH above 75%.
- Do not use ventilation in the evening or overnight.
- In winter (always with very light ventilation) one can introduce cold air of any RH – even up to 90% – so long as the indoor temperature remains at least 6°C higher than

the outside; this holds especially for cellars or any premises incapable of natural self-ventilation.

- *Forced ventilation in summer is always* **dangerous;** it can only be used for brief periods when the outside air has an initial RH no greater than 60% and the temperature gap is 4-5°C.

- When restoration requirements do not allow ventilation practice to follow the above guidelines (for example, when continuous nocturnal ventilation of a damp, over-crowded room is needed), the air must be dried before being introduced; thus one passes to air conditioning, which is beyond the scope of our subject.

- Avoid the formation of pockets and dead areas where the effect of ventilation does not reach by using local remedies and subsidiary measures (fig. 129, p. 190).

¶56. Summer heating to combat condensation.

— Strangely enough, summer heating is an excellent remedy for certain grave cases of humidity, such as those due to the condensation that afflicts cellars or basements. The best results are obtained by *transferring the necessary calories directly to the walls, instead of the air;* heating coils embedded in the floor, as in common radiant heating systems, resolve the problem to perfection. Naturally, the number of calories needed to combat summer condensation is much lower than for winter heating, and if a sole heating plant must be planned for the two diverse requirements – winter and summer – the furnace must be properly set up in advance. Separate furnaces are better.

When it is not possible to heat the wall mass directly, one must settle for heating the air. Electric radiators are most suitable for this task, if the installation is specifically constructed to deal with condensation. For premises of a certain extent, it is necessary to calculate the number of calories needed against summer condensation, using a procedure not unlike that followed for winter heating requirements. The difference is that, for summer heating, the base data are as follows:

temperature of outdoor air

temperature found inside

temperature desired

The temperature drop normally encountered in high summer between the outside temperature and that of premises suffering from condensation varies from 5°C to 8°C and even more. Usually, **reducing this drop by half** is enough to produce an extraordinary improvement in health conditions; the 'desired' temperature would thus be 3-4°C above the minimum found.

EXAMPLE

In the typical case of a basement exposed to the north, as shown in fig. 143, suppose that the temperature drop is 8°C:

temperature of outdoor air . . . . . . 30°C

temperature found inside . . . . 22°C

temperature 'desired'   . . . . 26°C

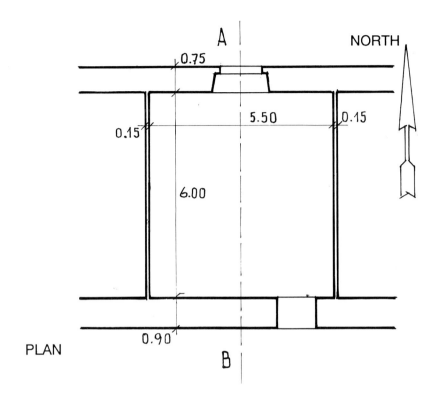

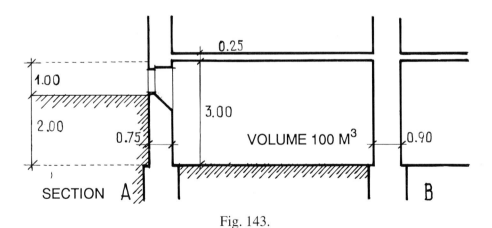

Fig. 143.

Example of typical subterranean premises subject to summer condensation. Character-istics and heating required:

- air volume 100 m^3
- outside air temperature in summer 30°C
- corresponding internal temperature 22°C
- hourly calorie requirement 646 kcal/h
- temperature obtained 26°C

The calculation of calorie requirements can be done the same way as calculations for winter heating, with which technicians are more familiar. To obtain the desired indoor summer temperature of 26°C, starting from 22°C, an addition of 646 kcal/h [750W] is needed; this figure corresponds to the difference between the heat leaving (868) and that entering (-222) the premises (=646). This calorie requirement is less than ⅓ that needed for winter heating.

In practice, since the temperature of floors and inner walls tends to increase gradually in summer, and since natural ventilation is often activated by opening doors and windows, the *calorie requirement can be held to be roughly equal to ¼-⅓ the winter requirement*, and thus around 6 kcal an hour per cubic meter of ambient air. This datum can be assumed for normal practice.

The limited quantity of heat needed to halve the summer temperature drop can be produced with electric heaters which permit easy calculation of power, keeping in mind that one kWh gives 864 calories with a 100% yield. One can empirically anticipate an installation of 1 kW for every 140-170 m^3 of space, divided among radiators with no more than half kW power, and which can be moved from one plug to another until the best result is obtained. This type of heating is expensive, but easily adjusted to a timetable when the premises are occupied.

In premises that have normal winter heating (as previously discussed), summer condensation can be avoided by extending the heating period for at least a couple of months beyond the date it is normally turned off; during this period the amount of heat can be gradually reduced.

¶57.   Four sins of inattention common to traditional heating engineers.

— This is a delicate subject and we do not wish to offend such valuable friends as heating engineers; we hope, therefore, that our remarks will be taken as constructive criticism. The four cases are as follows:

1) *The problem of 'cold feet.'* Dining halls in factories, schools, railroad stations, etc., are often located partially underground or at most on a mezzanine floor. Several years ago, German health experts observed the high incidence of sore throats in students who got cold feet from sitting in ground-floor or mezzanine classrooms. That there is a direct correlation between cold feet and weakening of general organic defenses against infection has been known since Pasteur's time. He demonstrated that, given the same air temperature and diet, hens kept for a few days with their feet on a damp floor became more susceptible to infection with anthrax than their counterparts whose feet were kept dry.

In a classroom, one remains relatively immobile for long periods, with the body's organic defenses lulled. The only parts of the body in direct contact with the structure are the soles of the feet – even though shoes are interposed. It is an error not to realize that the 20°C usually allowed for air temperature, and in which all the rest of the body is immersed, do not apply to the soles of the feet. There is always a few degree's drop in temperature between the air and the floor in ground floor and mezzanine rooms, and it is clear that even if the air temperature is 20°C, the floor will be 15°C or 14°C; the floor will carry off, either by its greater thermal drop, or principally by the major conductivity of direct contact, much more heat per cm of the sole than will be lost from a similar-sized body surface immersed in the air. Picture a company director sitting in his office (which is heated to 20°C) and listening to reports for two or three hours. Suppose he decided to get comfortable by swivelling his chair and leaning his back directly against an exterior wall. If he were idiotic enough to persist in that chilly position, he would certainly get pleurisy.

To return to the problem of cold feet, the routine error of heating engineers is thinking that the solution is to raise the air temperature by 2 or 4 degrees. This makes matters worse, for by increasing the dryness of the air one invites greater irritation of the throat, which is already strained by cold at the extremities.

Here, then, is the problem. What should be done about it? The answer is simple: apply an autonomous heating network of copper tubing under the floor in order to eliminate the difference in temperature between air and floor. Radiant electric wires, enclosed in sheathing, can also be used. The surface temperature of the floor should never exceed that of the air, i.e., 20-22°C. Can heating engineers understand this?

When an old building is involved and heating elements cannot be inserted into the floor, another expedient must be used: apply a thick (22 mm) parquet nailed over thin wooden strips or, more simply, planed fir planks (40-50 mm thick) connected tongue-and-groove along the edges. Thinner alternatives, such as 8 mm parquet squares attached with mastic or wall-to-wall carpeting, are useless. The phenomenon of cold feet is a health hazard, so we should not skimp on the solution.

2) *The problem of 'bastard cold.'* A bizarre error of heating engineers, linked to their routine, is that sometimes their carefully figured heat requirements, based on the minimum winter air temperature of a place, do not take into account the need for a strong supplement for what we call 'bastard cold.' Their diligent calculations can even be 20% too low. Here's why. Every civilized country has numerous weather stations which function very well and record everything: temperature and RH of the air, cloudiness, hours of sunshine or rain, and so forth. The height of rainfall is always registered, but neither the Public Works Department, nor the Agriculture Bureau, nor the Air Force are interested in distinguishing whether the rain arrives vertically or at a slant. All they need to know it that it arrives, and they are mainly concerned with its frequency and the annual total. Official climatology thus presents the strange oversight of not registering the amount of rain that falls at a slant and impregnates one or at most two sides of all the buildings in a given locality. In England, Norway, Poland and Italy, the phenomenon is quite prevalent and gives rise to a strange 'bastard cold' which acts in secret, carrying off great quantities of calories from the wet wall. Climatic cold (dependent on the air) is not involved here, but cooling of buildings; a thermometer attached outside a window *'doesn't notice anything.'*

Mother climatology, as is said, does not recognize this bastard child of hers, and so heating engineers, monument conservators, builders – all orderly people and all respectful of official records – do not even know that the child exists, or how sturdy and puzzling it is. In public housing with reinforced concrete frames, cooling due to driving rain is a frequent cause of uninhabitability for health reasons.

We have already mentioned that in any locality exposed to driving rain, the rain always comes from the same direction. Yet, the rain-beaten side is not always the one that, according to common sense, 'ought' to be the coldest, i.e., that included in the northern quadrant. How could common sense tell us that the coldest side of a building in Naples would be the southwestern one? Figure 126, p.180 points up the phenomenon, showing that the supplemental heat requirement for the premises on the rain-beaten side

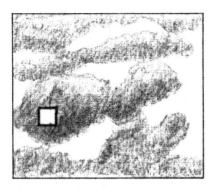

TYPE 1
cloudy stain covering entire wall
(Raised floor)

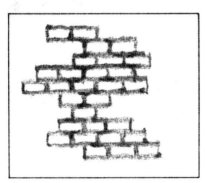

TYPE 2
pattern staining following the
mortar joints
(First floor)

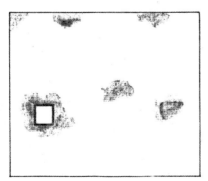

TYPE 3
scattered, rounded islands
(Second floor, top floor)

☐ two soundings in the areas most darkened with mold show that the inside is dry

Fig. 144.

Sometimes, even though the heating plant for an intermittent timetable has been well calculated, the northern walls are clouded with mold which forms various patterns depending on the construction material.

ranges from 10% to 20% more. But technicians still remain blissfully ignorant. In Chapter Eleven this subject was treated in detail.

N.B. In fairness, we must add an updating: in England, in recent years, quantitative data on driving rain is being collected on a short stretch of the Atlantic coast of Cornwall. The phenomenon is violent there, and causes the inhabitants serious discomfort.

3) *The 'climograph' problem and timetable errors when heating is discontinuous.* Sometimes a central heating plant with an intermittent timetable has been perfectly calculated, but the rooms exposed to the north, or having three or more sleepers, have their external walls clouded with green or black mold (fig. 144). For example, a nocturnal, 8-hour pause from 11 p.m. to 7 a.m. is allowed in the heating, as prescribed by the heating engineer.

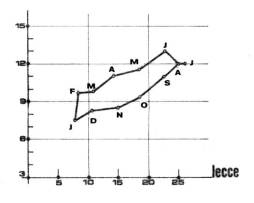

lecce

Unfortunately our friend *has not understood* the local climate, which in certain cases is not adequately described by the winter minimum. He has been mistaken, not in fixing the length, but the timing of the nightly heating pause (fig. 145). In short, the heating engineer is unfamiliar with what is called a 'climograph' – the best and most concentrated representation of yearly local climatic variations that the weather experts have been able to give us.

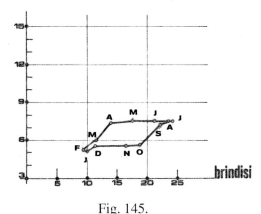

brindisi

Fig. 145.

The heating engineer has often been mistaken, not in fixing the length, but the timing of the nightly heating pause. To avoid this error and the ensuing mold, one must know the "climograph" of the place, which indicates when the boiler must be lit, even if it should be at night and go contrary to custom.

The horizontal axis of a climograph shows the *average temperature* of each month, and the vertical axis shows the *average daily fluctuation* in the same month – that is, the range in temperature from minimum to maximum over the course of a day. Let us examine the climographs of two southern Italian cities, Lecce and Brindisi, which are located near each other on the coast of Puglia, across from Albania. One immediately notices that Brindisi's climograph is smaller, rather pitiful and flattened along the bottom as if lying on the horizontal axis; this indicates *a mild and uniform climate.* Lecce's climograph, however, soars upwards and indicates an *extravagant climate, given to extremes.*

What is the difference between the two cities as regards their winter heating requirements, moderate though they may be? There is no practical difference in the amount of heat needed, because the monthly averages are about the same. The important difference, on the other hand, lies in the daily thermal fluctuation, which in February in Brindisi is only 5°C, but reaches 10°C in Lecce. The consequence: in Lecce the true cold is nocturnal cold because it lasts longer. In view of the fact that the nightly low occurs between 5 and 6 a.m., the heating should be in full operation at that time.

The total pause in the heating should therefore be divided into two separate periods, for instance at night from 11 p.m. to 4 a.m., and during the warmest time of the day, from 1 p.m. to 5 p.m. Will heating engineers learn to use climographs in combating the humidity of houses where the heat is turned off at night? We can, however, imagine the tenants' astonishment when the heat goes on by night instead of by day.

4) *Calculation errors for heating systems where there are damp walls.* In making calculations for the basements and mezzanines of old or historic buildings, the heating engineer is rarely aware that the walls have rising damp, or else this factor is not given much weight because most tables and guides are generally compiled for new, reinforced-concrete structures. Only after the heating is installed and operational is it found to be completely inadequate. The reason is clear. Damp walls disperse heat because the water filling their pores is 29 times more conductive that the air that would fill them if they were dry. In fact, the ratio between the conductivity of water and air is $\dfrac{0.52}{0.018} = 29$. Moreover, continuous evaporation requires further calories which are subtracted in not inconsiderable amounts from the air of the heated room.

For an exact calculation of the radiant surface needed in damp premises, or to check whether existing systems are adequate in borderline cases, two increases in hourly calorie requirements should be kept in mind:

- for greater dispersion through outer walls
- for the greater ventilation necessary to carry off water vapor

Dispersion. – To calculate the first increase, we should briefly recall that every wall disperses outward a given quantity of calories an hour, for every square meter and for every degree of temperature difference between indoors and out. This quantity often depends on the wall's thickness and on the material of which it is made. Every material has its own coefficient of internal conductivity (indicated by the Greek letter lambda, λ) which increases as the moisture content grows, especially when the material is porous.

A brick wall's coefficient λ of internal conductivity is about 0.6 kcal/mh°C when it is very dry (containing 1% water by volume). According to Cammerer, this condition occurs after not less than 15 months of drying in a new wall. The same coefficient is increased as follows with different moisture contents:

Percentage of moisture in relation to volume:						
1%	2.5% (normal)	5%	10%	15%	20%	25%
Coefficient of internal conductivity $\dfrac{kcal}{mh°C}$						
0.6	0.71	0.81	0.96	1.07	1.17	1.27

Consequently, in a damp brick wall, 50 cm thick, a 15% variation of moisture content by volume increases transmission heat loss by 50%. We shall see shortly the effect of this loss on the total deficit of a damp room.

Ventilation. – We must go on to calculate the second increase in heat requirements, i.e., that destined to replace heat lost through evaporation due to air exchange. Some air exchange is produced under normal circumstances through vents or special window fittings. When damp premises are involved, air flow must be encouraged by every available means. Without such an exchange, the inside air would absorb moisture from the walls up to and not beyond a given limit, becoming totally saturated; usually there is some continuous air exchange, so evaporation from the walls is also continuous and consequently subtracts heat from the air. As a rule of thumb, one usually figures that the air change should equal the volume of the room each hour when the walls are dry.

If the walls are damp, however, the air should be changed at least two or three times hourly to avoid the sense of suffocation produced by saturated air. To have some idea of the amount of heat increase required by a damp room as compared to the same room when dry, we could divide the total heat requirement of a given dry room very roughly as follows:

- 50% for dispersion through walls
- 25% for dispersion through windows and doors
- 25% for air exchange

In a damp room, in cases of average seriousness, we would have the following increase in heat requirements:

dispersion through walls goes from	50%	to	75%,
dispersion through windows and doors remains	25%		25%,
air exchange goes from	25%	to	50-75%,
Total from	100%	to	150-175%

To conclude: in average cases, *the radiating surface needed for efficacious heating of a damp room must be calculated with an increase ranging from 50 to 75% with respect to that needed for the same room when dry.*

We might add that, to make the premises comfortable, the furnace must be turned on 15 days before, and turned off not less than 45-60 days after the habitual heating period of the locality. The spring extension is particularly necessary for preventing seasonal forms of humidity, such as condensation of outdoor air and the tendency to spring/summer saturation, which afflicts cold premises, notably basements, when the warm weather arrives.

We hope that our friends, the heating engineers, will always notice in time when the premises they must heat are damp.

Chapter Thirteen

PROTECTION OF ART WORKS AND HISTORIC CENTERS

¶58.   Mural Paintings.

— Nowadays, proposals for restoration from moisture damage (real or presumed) should not be taken seriously unless the humidity has been verified and measured – *measured* above all. Sometimes, contrary to all expectations, there is no moisture; on other occasions, it is found where least expected. The experimental diagnostic system we introduced for rehabilitation of historic buildings is based on measurement of the water contained in the wall fabric. The author first applied this system to Leonardo da Vinci's Last Supper in the refectory of Santa Maria delle Grazie in Milan.

For four centuries it had been known that the refectory was unhealthful, and that moisture was responsible for the progressive ruin of da Vinci's famous painting, but it had never been possible to clarify exactly how or why, because the complex and elusive physical phenomenon had never been captured and quantified.

Following our method, soundings were made in the walls (outside the picture area, of course) and the moisture content of the samples extracted was measured. Surprisingly, a high moisture content (up to 10.9%) was found only in the lower area of the wall and no higher than two meters above the floor. Contrary to all expectations, the Last Supper, which begins above that height, was on a *perfectly dry wall* (fig. 146).

For the first time, albeit belatedly, it was demonstrated that humidity had not attacked the pigment layer from the rear, but from the front, having been deposited by condensation on the surface of the cold wall. The floor and the damp lower portion of the wall acted as a moisture reservoir. This experimental diagnosis resulted in a program for the overall drying of the refectory – the only remedy needed. Three simple masonry repairs were advised (fig. 147): the first two have already been done (1978) while, until the third is completed, the residual condensation on the Last Supper wall is temporarily offset by slightly raising the temperature of the wall mass with light heating from the rear. The general state of the hall has been greatly improved.

For art works on wall supports (mural paintings and stuccos), after inspecting the whole building, the diagnostic guidelines are as follows:

- **Measure the moisture content** of samples taken from within the wall (15-20 cm) in order to check whether there is moisture in the fabric.
- If the results are positive (excess of water in the fabric), go on to the second step: **location of the water supply** (rising from the ground? leaking roof? driving rain?).
- If the results are negative, i.e., if the wall fabric is dry, one is led by a process of elimination to suspect **intermittent condensation**. Then the usual question arises:

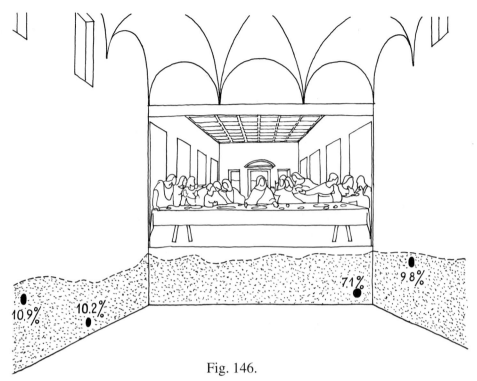

Fig. 146.

Contrary to all expectations, Leonardo's "Last Supper" was found to be on a perfectly dry wall. Moisture was present only in the lower portion of the wall and in the floor.

what is causing the condensation? There must be some cooling due to structural features or local weather conditions, and the cause must be identified.

The physical phenomenon of surface condensation always arises from a thermal drop between the air and a masonry surface – the physicist's 'cold wall.' Today, with optical scanning infrared thermometers, one can easily measure the *surface temperature* of the various structures: walls, floor, and ceiling, and locate which is the *cold wall.*

This new investigative technique is an ideal solution, for previously there were no instruments sensitive enough to low temperatures, and responsive enough to provide an instantaneous reading of every point on all the surfaces in a room. These new optical thermometers with thermoelectric pairs receive *at a distance* the infrared radiation emitted by a body and allow one to measure its temperature without actual physical contact. If the walls in a church do not contain water and the mural paintings are presumably being ruined by condensation, this kind of field investigation can firmly establish, for example, that the dangerous temperature is that of the floor, or part of the floor, and defensive measures can be limited to that surface alone. In fact, ambient air is brought to saturation by the heat reduction caused by that floor because it is the coldest structure in the entire church; when there is excess vapor, it is then deposited on the walls as well. This experimental diagnosis of the *cold wall* is another valid means of protecting mural paintings whenever the damage is generically attributed to moisture in some form.

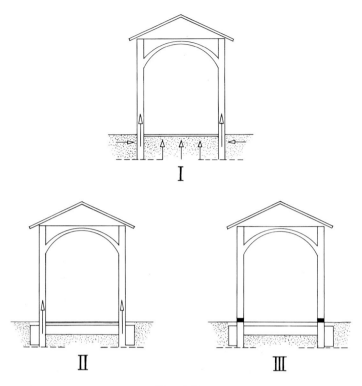

Fig. 147.

Progressive restoration of the Refectory of the "Grazie" (Last Supper) from moisture:
I) Before repairs, water entered by three routes. II) Now that a subfloor system has been
built and external perimeter drainage trenches have been installed around the building,
the water can rise only from the wall's foundation. III) When a damp-proof course has
been inserted in the wall, the water will have no means of entry.

Experimental diagnosis has a decisive value in indicating the proper approach to
restoration, but the following observations should also be kept in mind, as they influence
the restoration:

- Even though humidity can act on the pigment layer from the *back* (moisture in wall
  fabric) or from the *front* (moisture in the intonaco, or condensation), the alterations
  are similar.

- Deterioration of the pigment layer, often attributed too exclusively to humidity, is
  frequently linked to a joint cause.

In the case of the Last Supper, this joint factor is perhaps attributable to the
preparation of the ground, which was done in too many thin layers, or according to others,
to some unknown binder added to the tempera. The humidity of the refectory alone would
not be sufficient to destroy Leonardo's painting; indeed, the refectory also houses the
Montarfano Crucifixion in a perfect state of conservation opposite the Last Supper, which
is sadly deteriorated. The former mural painting was done with normal methods, and no
innovative techniques were used. Naturally, remedies for protecting mural paintings

against humidity (apart from the action of the joint factors mentioned above) are the same as those recommended for overall protection of damp premises, depending on whether rising damp (wall fabric) or condensation (plaster) is involved.

For rising damp, we recall the original wall treatment (¶29) with which the architect Koch saved the Domenichino frescos in the church of San Luigi dei Francesi in Rome. Three arches were cut in the wall below the painting, thereby eliminating contact between the damp foundation and the frescoed wall area (fig. 50). Today, the Massari technique of rapid core drilling followed by insertion of polyester resin has been perfected, as explained in ¶30. It is no longer necessary to save individual frescos with the 'strappo' technique, which has been rather abused of late. In many cases it is preferable to block the rising damp with a U-shaped cut around the fresco: two vertical cuts on the sides joining a horizontal cut below the fresco. This technique was used in Florence to save Perugino's Crucifixion in the refectory adjacent to Santa Maria Maddalena dei Pazzi. (See description in ¶77, where the large-scale work on the church of Santa Caterina at Galatina, near Lecce, is also discussed.) Other diagnoses and restoration programs for mysteriously damp mural paintings are given in ¶72 (the Palazzo Pubblico of Siena), ¶75 (a Thracian tomb in Bulgaria) and ¶76 (the frescos of the Palazzo del Te in Mantua).

It is very difficult to protect mural paintings against the condensation of outside air or sea breezes. We refer the reader to the general guidelines in the chapter on condensation and emphasize, once again, that in such cases ventilation of the premises should be reduced to a minimum, the direct action of wind should be blocked by windows, and finally (whenever possible) the wall mass subject to condensation should be lightly heated. This last remedy is the most definitive. N.B. **the walls must be heated directly**; this approach is much more difficult but much more effective than heating the air. Heating systems should be planned case by case to bring the necessary calories to the back of the wall, using hot-air shafts, heated linings, electric heaters with reflectors, or electric resistors embedded in the wall. Rather than supplying a few calories to the back side of the wall that bears the painting, it may be more practical to heat the *floor* mass thoroughly with a normal radiant heating system. See in Chapter 15, ¶73, the example of the authors' rehabilitation of the church of Santa Maria della Rotonda in Albano Laziale.

In our own experience, the greater part of humidity-related deterioration of mural paintings can be attributed to *condensation,* principally because historic buildings, refectories and, in general, any premises that are no longer inhabited are often little better than refrigerators. We advise light radiant heating with embedded coils (which heat the masonry instead of the air) as the most rational and effective remedy for this problem.

¶59. Surface protection of outdoor stone sculpture.

— Superficial attack of stone can occur due to two different mechanisms: the action of rainwater or the action of water vapor in the air. If given percentages of dust or soluble gases are present, the mechanism can become deadly. For example, the anhydrides diffused in the air around industrial plants become corrosive when they combine with traces of moisture on a wall, a stone cornice, a marble statue or a bas relief, and form the corresponding acid. Among these anhydrides, the most common is sulfur dioxide, which forms sulfuric acid in contact with water and oxygen. This acid specifically attacks carbonates and is therefore a threat to plaster, marble, travertine and many of the natural stones used in historic buildings.

On the whole, it has been found that *stone sculpture, when dampened by rainwater, is eroded by carbon dioxide, which is more damaging than originally thought; sculpture sheltered from the rain is attacked by sulfur dioxide.*

Protective measures involve chemical or physical treatment. Either type is undoubtedly effective but there are always difficulties to overcome, independent of the merits of the procedure in itself. There are two basic problems: the height of the construction in need of protection (one thinks of the Greek temples of Athens or Agrigento), which raises a question of expense, and the short life-span of protective treatments, all of which must be repeated sooner or later, thus also raising a question of expense. In short, truly effective protection is always very costly, whether it is done by physical or chemical means.

Given the general nature of this book, we cannot go into particulars here. We refer the reader in search of more precise information to the proceedings of scientific meetings, published by the Cesare Gnudi Center for the Conservation of Outdoor Sculpture (via dei Pignattari 1, 40124 Bologna). Rather summarily, we shall limit ourselves to a brief review of the different characteristics of the two types of protection.

1) *Protection by physical means.* This type of protection is based on the formation of a surface coating that blocks capillary action by making the surface water-repellent: paraffin or wax in a suitable solvent (benzene, toluene, paraffin oil, etc.) are commonly employed. Linseed oil and transparent paints were also used but frequently they are damaged by weathering and produce unpleasant optical effects. The ancient Greeks (even though carbon fossil fuel was not used in those times) protected the creations of all three of the arts – architecture, painting, and sculpture – with surface coatings, colored or clear. Their choice of coatings seems to us purely aesthetic in some cases, but in other cases can only be explained as a practical concern for conservation. A small spatula, called a 'kestrom,' was heated over a flame and used to apply the coating. Perhaps even today no product can compete with plain paraffin, which is notably inert chemically (*parum affinis*), and provides a soft, innocuous veil, having no mechanical strength by i   . Not all specialists, however, agree on this preference for paraffin.

Indeed, from one day to the next, one is tempted by an array of new products that are much more adhesive and durable than paraffin; these include acrylic and vinyl resins and the impressive range of silicones. Time will tell how well these new products perform.

2) *Protection by chemical means.* This protection is obtained by means of substances that can combine with components of the stone and form hard compounds, impermeable to water and vapor. Of the fluosilicates employed for this purpose, those of sodium and potassium have the desirable property of being very soluble and of hardening the mass of marble treated. Unfortunately, they later produce unpleasant efflorescence, and are therefore no longer used. On the other hand, fluosilicates of magnesium and zinc are not very soluble and thus require a great deal of water, but they effectively consolidate

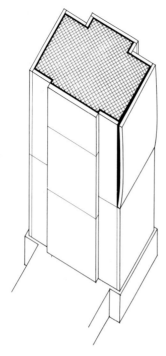

Fig. 148.

Typical swelling of slabs due to condensation. Greek marble around a pillar in the church of San Marco in Rome, before restoration.

stone without producing flowing beards later on. At one time, attempts were made to spray the sculptured elements of buildings with fluosilicate, but this was rather ineffective because the liquid flowed down without penetrating the stone. To obtain the proper penetration, a special technique was used on Donatello's magnificent outdoor pulpit on Prato Cathedral. Instead of spraying, a watertight case was built around the pulpit and filled with fluosilicate, in which the sculpture was immersed for the requisite time.

For the Basilica of San Marco in Venice, the chemists of the University of Padova advised dismantling the decorative marble piece by piece, extracting the air under vacuum and providing deep impregnation with liquid resin.

¶60. Protection of interior marble decoration.

— Ground floor premises with marble facings rarely escape condensation *unless they are heated during the winter and late into spring*. The phenomenon is accentuated in crypts, in partially underground churches, in embanked apses, in monumental atria and in convent chapter rooms or refectories with small, high windows.

It should be remembered that the interesting point of the diagnosis, once condensation has been found on the marble, is to discover the source of the water vapor. There are two possibilities: either it arises within the premises (evaporation from floors and skirting, as usual) or it enters from the outside with the warm, moist air of a winter 'sirocco' or spring breezes. We know that the doubt can be resolved by analysis of the wall's moisture content, taking samples from behind the marble that lines the walls and floor.

Restoration will be aimed at cutting the route of rising damp, if that has been found; in such a case, masonry works will be called for (subfloor air spaces, breach cutting, drying, etc.). If the problem is condensation due to cooling of outside air upon entering the premises, efforts will be made to modify the room's thermal inertia. In the latter case, especially for ground floor premises, the definitive remedy is to install a radiant heating system embedded in the floor. Therefore, at the risk of being repetitive: *do not heat the air, but directly heat a large masonry mass in the premises, i.e., the floor.* A normal heating plant with horizontal pipes can be used, or else electric resistors in silicone sheathing. A temperature of 14-15°C will suffice – for restoration purposes, that is – but the heat should continue 40-50 days longer than the normal period so that the masonry remains warm at the most critical time in late spring and early summer. In some cases, light heating might also be necessary in full summer.

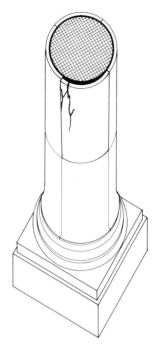

Fig. 149.

Swelling and breakage of a lining of Sicilian red jasper on a column in the church of San Marco in Rome.

The remedy of radiant floor heating can be used, in desperate cases, even when the floor is dry and the master walls are soaked with rising damp, so long as there is the *indispensable* air exchange provided by vents or windows kept slightly open. A technician who must plan such work should remember that it does not involve a heating plant, but a 'reclamation' plant to control condensation. A heat level of 4-5 calories [5-6 W] per hour per m^3 of air will suffice to activate the necessary exchange of damp air. See the example of Santa Maria della Rotonda in Albano (¶73).

As to the minor restoration work needed for the marble decoration, we should remember that the marble is damaged in two ways:

- physical
- chemical

The first includes actual mechanical damage: swelling and breakage of slabs (figs. 148-149), warping of balustrades (fig. 150) and so forth. The second causes flaking of breccia marble, powdering, clouding, etc. A complete sampler of condensation damage was formerly visible, before restoration work was completed, in the Roman church of San Marco, which was extremely damp because its floor was 2 m below street level.

Restoration plans for this church grew out of the authors' experimental observations on its air and masonry. It was found that currents of damp air, originating in the underlying cellar, entered the church through grills which had been erroneously inserted during a previous restoration with the idea of improving the air circulation. Analysis of the masonry (13.9% moisture in the church, and a good 30% in the cellar) led to a diagnosis of serious rising damp and contemporaneous condensation. Heating was ruled out because

Fig. 150.

A rail warped by the pressure of rusted iron pins, again in San Marco, before restoration.

of the notable amount of water continuously supplied to the walls. The project, which has now been virtually completed, included:

- blockage of all air passage from the cellar to the church
- independent air exchange in the cellar by means of natural draft ventilation chimneys (figs. 141-142)
- increasing the thermal resistance of the floor by construction of an anti-condensation subfloor
- summer heating of the subterranean crypt, which was subject to condensation

See ¶54 on the calculations for the ventilation chimneys. To our knowledge, these were the first such chimneys constructed in Italy to protect a large historic building from humidity.

¶61.   Beware of pseudo-scientific commercial treatments for rising damp.

— Given the plethora of new products sold for repairing damp walls, it has always been difficult for the uninitiated to avoid controversy and disappointment. Today, however, it has also become difficult even for people in the field itself to avoid confusion. The pseudo-scientific halo that surrounds the presentation of the most peculiar inventions sometimes makes an impression in outlying technical offices. After the logical and traditional methods fail to free the mold-filled and eroded apse of an old church from humidity, why not try the latest innovation? For instance, what about those tubes that are inserted at a slant in the wall, and which a salesman describes as true drainage? They really don't cost very much and, at worst, they cannot do any harm. So why not try them? Even more persuasive is the salesman who speaks, in all good faith, of ions, electro-osmosis and water movement across a porous membrane. Then, when he demonstrates with instruments that there is a difference in potential between the base and the upper part of your wall, the argument is technically irresistible. Electricity is *clearly* entirely to blame. Those two or three hundred millivolts, shown on the meter, have made the water rise in the wall. Therefore, all one needs is to create a short circuit between the upper wall and the base and the difference in potential will disappear within a few days. The humidity, servant of potential, will inevitably leave the wall.

It would be interesting to calculate the millions that, among churches, convents, historic buildings, old hospitals, ancient barracks, etc., are squandered annually world-wide with perfect administrative propriety. There are many stewards and maintenance officers who have not kept up with recent developments and can be sold a bill of goods under the guise of science.

Since it is difficult for the architects in charge of restoring historic buildings to distinguish between true science and false, the author presented the following **cautionary formula** to the International Congress of Restoration Technicians, held in Venice in 1964. This formula applies to new discoveries and commercial devices for combating rising damp in masonry:

"Before accepting the new specialties and devices on the market, one must officially determine the humidity state of the structure being restored by taking at least five samples from 15-20 cm deep in the wall at given heights above the floor, for example at 0.40, 0.80, 1.20, 1.60, 2.00 m. The samples, closed in airtight glass jars, should be sent to a qualified hygiene or chemistry laboratory at a university or public agency, with a request for measurement of the moisture content percentage by weight. Then, when the new restoration device or commercial specialty has been applied, repeat the procedure, taking the same number of samples at the same heights as before, and sending them for measurement to the same laboratory. The second sampling must be taken after a reasonable length of time in order to judge the efficacy of the device, for example after at least a year.

The device will be presumably valid if the sample's moisture content is clearly diminished. The testing must be controlled by the administration in charge of conserving the monument, and not entrusted to the person or firm applying the device on trial."

The above formula codifies trial testing methods for restoration work and protects the administration from any criticism if the work fails; yet it also leaves open an avenue for prudent experimentation and scientific research in a field where they are greatly needed.

Sometimes, to demonstrate the efficacy of a patent or a specialty, the salesman or applier will show a few examples of recent work where the humidity has indeed disappeared from the plaster surface and does not show on surface meter readings. The wall fabric, however, is not necessarily dry at all; see the case described in ¶74 of the Accademia di San Luca in Rome. Such examples of 'restoration' from rising damp are technically and legally worthless unless *at least three years have passed since the work was done, whenever the work included renewal of the plaster.* Until recently, one of the most heavily abused techniques for reassuring a doubting client consisted of dismantling the old, stained and ruined plaster and replacing it with new plaster, usually mixed with cement, hydrofuges or some other 'special' additive. This involved a banal face lift, while in reality the fabric was still impregnated with the *same amount of water as before treatment.* Not everyone knows that new plaster spread over a damp wall has ideal setting conditions; it sets slowly because the layer beneath does not extract water from the plaster as it would if the wall were dry. After 4-6 months, the plaster is completely hardened and dry on the surface to a depth of a few mm (as can be verified with a meter) and gives the impression of a true cure. Only later, when the entire thickness of the plaster is dry, is its capillary network again open to invasion from the rear, i.e., from the still-damp masonry. The reconquest is inexorable, but slow, and several more months go by before the water from the fabric gradually reaches the surface. The effect of the face lift lasts three years or, exceptionally, four, after which the plaster first darkens (fig. 151, example of renewal with hydrofuge plaster which darkened around the edges four years later) and then,

Fig. 151.

The masking of masonry dampness with hydrofuge rendering lasts an average of 3 or 4 years, after which the rendering comes loose or staining reappears around the edges.

depending on the case, comes loose and swells, or decays and is decorated anew with mold or erosion. This is why, for any contract involving work specifically to cure rising damp, the administration in charge must fix a *minimum guarantee period of at least three years* before definitive test results are examined.

In Europe, a constructor is held responsible for structural stability for a decade or so, because experience has shown that cracks can take years to appear if there are hidden defects. Today, a similar long-term responsibility should devolve on the contractor or humidity specialist who restores an historic building or a work of art that will be seriously damaged if humidity is not brought under control. Three years is the minimum guarantee period during which the contractor or specialist is held responsible because visible dampness *usually returns* within this time if the restoration has not been effective.

¶62.   The problem of daytime heating designed for human comfort and often damaging to cultural heritage in churches, museums, archives and libraries.

— Museums, libraries and archives in Europe are often housed in ancient historic buildings with very thick walls and high thermal inertia. These buildings are not well suited to their new roles, but public administrators utilize them indefinitely after gutting, relining and adapting them as best they can to house pictures, books and important files. Heating plants are almost always installed, increasingly so in churches, whether outstanding works of art are present or not, and today's fashionable systems involve blowing hot air over the heads of the congregation. In planning these heating plants, a typical but serious thing happens: even if the firm employed is reputable, technically competent and perfectly honest, the heating engineers instinctively and routinely install *hygienic type* systems suitable for humans and their physical well-being. Thus these plants function *by day* on a *bureaucratic timetable*. The architect Emile André, conservator of Lausanne Cathedral, has described the serious consequences of one such system, recently installed for climatization of his cathedral.[1] In winter, the heat is turned on during services for only three hours a day. Then, each time it is turned off, some 180 liters of condensation are deposited on the walls. The water, combining with air-borne smog, destroys the soft-stone statues. Unfortunately, historic palaces and old churches always have massively thick walls and suffer from that variable and capricious form of humidity, condensation, which is a decidedly nocturnal and notably pre-dawn phenomenon. Broadly speaking, condensation in churches damages marble, mural paintings and metal; in old buildings it affects art collections, parchment, books, and files of documents (figs. 152-153). Furthermore, it can be said to damage 'cultural heritage' in general. It will be realized that these are *inert objects* and their protection from cold and humidity is unrelated to human requirements or physiology, warm-blooded animals that we are. Heating to protect cultural heritage from condensation moisture must therefore be of the *industrial type* and include a *nocturnal timetable* related to the local climate; it should operate, for example, from 2 to 8 a.m. at a *low temperature* within a range of 12° to 14°C. The system should also be independently controlled by an automatic timer, so that one need not rely on night watchmen or special employees. Today's daytime, regular and *ad hoc* heating is indispensable during working hours for people such as readers, visitors, museum personnel, librarians and archivists; it is also needed by the priest and congregation in churches. Once again, we must stress that this is entirely different from, and quite unrelated to, the protection of works of art and culture.

Henceforth, the sensible solution would be to create two separate heating plants: a major one for people during the day (which should not cause the kind of damage found in Lausanne Cathedral), and a minor one for objects of cultural heritage, which functions

---

1   "Premiers essais de traitement de statues en molasse à la cathédrale de Lausanne," *Proceedings of the International Study Conference for Conservation of Outdoor Sculpture,* Bologna, October 1969, p.200.

Fig. 152.

*The heating of historic churches today is always **daytime heating** on timetables deter-mined by the hours of worship. The art works undergo a kind of sauna: dry heat when the church is full and well heated; damp cold after the congregation leaves and the heating abruptly ends.*

Fig. 153.

At night, the church falls into a sepulchral chill. Smog, sulfur dioxide and condensation attack marble, stuccos, frescos and metals. The priest, the congregation and the conservator of the monument sleep snugly in their beds.

automatically at night. The basic problem is then not so much the greater cost of a double installation as double running costs; it is indispensable that the heating power installed to protect art works be reduced to the *minimum,* as it is often run continuously. Control of this part of the heating plant must be entirely automatic, relying on the combined action of thermostats and humidistats.

It must be remembered that condensation on marble and mural paintings in an old historic building can occur well before the RH reaches 100%. Deliquescent salts (such as nitrates and chlorides) in the surface layers of walls and plaster subtract water vapor from the air at *an RH below 100%.*

In Venice, where granules having very high concentrations of sodium chloride (perhaps from aerosols) are sometimes found on marble in churches, hygroscopic absorption of water can even begin at an RH of 76%, which corresponds to the equilibrium vapor pressure of a saturated solution of this salt. Thus in Venice, automatic devices should be set, in principle, to trigger the protective heating system whenever the RH rises above 75%, as suggested by Torraca. We might add that the RH should not be measured in the middle of the church, but in the 8 cm thick layer of air next to the surface of the floor or wall attacked by condensation. Kettenacker's experiments (see ¶19) have proven that this restricted area of *still* air is the site of thermohygrometric phenomena of reciprocal action between a cold surface and water vapor in the air. The entire central air mass in the church is not involved in what happens right next to the wall.

By heating only the 8 cm air layer adjacent to the wall, the hourly calorie requirement for the building amounts, in power installed, to ¼ or ⅙ that necessary for the requirements of worship.

Of course, the heat produced for the building's protection also contributes to the well-being of the congregation during church services, thus decreasing the amount of heating required for the latter purpose. Low-temperature radiant heating systems embedded in the floor can reconcile the twofold need to assure the building's welfare and warm the people in it as well.

¶63. The windshield effect in the defense of marble, mural paintings and stuccos.

— The windshield effect is familiar to anyone who has ever de-fogged a car windshield in winter with a veil of hot air from the heater. Similar treatment for the decorated walls in a church, especially if they are marble, allows for effective defense against condensation with a minimal expenditure of heat. Traditionalistic heating engineers have neither formulas nor tables on this subject. Experiments we conducted in Rome indicate a requirement of between 50 and 400 kcal per linear meter of wall. The ways to supply the heat are infinite: in some cases, hot air (however produced) can be forced upwards through a slot in the floor adjacent to the baseboards. In other cases, individual thermo-convective heaters can be used.

From testing in Rome, one can deduce that the initial temperature of the forced air should not exceed 40°C, and that a low initial air speed (so as not to disturb the congregation) is effective up to 4-5 m high. By 'effective' we mean that the air temperature is still at least 1°C higher than the temperature of the static air in the middle of the church.

Under some circumstances, one can do without forced hot air and fans – for instance, where there are mural paintings (which are more delicate than marble) on a limited wall area, and the environment is a small chapel with no drafts or windows. This was the case in the Pinturicchio chapel of Santa Maria of Spello, where a very light, self-rising veil of warm air was created by installing a radiant heating strip in the floor next to the painted wall. The heat is emitted from electric resistors embedded directly beneath the tile paving. This involved a mere 1500 watts installed along a 15-meter strip which supplied continuous but minimal heat, given the delicate state of the mural painting affected by condensation. The running costs are also minimal, and should be considered as a reasonable part of the building's maintenance budget (figs. 154-155).

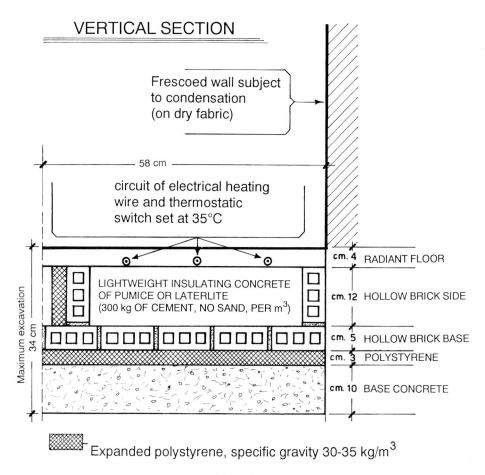

VERTICAL SECTION

Frescoed wall subject to condensation (on dry fabric)

58 cm

circuit of electrical heating wire and thermostatic switch set at 35°C

LIGHTWEIGHT INSULATING CONCRETE OF PUMICE OR LATERLITE (300 kg OF CEMENT, NO SAND, PER m^3)

Maximum excavation 34 cm

cm. 4 RADIANT FLOOR

cm. 12 HOLLOW BRICK SIDE

cm. 5 HOLLOW BRICK BASE

cm. 3 POLYSTYRENE

cm. 10 BASE CONCRETE

Expanded polystyrene, specific gravity 30-35 kg/m^3

Fig. 154.

A rising veil of warm air, intended to prevent condensation on the walls of historic churches (windshield effect), can be generated by electric resistors embedded in the floor along the base of the wall being protected. To save on running costs, it is wise to impede the downward dispersion of heat with a floor system such as that shown in the diagram.

Fig. 155.

In some cases, a 20-30 cm wide strip of floor, adjacent to the wall being protected, is equipped to emit heat, especially at night. This brings about the windshield effect and impedes condensation.

Limitations of applying the windshield effect

The point of this paragraph is the utilization of heat as a specific cure for condensation in historic buildings. It must be stressed that *heat is powerless against rising damp* as opposed to condensation. Indeed, it can be damaging, to mural paintings in particular, because it forces surface evaporation of the water inside the wall and provokes crystallization of the salts transported by the inexhaustible flow of ascending capillary water. In some cases the pigment layer eventually shatters and in others it is covered by a hard and opaque veil like a cataract. Therefore: *never attempt to use heat to cure rising damp.*

There is one exception to this rule. If the water supply has been cut off by insertion of a damp-proof course, the flow of water stops completely and at once. Every thread of capillary water, a true conveyor belt bringing water and salts to the painting's surface, is arrested. The water still bottled in the wall becomes inert. This residual water will decrease extremely slowly as the wall gradually dries by evaporation, but the salts are no longer a threat because they do not have a vehicle – water – and remain stranded inside the wall. The mural painting is safe, even though momentarily dimmed by dry surface salts which must be removed by a restorer. After insertion of a damp-proof course, heat supplied by the windshield effect is very beneficial because it speeds the departure of harmless residual water above the cut, water that otherwise might take years to leave. It is advisable, however, to stimulate evaporation on the side of the wall that is not painted.

Mural paintings are often attacked contemporaneously by rising damp (on average up to 2-3 m above ground) and by condensation (usually isolated stains at variable wall and ceiling heights. In such cases of double attack, the correct restoration technique is first to eliminate the water rising from the subsoil, using a damp-proof course in the prescribed manner, and second to eliminate condensation with heat, using the windshield effect. A two-pronged operation of this sort has been tested in the church of Santa Maria dei Miracoli in Venice.

To sum up: do not use the windshield effect against active rising damp. The use of heat is effective and indispensable as soon as the rising damp has been cut off. Finally, it is clear that a warm air veil is inappropriate for walls where there are large painted canvases or wooden panels or any movable art works on organic supports that would be affected by the heat.

Conclusion

In Europe, little has been done to date to control condensation damage in churches and monumental halls because there have been *no guidelines of any kind.* Even liquid gas heating has been tolerated, although it is disastrous for marble; the combustion of every kg of gas unloads 800 g of water vapor into the air of a church and causes enormous damage.

To the contrary, dry heat accompanied by a quota of air exchange *can arrest any condensation damage* and permit restoration specialists to recover and, above all, to stabilize works of art. We must accustom ourselves to the idea of the indispensability of heat, applied not routinely but with new criteria, and accept the related operating expenses for seven or eight months of the year. No one is surprised that drainage pumps in low areas of Holland function virtually year-round to keep water from flooding the reclaimed land. There are two imperatives to be respected. One is *economic*: running costs must be kept as low as possible in view of the lengthy heating period, because cost is the basic element in administrative decisions for or against a heating plant. The other is *technical:* as one must use extremely little heat, yet on an extended timetable, the calories must be fired against one enemy alone: the 'cold wall.'

Thus one calls on radiant warm air for walls, using the windshield effect, or (depending on the case) marble skirting and floor with the barest minimum of radiant heat.

¶64. Historic centers chronically afflicted by humidity. The danger of pseudo-restoration.

— Rising damp is a serious component in the general deterioration of historic centers but has been little known till now due to backwardness in investigation. Rising damp is serious from a technical standpoint because it is costly and difficult to eliminate; it is serious from a legal standpoint because the financial responsibility for the necessary repair work must be allocated equitably. Moreover, the damage caused by rising damp is not purely aesthetic, but primarily economic, for it reduces the value of ground-floor rental properties. This subject was treated for the first time by the authors in a report, "Defense of Historic Centers from Humidity Damage," read in the Rome Congress of 1968.

The new aspect of the question seems to be the following: When ground moisture does not originate from a uniform groundwater table (as it does in perfectly flat cities or even Venice) but originates from dispersed surface water in hilly cities such as Rome, there is a joint responsibility and thus a precise obligation on the part of cities as managers of the sewer system and all underground services. Sometimes the water companies are also involved, for very old water systems can lose up to 15 or 20% of their capacity. In Rome, for example, we are inclined to believe that the sieve-like subsoil of the old city streets is responsible for decades of steady irrigation of foundations, unbeknown to public or private property owners. One confirmation of this belief was provided by the case of the building of the Accademia di San Luca on Vicolo Scavolino. For almost a century, the ground-floor premises of the academy were unusable due to dampness; they were instantly restored in 1962 after measurements demonstrated that the water came from an unsuspected subsidence of the sewer on Vicolo Scavolino itself. Once the sewer was repaired, the moisture disappeared (see ¶74).

As regards functional and economic restoration of historic centers, the city's job is to intervene wherever rising damp has attacked all or most of the buildings along a street. Certainly in such cases the first step towards restoration is to dig up the drenched subsoil of the old street and renew the ancient sewer system which is no longer up to its task. Perhaps a part of the expense might be shared among the building owners in an equitable way, for the work will undoubtedly improve property values.

In any event, the problem should first be studied at executive headquarters for restoration of the historic center; it merits the methodological premise that phenomena should not be judged offhand but on the basis of objective measurements, followed by a precise diagnosis for each building. Second, when *condensation humidity* has been diagnosed, the proprietor should undertake the necessary restoration (and the related financial burden) because this type of humidity comes from the air and depends on inadequate heating or insulation of the structure: it is always an individual defect of the building. This is also true, contrary to common belief, of driving rain, which seldom passes through walls but rather cools them and provokes internal condensation only on the rain-beaten side. Third, if rising damp is diagnosed, the cost of eliminating it can devolve entirely or in part on the city, to the extent that rising damp involves dispersed water originating from below street level.

This rather specialized subject calls for precise measurements of the cause of humidity to be combined with restoration projects for historic centers. These measurements and suitable plans for repair work should be compiled on the basis of analysis in specialized laboratories.

The danger of pseudo-restoration

Without proper measurements and laboratory analysis, a planner is almost certain to make glaring errors as to the cause of the humidity that affects a single church or historic building or an entire row of commercial buildings that have sunk in value. It would be interesting to calculate the funds squandered yearly by stewards and maintenance offices on useless repairs for historic buildings with very thick walls. They mistake condensation for rising damp in ground floors and basements. They mistake humidity and mold in upper floors for penetration of driving rain, and so apply excellent waterproof paint, acrylic or vinyl resin, loaded with star dust, quartz, mica or some other expensive substance. So it happens that errors are perpetuated … and maintenance funds vanish by the millions.

Chapter Fourteen

CONTROVERSIES

¶65. The use of storerooms despite humidity.

— People sometimes ask to have conditions improved in a mold-infested storeroom or warehouse, but clearly state that they do not intend to do any masonry repairs. In such a case the doors and windows are sealed and a certain number of electric 'dehumidifiers' (Leonard, Chrysler, etc.) are distributed throughout the premises. These machines draw in and cool the air, extracting by condensation a good deal of its water vapor (which is collected in a pail), and then recirculate the air after reheating it over electric resistors. When one wishes or is obliged to continue using damp premises without dehumidifying systems, the following five precautions should be observed to keep damage to a minimum.

- Move all open or closed furniture, including bookcases, 20 cm from the walls.
- Clear all lower shelves up to 40 cm above ground; keep crates raised above the floor.
- Move the goods or books around at least twice yearly, in spring and autumn.
- Allow for abundant air passage through internal and external fixtures, regardless of the season or weather, except when there are warm, moist marine winds in winter that are known, in local experience, to cause condensation.
- Remember that winter heating is sometimes damaging because it creates favorable conditions for mold when there is not enough ventilation; in summer, forced ventilation from outside is always damaging in cellars or basements.

¶66. Rental of damp housing.

— Litigation between tenant and landlord often arises over the cause of decay of furniture and goods, or even over the origin of illnesses that strike people residing in unhealthful environments. The case of a newly constructed building must be distinguished from that of an older one.

In new buildings, the question raised is this: can a tenant seek damages when a rental property is proven to be unhealthful if the landlord, having complied with all the city regulations, has an occupancy permit? The answer is undoubtedly affirmative, i.e., the tenant can claim damages. This is so because an occupancy permit is usually given for an entire building, a certain time after completion of the fabric, without specific investigation of the particular environments that, due to their situation or exposure, dry out more slowly than the average. Such environments would be as follows: sunless basements, ground floors and first floors; premises on any floor on a side beaten by driving rain or simply by damp winds; rooms closely overlooking tree-lined streets or gardens; premises situated on courtyards with insufficient ventilation.

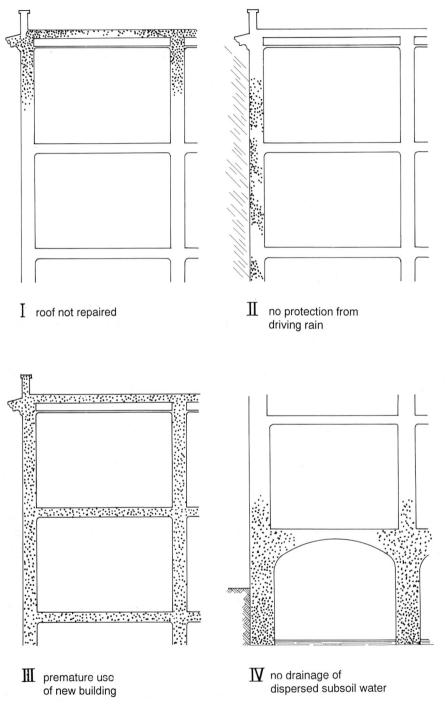

I   roof not repaired   II   no protection from
driving rain

III   premature use   IV   no drainage of
of new building   dispersed subsoil water

Fig. 156.

A scheme for litigation: four cases of dampness that can be blamed on the landlord because of a verified excess of moisture in the masonry fabric.

If a dispute arises, an inspection of humidity conditions in the premises must be conducted (using the criteria stated in ¶21 and elsewhere), *and the deciding factor will be the moisture content percentage revealed by analysis of depth samples from the wall.*

Should it happen that newly built premises have been rented without an occupancy permit, the landlord will be even more likely to suffer the consequences of disregarding regulations. Even if tenant's claims are objectively unfounded, they will find such negligence a good pretext for litigation.

As regards older buildings that in their day were properly certified, and thus in which humidity is presumably not due to construction but to invasion, the interested parties can request a court survey or an inspection by the local Health Board. Still, not all municipal health regulations, as we have already seen, include precise standards and numerical limits for assessing humidity conditions; where clear guidelines are absent, there can be contradictory interpretations of moisture figures for air and walls. The practical rules and tolerances indicated in Chapter Five compensate for this lack and assure precision and objectivity in health assessments.

Different combinations of problems can arise out of the basic observation, repeated frequently in this book, that the dampness of an environment originates either in the walls (moisture in the fabric) or from the air (moisture irregularly appearing on the wall surface). Infiltration from the roof, lateral penetration of driving rain, dispersed water around the foundations – all problems attributable to construction defects – give rise to an equal number of instances of moisture in the wall fabric for which the landlord is responsible (fig. 156). The trouble that follows consignment of premises that are still damp after construction or restoration may also be laid at the door of a landlord who, through ignorance or greed, rents his property prematurely.

Controversies arising from dampness due to air cooling (pseudo-condensation or true condensation) are more difficult to resolve because other factors are sometimes involved. Such factors might be construction defects, a bit of dampness in the fabric, or errors in use. When combined factors are not present, the problem is simplified. In figure 157, three simple cases of cooling are sketched. These result solely from construction error or negligence, and the builder is accountable for the unwholesome condition. In Case I, the cooling occurs through the floor, which does not have a proper subfloor. In Case II, the ceiling lacks insulation. In Case III, the exterior wall is not thick enough. All three are typical construction defects.

On the other hand, the two cases shown in figure 158 are examples of improper use on the tenant's part; here, instead of cooling, there is so much vapor produced that the walls are covered with a veil of water, despite their adequate thermal protection. Not only is the tenant unjustified in complaining, but he or she may also be held responsible for any damage to the building, such as deterioration of wallpaper, curtains and decor, short circuits, plaster deterioration, and so forth.

In Case I of figure 158, the 20 dancing couples (hard work …) deposit over 4 liters of water on the walls every hour. In Case II, an irresponsible tenant, who has put a gas stove in an unventilated room, irrigates the space with three or four liters of condensation water daily.

Interpretation of symptoms (stains, mold, erosion, etc.), analysis of RH, but, above all, analysis of the moisture content of the walls and calculation of thermal protection, will *always* permit controversial cases to be resolved.

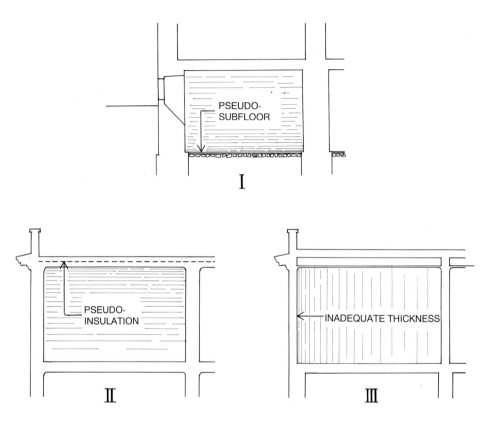

Fig. 157.

A scheme for litigation: three cases of dampness from cooling that can be blamed on the landlord because of verified construction defects.

When stored goods are involved, as for instance in a *storage contract,* deterioration may depend on the amount of moisture present and on the nature of the goods immersed in it. When such an eventuality is foreseen in advance, the contract can be written with suitable provisions for the periodical removal or inspection of packages, or a given air exchange. Indeed, it must be borne in mind that air circulation can be cut off in any environment, even a perfectly dry and healthy one, simply by filling the available space with furniture or crates – as ultimately happens in any storeroom. Once air circulation is reduced, the slightest, unforeseen moisture reserve can cause localized saturation and extremely damaging permanent stagnation. Many storerooms are decreed to be 'damp' when they are merely closed too tightly and forgotten.

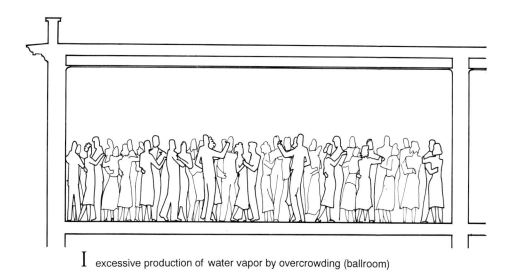

I excessive production of water vapor by overcrowding (ballroom)

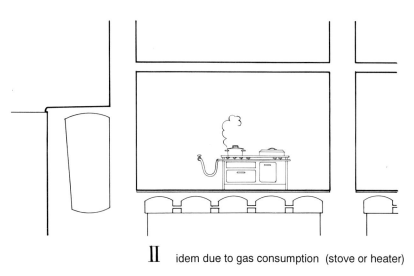

II idem due to gas consumption (stove or heater)

Fig. 158.

A scheme for litigation: two cases of dampness that can be blamed on the tenant because of improper use of the premises.

In normal *rental* contracts for living quarters, i.e., actual habitation or continuous daily presence for work, the tenant is only justified in claiming damages from the landlord in either of the cases below:

- when **analysis** has demonstrated that dampness in the wall fabric is beyond the limits of tolerance (recent construction, dispersion of improperly drained water, lack of insulating layers on the prescribed surfaces)
- when **calculation or measurement** has demonstrated that there is insufficient thermal protection in any surrounding structure: wall, floor or ceiling (winter condensation in upper floors or exposures to north and east, tendency to spring/summer condensation in lower floors and basements).

Chapter Fifteen

TYPICAL EXAMPLES OF DIAGNOSES
AND RESTORATION PROGRAMS

PRIVATE HOMES

¶67. **A large stately home in reinforced concrete on Lake Geneva (condensation).**

— This was a case of recent (1963) and representative construction, inspired by traditional, eighteenth-century French architecture and finished in every detail with great care and taste. There was only one floor above ground, with a framed structure and cavity infill walls lined with expanded polystyrene.

In order to stay within the height allowed by the building code, the ground floor was built at a level with the surrounding ground. As a result, the large, well-heated rooms beneath, destined by the owners to be their private quarters, were unhappily located in a true cellar, poorly ventilated, with cold bare walls of reinforced concrete. The cellar had a continuous embanked wall, cased in reinforced concrete 25 cm thick.

SIGNS OF DAMPNESS. MEASUREMENTS. The investigation was made during a hot dry period in early August. Measurements in the cellar indicated the presence of water in the stained plaster, up to 14% at some points, which showed that *water was being actively supplied.* This fact was even more serious because the basement was designed with a continuous reinforced concrete wall precisely in order to protect it from water penetration, like a watertight box immersed in clay. A pebble drainage system next to the exterior wall (fig. 159, top) was meant to carry off any outside water. The presence of scattered, very damp stains on the interior plaster demonstrated that the external drainage was not functioning properly. Moreover, the damage was not so much the visible stains as the invisible cooling and consequent stratification of the basement air, as if in a cup. The air was almost saturated near the floor. Measurements indicated the RH was 80% near the ceiling and 92% near the floor, while the surface temperature of the reinforced concrete wall decreased from 21°C near the ceiling to 17°C near the floor – an enormous drop of 4°C. This exceptional stratification, and the general cooling of the entire floor made it unpleasant to be in the basement and decidedly unhealthy to live there. The external water drainage system was shown to be *counter-operative.*

REPAIRS. The work was conceived to eliminate the causes of the cooling that produced condensation in the basement rooms: both the permanent cooling due to the flow of water in the drainage system and the intermittent spring cooling due to the tremendous thermal inertia of the continuous reinforced concrete wall.

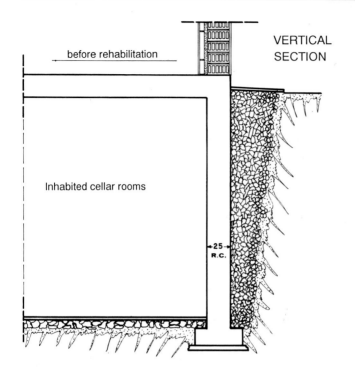

VERTICAL
SECTION

before rehabilitation

Inhabited cellar rooms

25
R.C.

Fig. 159.

Geneva, Switzerland: section of external perimeter trench (left) which was damaging because it brought cold water into contact with the wall. Below, the trench after reconstruction to keep the water away from the house.

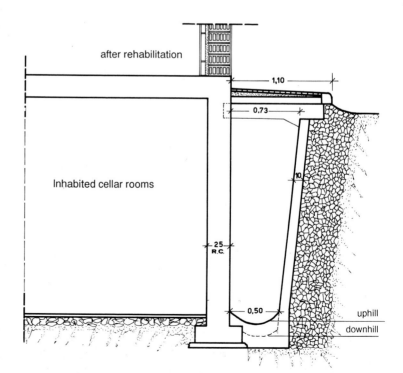

after rehabilitation

Inhabited cellar rooms

1,10

0,73

10

25
R.C.

0,50

uphill

downhill

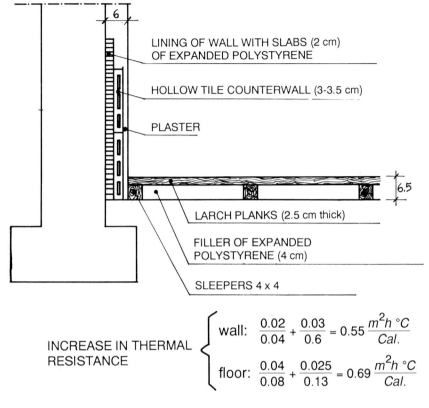

LINING OF WALL WITH SLABS (2 cm) OF EXPANDED POLYSTYRENE

HOLLOW TILE COUNTERWALL (3-3.5 cm)

PLASTER

LARCH PLANKS (2.5 cm thick)

FILLER OF EXPANDED POLYSTYRENE (4 cm)

SLEEPERS 4 x 4

INCREASE IN THERMAL RESISTANCE

$$\text{wall:} \quad \frac{0.02}{0.04} + \frac{0.03}{0.6} = 0.55 \frac{m^2 h\,°C}{Cal.}$$

$$\text{floor:} \quad \frac{0.04}{0.08} + \frac{0.025}{0.13} = 0.69 \frac{m^2 h\,°C}{Cal.}$$

Fig. 160.

Geneva: work to prevent condensation in the subterranean area. Increase of thermal resistance of the floor and exterior wall.'

Four points for restoration:

- *Outside,* replace the pebble drainage with an empty trench and transfer the drainage system to the far side of the trench (fig. 159, bottom).
- *Inside,* line the walls with expanded polystyrene (2 cm thick) and an adherent counterwall of hollow tiles, as in figure 160.
- Over the present floor, which does not have a true subfloor, place wooden boards (inexpensive in Switzerland) no less than 2.5 cm thick, after filling the underlying space 4 cm high with polystyrene chips (also fig. 160).
- Every year, after the central heating is turned off, produce air exchange by using small portable electric heaters, no more than 1 kW per room, including the hallway. In a cellar such as this, the air tends to stagnate in spring and summer, even when the walls are perfectly dry.

Dehumidifiers are not recommended, because the windows must be closed, and the rooms are thus unhealthful for residence. Electric heaters, turned on occasionally, reactivate air exchange by drawing in outdoor air; such exchange is indispensable for people and also for good conservation of furniture and books.

¶68. Public housing in Viareggio (cooling from driving rain).

— Viareggio's climate would be excellent if it were not for the rather violent driving rain prevailingly from the northeast. The humidity problems encountered in the building derive from the use of hollow fired-clay blocks in the outer infill walls of the framed structure.

SIGNS OF HUMIDITY. MEASUREMENTS. The effect occurs only on the rain-beaten side and can be seen on the outside in a grid pattern of damp with a mesh corresponding to the outlines of the building blocks: 13.5 x 40 cm. The blocks are 27 cm thick and the fully plastered wall is 30 cm thick. The humidity *does not show in a grid pattern* on the inner walls, as should happen if rainwater penetrated the mortar joints by capillary action to the inside. There, it is seen as a random cloudiness which is completely unlike the geometric exterior (fig. 161).

This radical change in the appearance of humidity in its passage from outside to inside leads one to expect that the usual phenomenon is involved: surface soaking of the outer wall by driving rain and subsequent cooling by evaporation. The cooling is transmitted to the internal wall face and provokes condensation of water vapor in the air, especially in bedrooms with two or three sleepers. The measurements taken confirmed the prediction exactly: on the first floor, in a three-person bedroom heavily clouded with damp, we found the moisture content shown in figure 162, using a regular electrode meter on a vertical wall. The uniformity of moisture in the central part of the first floor wall *confirms the phenomenon of condensation: the percentage of 18% is extremely high.* The stains are repeated on the upper stories, but there is less water present in the plaster – never exceeding 15% (fig. 162). The distribution is also less uniform.

The first-floor room, where a maximum and almost constant 18% moisture content was found, is subject to two cooling factors at the same time. The eastern wall loses heat because it is beaten by the rain accumulated on the facade, and the floor loses heat because it is above the porch. For this reason, the humidity is greater and more uniform on the first floor than on the upper floors.

Measurement of surface temperatures with a rapid-response bimetallic thermometer confirmed that the temperature of the floor was always 1°C lower than that of the wall.

RESTORATION WORK. For both financial and architectural reasons, it did not seem opportune to recommend an external facing. The following measures were suggested for the condensation:

- Lining with heavy expanded polystyrene slabs (at least 20 kg/m^3), 1.5 cm thick, applied with a few dabs of pure cement on the plaster of the inside walls; an adherent counterwall of hollow tile was then applied without leaving an air space. The total loss of space is 6 cm, the least possible; here, a lining is also indispensable under the windowsills.
- Protection of the underside of the first floor, where it overhangs the porch, with insulating layers that provide additional thermal resistance of at least $R = 0.12$-0.15.

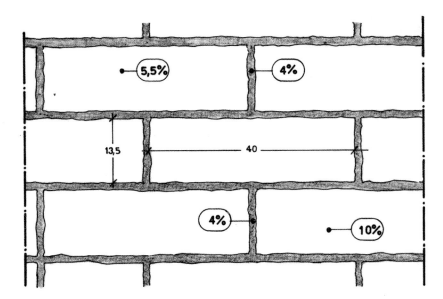

Grid pattern staining of outer rendering under the action of driving rain, and moisture content (%) after 8-9 days of clear weather.

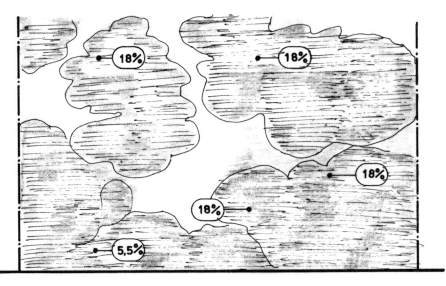

On the inner wall, no traces of a grid pattern, although the stains are moving : cloud-shaped stains with a uniform, very high percentage of moisture.

Fig. 161.

Viareggio, Italy: differing appearance of dampness indoors (below) and outdoors (above) on a rain-beaten wall.

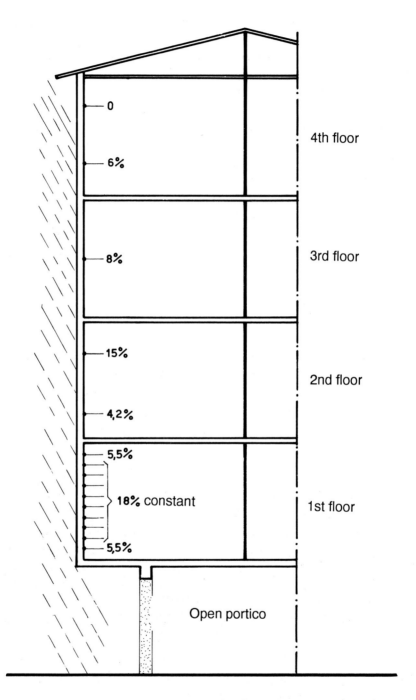

The moisture content of the plaster on the inside wall is highest on
the 1st floor, above the open portico.

Fig. 162.

*Vertical section of the building on the side exposed to driving rain: percentage distribu-
tion of moisture in the plaster of the inside wall.*

The work is tedious to carry out: it can be resolved with 1.5 cm thick thermal insulation boards (e.g., ERACLIT, POPULIT), or 1.5 cm high-density expanded polystyrene protected by a rendering armored with fiber glass. At worst one can use 2.5 cm of light rendering: for example, lime with fine sifted pozzolana and perlite, or vermiculite for renderings with cement and hydrated lime.

¶69. A sampling of damp houses in Avellino (cooling from driving rain).

— This city is situated in a basin, and has an average winter temperature 3°C lower than that of Naples, even though the two cities are aligned on the same parallel. Driving rain is frequent here, prevailingly from the southwest. From a construction standpoint, the cold and rain are the two salient characteristics of the climate. The traditional buildings in the old city were ably protected by very thick walls of excellent local tuff; from 60 to 65 cm on the ground floor and never less than 50 cm thick on the top floor. Large cornices abounded, and there were almost always blind walls on the SW side, sometimes rather unattractively lined with sheet iron.

After the devastation of the Second World War, the housing shortage was so acute that new public housing had to be rapidly supplied. Planning was centralized in Rome, and completely ignored the peculiarities of the Avellino climate. Thus the new buildings had no cornices and were made of reinforced concrete frames with light, infill walls and no heating (because it's warm in Naples). All four sides of the buildings were built in the same way. The planner and the works supervisors knew nothing about the driving rain, nor had anyone told them, as might have been done if there were seismic dangers or if the subsoil were treacherous.

THE FIRST DAMP HOUSES OF THE POST-WAR PERIOD. An early group of buildings, constructed in 1955 in the Madonnelle quarter of the San Tommaso district, had a pleasant architectural style and a sensible interior design. Unfortunately, the buildings were found to be tenaciously and permanently damp, though at first the humidity was thought to be transitory and due to over-hasty occupancy. The exterior walls were built of hollow cinder blocks of the type shown in figure 163, doubly wrong both for their poor resistance to surface rain penetration and for their insufficient thermal protection with respect to the local climate. The construction firm, which had built the entire quarter, requested the author to propose solutions for definitive restoration. The drastic measures suggested are schematized in figures 164 and 165. Each of the solutions had advantages as well as practical drawbacks due to the fact that the buildings were all occupied. The solution shown in figure 165 was eventually chosen, even though it was statically more complex.

In 1955, the Madonnelle quarter, with 140 apartments, had cost roughly 350 million lire. In 1959, four years later, an additional 70 million was spent to protect the quarter from rain humidity. The defect was insufficient thermal protection, more accentuated on the rain-beaten side due to the phenomenon of psychrometric cooling by evaporation.

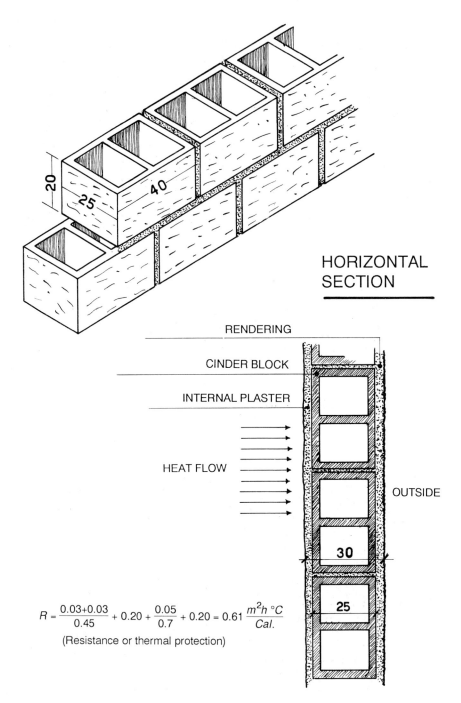

Fig. 163.

Type of wall in hollow cinder block, effective sp. gr. 1200 kg/m³. Maximum thermal resistance R = 0.60, a theoretical value supposing that the joints are perfect, the rendering intact and the air in the cells immobile. Extremely insufficient with respect to the necessary R = 1.

Fig. 164.

Basic restoration of houses built with hollow cinder block and made unhealthy by driving rain. Interior and exterior masonry work: 1) application of outer facing of ship-lapped ceramic tile, joints grouted with cement 2) closed air space 3) counterwall of 4-cell hollow brick 4) normal lime plaster without cement 5) filling of very dry wood charcoal up to about 15 cm.

Drawbacks of this solution: *considerable disturbance to the tenants during the interior work; about 15 cm of space lost because of the counterwall.*

Advantages to this solution: *no static problem.*

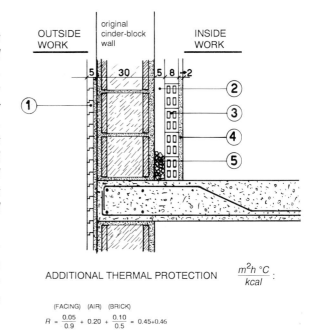

ADDITIONAL THERMAL PROTECTION $\dfrac{m^2h\,°C}{kcal}$:

$$R = \underset{\text{(FACING)}}{\dfrac{0.05}{0.9}} + \underset{\text{(AIR)}}{0.20} + \underset{\text{(BRICK)}}{\dfrac{0.10}{0.5}} = 0.45 + 0.46$$

Fig. 165.

Another solution for basic restoration of houses built of hollow cinder block. Only exterior work is involved: 1) preparation of cement mortar 2) facing of 4-cell hollow brick on edge 3) preparation of cement-lime mortar 4) facing of heavy pressed brick with thin beds and mortar also in the vertical joints; cement stucco.

Drawbacks of this solution: *static problem of supporting the extra weight.*

Advantages: *no disturbance to the tenants and no space wasted inside.*

Additional thermal resistance about R = 0.38, somewhat less than the preceding solution, but still sufficient.

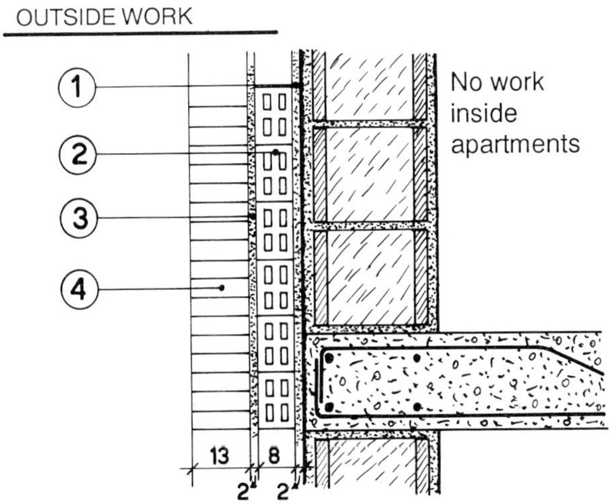

OUTSIDE WORK

No work inside apartments

Weight = 400 kg/m^2

~ 4,000 kg/ linear meter of outer wall = load to be borne by frame, bulb or ground.

¶70.   Houses heated from open kitchens in Venice.

— There was a time in the post-war era in France and Italy when the housing shortage was so acute that building was done in haste, in great quantity and very badly. Houses were damp because their walls did not provide sufficient thermal protection, but French builders laid the blame on the occupants, claiming that kitchen doors were left open and steam from cooking pervaded the homes. The dampness was the tenant's fault. See the amusing propaganda of figure 166.

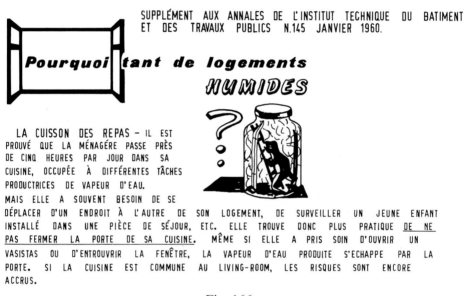

SUPPLÉMENT AUX ANNALES DE L'INSTITUT TECHNIQUE DU BATIMENT ET DES TRAVAUX PUBLICS N.145 JANVIER 1960.

Pourquoi *tant de logements*
HUMIDES

LA CUISSON DES REPAS – IL EST PROUVÉ QUE LA MÉNAGÉRE PASSE PRÈS DE CINQ HEURES PAR JOUR DANS SA CUISINE, OCCUPÉE À DIFFÉRENTES TÂCHES PRODUCTRICES DE VAPEUR D'EAU. MAIS ELLE A SOUVENT BESOIN DE SE DÉPLACER D'UN ENDROIT À L'AUTRE DE SON LOGEMENT, DE SURVEILLER UN JEUNE ENFANT INSTALLÉ DANS UNE PIÈCE DE SÉJOUR, ETC. ELLE TROUVE DONC PLUS PRATIQUE DE NE PAS FERMER LA PORTE DE SA CUISINE. MÊME SI ELLE A PRIS SOIN D'OUVRIR UN VASISTAS OU D'ENTROUVRIR LA FENÊTRE, LA VAPEUR D'EAU PRODUITE S'ECHAPPE PAR LA PORTE. SI LA CUISINE EST COMMUNE AU LIVING-ROOM, LES RISQUES SONT ENCORE ACCRUS.

Fig. 166.

The French also have problems with damp public housing: a curious attempt to chastise tenants so they will keep their kitchen doors closed.

In Italy, on the other hand, some scatterbrained architect went even further in designing new worker's housing for Mestre, near Venice. The kitchens were left open to the hallways, on the grounds that the entire apartment could be heated by the warm kitchen air. Thus the expense of a heating plant was saved where the average January temperature was 2.5°C. This was certainly a clever trick! In addition, since the houses were beaten by driving rain, the wall structure shown in figure 167 was invented. The houses immediately filled with mold.

When called to examine the case, we found mold ornamenting only the walls on the side exposed to driving rain and short portions of the partition walls where they joined the others, as shown in figure 168. Moreover, the day after a violent rainstorm, the outer, rain-beaten wall contained 4% water, while there was 15-16% at the corresponding point on the inner wall face: true condensation.

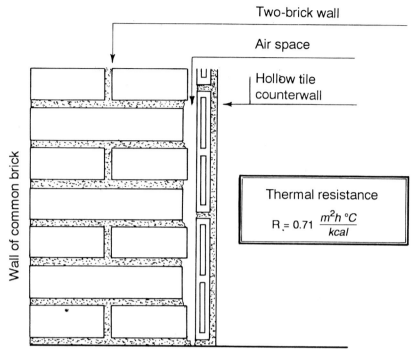

Fig. 167.

Mestre, Italy: to protect unheated houses from driving rain, it seemed sufficient to add a hollow tile counterwall during construction. This was done only on the exposed side.

The prescription:

- Immediately install a good central heating plant. In view of the January isotherm of 2.5°C in Venice, the planners's claim to heat the whole apartment with a gas stove was absurd.
- Partition off the kitchen and put a spring-closing door to the hall.

The mold disappeared immediately.

¶71. Case studies of unusual errors in mass-produced public housing.

— In great nations with good central organization, there are occasional urgent requests for low-income housing, of the type called HLM in France, after disasters such as earthquakes and wars. Governments respond with centralized architectural planning, offering the best standard-type housing without adapting it to the locations where it will be built. Local climate and construction materials are not taken into account because reinforced concrete frames are normally used to speed construction. The central planner must be informed, however, if the zone is subject to earthquakes, because this factor is mentioned in previous laws which must be respected. A few examples are given below of buildings born damp because the planner was unfamiliar with the place and the true climate where they were to rise.

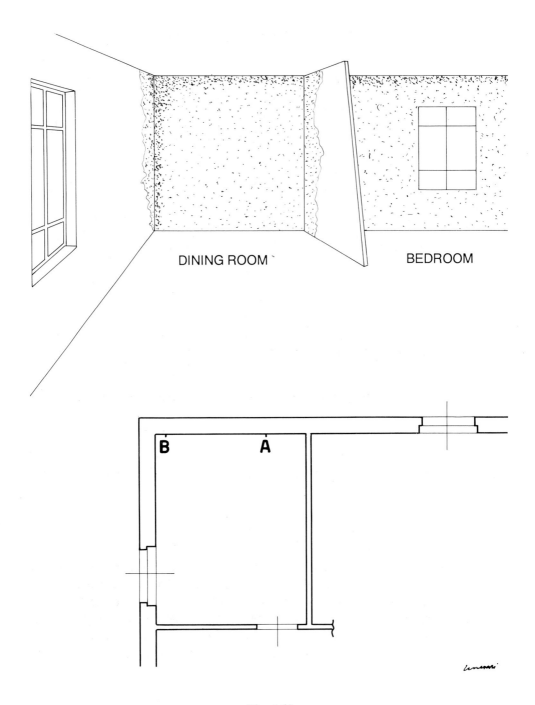

Fig. 168.

Distribution of mold on walls and partitions, as found in public housing in Mestre.

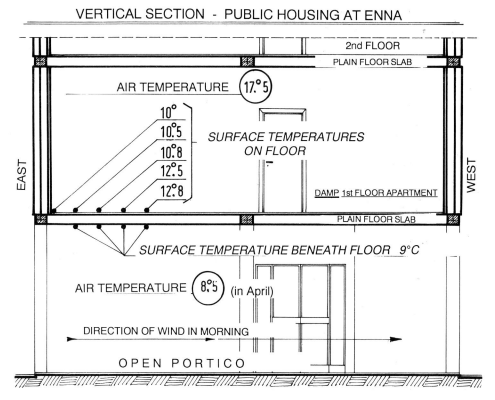

Fig. 169.

At Enna, Italy, the dampness of first-floor premises above a portico was due to cooling of the floor, which had been constructed exactly like all the others – without the greater thermal protection required for exposure to the outside.

Example 1

Figure 169 shows a low-income apartment building in Enna, Sicily, 930 m above sea level, with a magnificent portico open to the wind. The floor above the portico was built exactly like all the others and did not have adequate thermal protection for its position. Cooling of this floor thus made all the first-floor quarters damp – a small factor overlooked in the planning. It would have sufficed during construction to give the first floor an extra base layer of lightweight concrete mixed with pumice, expanded clay or vermiculite.

Example 2

Figure 170 shows the case of the entire quarter of San Licandro in Messina. The walls were constructed according to anti-seismic regulations and contain an enormous

INTERNAL VIEW OF WALL TYPE SUBJECT TO MOLD

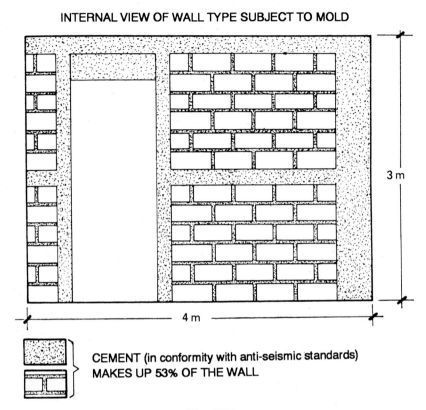

3 m

4 m

CEMENT (in conformity with anti-seismic standards)
MAKES UP 53% OF THE WALL

Fig. 170.

In earthquake zones such as Messina, dampness in public housing is due to the strong thermal dispersion of the masonry; given anti-seismic regulations, cement justifiably prevails. Legislators save the tenants from earthquakes at the expense of rheumatism and heart disease.

amount of cement concrete and cement mortar, both cold and dispersive materials. Here, regulations have spread dampness in the living quarters. A joint cause of cooling, which overstrains the situation, is the driving rain which affects only one side of the building. There is no point in protecting the other three sides at great expense.

The remedy was to line the interior walls of the rooms with slabs of expanded polystyrene, 3 cm thick, then with rigid polyvinyl panelling.

Example 3

Another recondite factor contributing to dampness is the *division of heating into separate systems*. The heating of a building should be indivisible, just as the roof is indivisible; otherwise, each tenant heats in his own way and at his own timetable – perhaps for only three hours while eating supper and watching television, as was found in Avellino. The underheating of a building with autonomous systems is schematized in figure 171.

Some agencies may have chosen to install separate heating systems in order to avoid administrative headaches, but more serious and well-justified disputes arise later on, when health and goods have been damaged by humidity. Even with the best of intentions, it may be difficult to resolve such questions when one is hindered by the insistence of tenants and old builders alike that 'the rain comes in the walls.' From this mistaken persuasion one passes *logically* to external waterproofing. This is the hour of synthetic resins: beautiful, sufficiently long-lived colored mixtures, based on mica, quartz powder, etc., and bound with vinyl or acrylic resins that are truly elastic, do not crack and are also waterproof: magnificent products indeed. *But what use are they when condensation comes from the inner wall face instead of the outer one?* And condensation appears on the inner wall face because *the building as a whole is underheated,* due to the individualistic management of autonomous heating systems. The tenant does not know that only half the quota of heat he needs is produced by his own furnace; the other half comes from above, below, or next door: in short, from the neighbors.

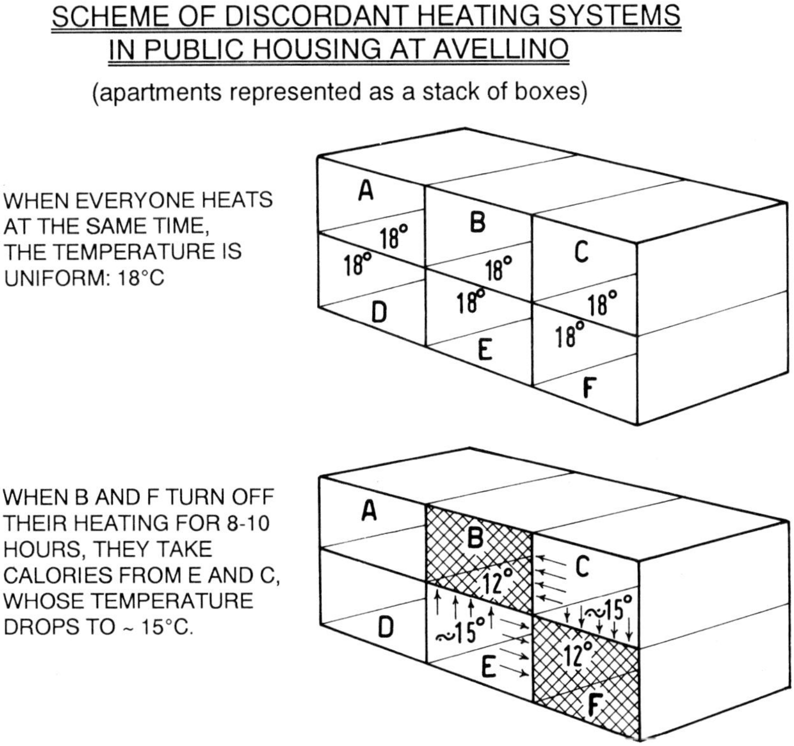

SCHEME OF DISCORDANT HEATING SYSTEMS
IN PUBLIC HOUSING AT AVELLINO

(apartments represented as a stack of boxes)

WHEN EVERYONE HEATS AT THE SAME TIME, THE TEMPERATURE IS UNIFORM: 18°C

WHEN B AND F TURN OFF THEIR HEATING FOR 8-10 HOURS, THEY TAKE CALORIES FROM E AND C, WHOSE TEMPERATURE DROPS TO ~ 15°C.

Fig. 171.

Autonomous heating systems, used on erratic timetables, lead to general underheating of the building and subsequent condensation, with stains and mold on the coldest sides, in particular those beaten by driving rain. Administrations that avoid accounting problems by installing separate heating plants later face much greater health problems and complaints to resolve.

Example 4

In the village of Agri in Calabria, 800 m above sea level, a beautiful, granite-like local stone was always used for building. The zone is subject to earthquakes, so the buildings were robust and carefully constructed.

This stone has high compressive strength (and thus requires a minimal wall thickness) and is beautiful to behold, but it is not at all desirable in terms of health or thermal protection. Laboratory analysis gave the following results:

- specific gravity 2,900-3,000 kg/m^3
- water absorption 1.1% (i.e., none)

The stone is a sort of granite, as mentioned above, of extremely high specific gravity, absolutely incapable of absorbing water, and having high internal conductivity.

In the recently built damp houses that we were asked to examine, calculations indicated that the thermal protection on the top floor wall, which was 45 cm thick, was equivalent to a solid one-brick wall, i.e., 14 cm of brick. This type of public housing, built with such faithful adherence to anti-seismic prescriptions, is a fortress with respect to bombardment and earthquakes, but a shanty-town hut with respect to cold.

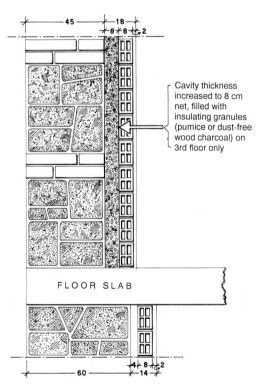

Cavity thickness increased to 8 cm net, filled with insulating granules (pumice or dust-free wood charcoal) on 3rd floor only

FLOOR SLAB

Fig. 172.

Vertical section of an anti-seismic granite wall in Agri, with a counterwall added to eliminate condensation

Humidity stains were found in all the new buildings, on all three stories, exclusively on the northern exposure. The stains were highly accentuated on the top floor, where the masonry, as stated, was only 45 cm thick.

The diagnosis of condensation was confirmed by the distribution of the humidity, which was accentuated on the brick courses, as always happens where two materials of very different specific gravity touch.

The restoration plan was to increase the thermal protection of the outer walls, somewhat more on the top floor and less on the lower floors.

The work consisted of a simple interior counterwall of 4-cell hollow brick, unencumbered by debris. The thermal resistance of the cavity on the third floor was increased by enlarging the cavity to 8 cm and gradually filling it, while the counterwall was being built, with wood charcoal, which abounds in Calabria. Extremely dry and clean charcoal was used (fig. 172).

Example 5

Buildings in the town of Ascoli are usually constructed three stories high with the excellent local bricks in bearing walls, without a frame and with no external rendering. The walls are 42 cm thick on the lower floors and 28 cm thick on the top floor. Italians jokingly say that the inhabitants of Ascoli are tightfisted and save on everything – even the thickness of their walls. It is cold in Ascoli, however, and a strong wind blows from the west, often carrying rain.

The buildings are heated. The reduction in outer wall thickness from 3-brick on lower floors to 2-brick on the top – a perfectly logical tradition from a static point of view – is irrational from a thermal perspective. The top story invariably suffers from reduced thermal protection for three reasons: cold from the attic; exterior wall thickness reduced a third; lack of the reciprocal shielding from nearby buildings that helps protect the lower stories. In fact, the only damp lodgings found were all on the top floors.

The three works recommended for restoration (indicated in fig. 173) are as follows.

- internal lining of all outer walls exposed to the west with 2 cm thick slabs of heavy expanded polystyrene. Over this, placing an adherent counterwall of hollow tile, leaving no air space. Total encumbrance: 7 cm
- application of the same lining on the rolling shutter housings
- laying polystyrene slabs over the attic floor. The slabs are held down simply, with a few bricks here and there.

Example 6

Tricks played by movement joints in low-income reinforced concrete row housing. – The entire zone behind the Gulf of Naples is heavily beaten by westerly driving rain from the sea. At the invitation of the local construction board, we visited a large housing development with rows of buildings, three stories high above porticos which were given over to parking. These buildings were well constructed but, unfortunately, very damp. Each row (fig. 174) was formed of seven or eight identical buildings, set tightly side by side. The technicians from the construction board followed our measurements with interest, and seemed convinced by our explanations about the cooling action of driving rain exclusively on the western side. At the end of our inspection, however, they somewhat gleefully led us to a few inner walls, transverse to the row, that were scandalously damp and moldy, even though completely protected from the wind by their internal position. After recovering from our initial surprise, we went outside to look at the building at a point corresponding to a damp transverse wall. There we discovered that the damp wall coincided with a movement joint between two reinforced concrete frames (fig. 175); such joints are required by the building code when the long side of a row building exceeds a certain length. The 2 cm gap of the joint had remained open and could be seen from below in the portico ceiling. Naturally, the joint coincided with the dividing line between two contiguous apartments, and the tenants were completely unaware of it. Cold outdoor air circulated freely in the open joint.

Obviously, the lavish growths of mold on the walls of the two adjoining rooms were due to the thinness of those walls. Each was only 14 cm thick, being composed of

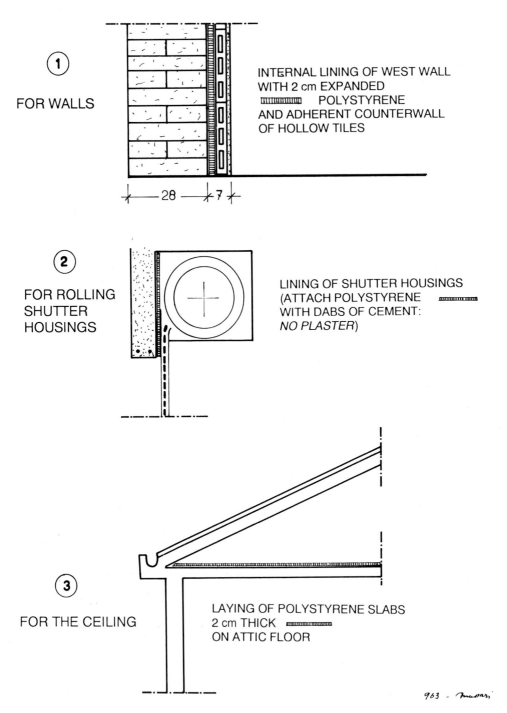

1

FOR WALLS

INTERNAL LINING OF WEST WALL
WITH 2 cm EXPANDED
POLYSTYRENE
AND ADHERENT COUNTERWALL
OF HOLLOW TILES

28 — 7

2

**FOR ROLLING
SHUTTER
HOUSINGS**

LINING OF SHUTTER HOUSINGS
(ATTACH POLYSTYRENE
WITH DABS OF CEMENT:
NO PLASTER)

3

FOR THE CEILING

LAYING OF POLYSTYRENE SLABS
2 cm THICK
ON ATTIC FLOOR

963 - massan

Fig. 173.

*Interior insulation in damp premises to compensate for the insufficient thermal protection
of the outer brick wall.*

PERIMETER OF A ROW OF LOW-INCOME APARTMENT BUILDINGS

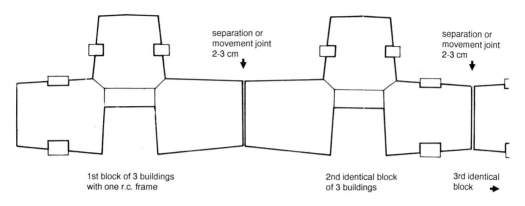

1st block of 3 buildings
with one r.c. frame

2nd identical block
of 3 buildings

3rd identical
block

Fig. 174.

Low-income row housing in Mercato S. Severino in the area behind Naples. Three buildings are combined in each row.

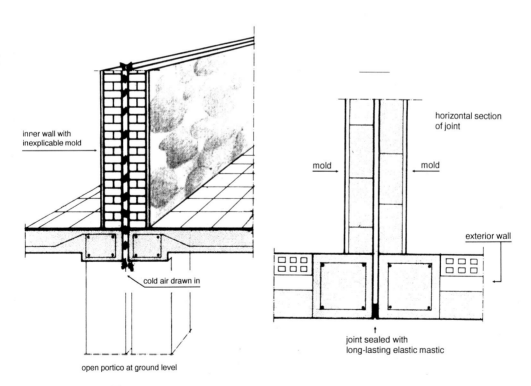

Fig. 175.

Fig. 176.

Vertical section of the inner transverse walls, which had heavy mold on the side corresponding to the movement joint between two reinforced concrete frames.

To eliminate the mold, we merely sealed all the movement joints between the buildings. Good, long-lasting elastic mastic was introduced to a depth of 5 cm.

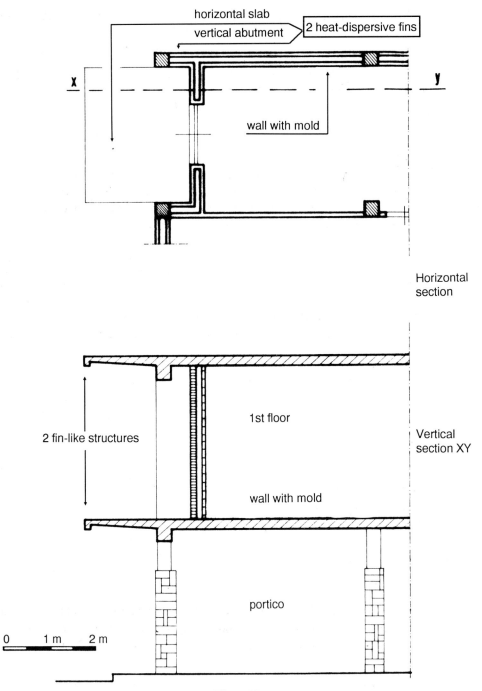

Fig. 177.

There are whimsical architects who inadvertently become wizards in reinforced concrete. Unfortunately, they forget that large, out-thrust balconies and vertical abutments between the balconies of adjacent apartments are rather dispersive of heat – so dispersive that they make an apartment unlivable due to damp and mold, as in the case shown here.

one brick laid flat, as shown in figure 176. In actuality, from a thermal standpoint, the rooms had no better protection on that side than the walls of a shack.

Restoration was very simple. The crack was merely filled all around with an elastic sealant, blocking the air inside. In such cases it is advisable to apply some type of polyethylene sulfonate sealant with a caulking gun to a depth of about 5 cm. Plaster, lime, cement and bitumen are forbidden.

Example 7

A vertical decorative abutment in reinforced concrete becomes a cooling fin. – Again near Naples, and again in a zone exposed to driving rain, we happened to see another curious source of humidity due to reinforced concrete. The architect had whimsically decided to enclose part of the short sides of large, outthrust, panoramic balconies with a blind vertical abutment (fig. 177). The decorative abutments provided the balconies with a certain privacy in the corners so enclosed.

As can be seen in figure 177, between the horizontal balcony and the vertical abutment, a large surface area was exposed to cold outdoor air in winter. This structure acted as a perfect heat dispersal fin, subtracting heat from the adjacent room much the way cooling fins work in an automobile cylinder (fig. 178). The dispersion must have been considerable, for the adjacent wall of the room was full of thriving mold.

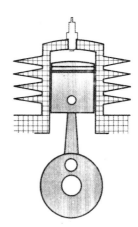

Fig. 178.

In the cylinders of percussion engines, maximum cooling is obtained by adding fins. Wizards in reinforced concrete treat homes as if they were motors that need cooling.

The prescription was to fill the wall cavity with expanded clay granules, to line the wall with polystyrene and wood panelling, and finally, to increase radiator surfaces by 50%. Good results were obtained, as the mold did not reappear the following year.

Example 8

A general climatic observation for maritime localities. – Not all administrators know that the principal cause of humidity in new houses was revealed by a statistical inquiry in 1964, done by the National Research Council of Italy. In 90% of all cases, persistent humidity in living quarters was found in only one or at most two sides of the building: the sides regularly beaten by driving rain. Chapter eleven of this book is entirely devoted to stressing that *driving rain never passes through well-built walls* but cools them greatly, giving rise to condensation on the inner wall face. It is extremely difficult to convince tenants that the liquid water they find on the bedroom floor in the morning has come from gas burned in the kitchen and from their own lungs. Often, even engineers are not easily persuaded. This is why there is a need for laboratory analysis and direct measurements.

Another thing many administrators do not know is that, in localities with moderate maritime climates (average January temperature above 6°C), it is a serious mistake to follow the recent building industry trend of lowering the free height of all stories to 2.40 m, while at the same time tucking kitchens and bathrooms into windowless interior rooms with forced ventilation so as not to waste the view. This involves a savings of 5% in the construction costs of high-density public housing.

This approach may work in Stockholm, but is quite wrong for Lisbon or Marseilles or Naples, where the winter heating period is brief. After the heating is off, such maritime localities still suffer from sudden cooling in spring and early summer (often caused by driving rain). At those times, windows must be kept closed, and consequently there is a serious rise in nocturnal RH in overcrowded, low-ceilinged rooms. Then follow mold and … rheumatic pains due to bad air! This is hardly progress in building, to reduce the useful height of rooms in temperate climate zones with intermittent winter heating! If building industry specialists were given a free hand, tenants would eventually be reduced to the status of hens in a coop.

HISTORIC BUILDINGS

¶72. Inexplicable humidity in a fresco on the first floor of the Palazzo Pubblico in Siena.

— The Spinello Aretino fresco depicting the arrival in Rome of the Sienese pope, Alexander II Chigi, was already greatly deteriorated when examined in 1960. Dampness was evident in the darkening of colors in scattered, irregular patches. The 'common sense' conviction in Siena, shared by all those troubled by the progressive deterioration of this fresco, was that there was moisture coming from below: rising capillary damp. Some scholars maintained that it came from the room directly beneath the fresco on the ground floor (fig. 179), where the Sienese Republic had stored salt for a few centuries. Their idea was that the room was probably still impregnated with salt, which draws moisture. Technicians favored the theory that the humidity was still active and rose from the large drain that collects all the rainwater from the nearby square (Il Campo); this drain passes beneath the building along the foot of the thick wall that bears the fresco on the first floor.

Both hypotheses were fairly reasonable and could be easily confirmed by measuring the moisture content of the wall in the lower floor, but such measurements had never been taken before.

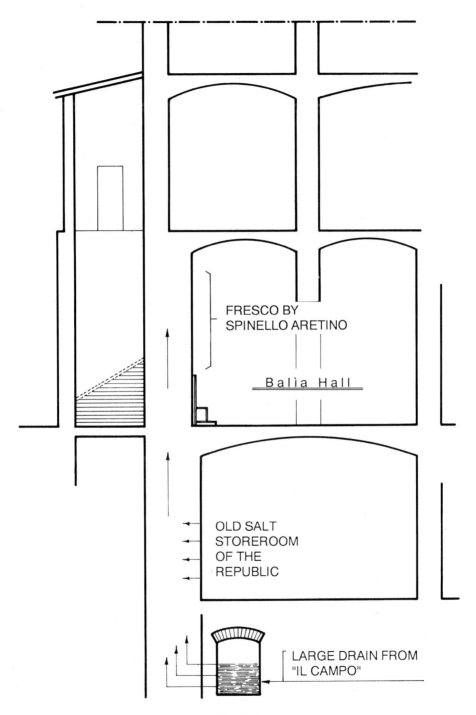

Fig. 179.

Vertical section of the wall with the damaged fresco in the Palazzo Pubblico of Siena. The conventional "common sense" diagnosis was rising damp, fed, it was said, either by hygroscopic water in the old salt storeroom or by water from the underground drain.

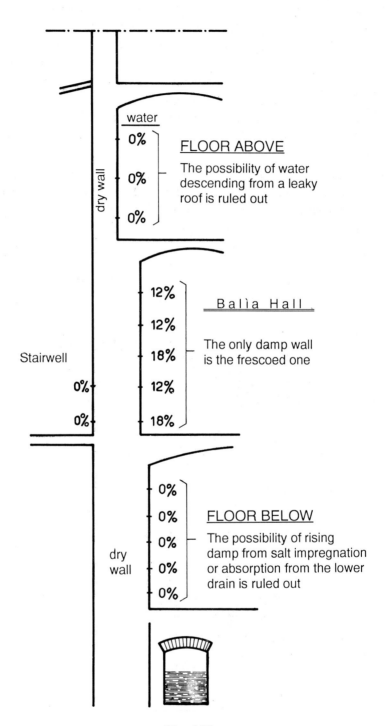

Fig. 180.

Measurement of the moisture content is negative: the walls are perfectly dry in the rooms above and below the Balìa Hall.

MEASUREMENT OF THE WATER IN THE PLASTER. To universal surprise, the measurements were completely negative, both in the masonry of the room below and in that above (fig. 180). Not only was the hypothesis of rising damp ruled out, but a newly proposed hypothesis that water descended from above, due to a leaking roof, was also disproved.

The problem became even more puzzling when further measurements in the back of the frescoed wall, towards the stairway, showed that the wall was perfectly dry on that side. Moisture was found *only on the fresco,* but there high amounts were measured: from 12% to 18% by weight.

In the second phase of the investigation, we decided to check the inner part of the wall by cautiously drilling in the undecorated lower area, which was normally covered by the backrest of a large, wooden antique bench, 2 m high.

DISCOVERY OF THE COUNTERWALL. The hole was begun gently, with a low-speed electric drill, and everyone was astonished to discover that the structure was not solid, but composed of a counterwall of heavy, fine-grained Sienese bricks, 6 cm thick, laid on edge with plaster. Behind them was an uneven cavity. Thus the fresco was *painted on this heavy counterwall.* Beyond it was the true master wall, about 1.65 m thick on average.

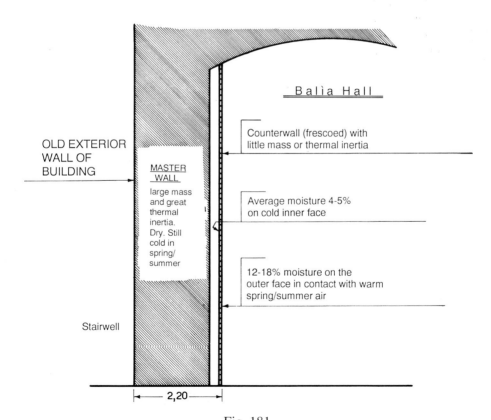

Fig. 181.

A diagnosis of condensation makes sense after the discovery that the fresco is not painted on the master wall, but on a counterwall subject to different temperatures on its two faces.

Ulterior measurements of water distribution revealed that:

- The master wall was perfectly dry.
- The back of the frescoed counterwall had an average moisture content of only 4-5%, while the front contained 12-18%.

The latter finding (fig. 181) was of decisive importance, for it clarified the fact that *the water came from the fresco surface and spread* towards the inside, diminishing in concentration in the limited thickness of the counterwall.

SIENA'S CLIMATE AND THE BUILDING'S EXCEPTIONAL THERMAL INERTIA. Climatic tables give Siena an average temperature of 4.7°C for the coldest month (February) as against 5.6°C in Florence. Siena's climate, therefore, is hardly mild and this fact has some weight in relation to the massive structure of the Palazzo Pubblico and to the lack of heating therein. The most solid and monumental reinforced concrete public building of today is a mere plaything from the thermal standpoint in comparison to Siena's Palazzo Pubblico, where all the physical phenomena of cooling and warming must be measured by an appropriate yardstick.

As has been stated, once measurements had ruled out the first simplistic theories as to the origin of the humidity (water from the roof, leaking pipes, ancient salt deposits, capillarity from the drain, etc.), and the enormous thermal inertia of the masonry was taken into consideration together with the discovery that the fresco was painted on a counterwall, a diagnosis of condensation began once again to make sense. Condensation would be unlikely if the fresco were painted on a master wall with equal surface temperatures on both sides, but would not be so surprising on a diaphragm such as the counterwall.

MICROCLIMATE OF THE CAVITY. In reality, the condensation is due to the difference in air temperature on the two sides of the counterwall, and is a seasonal phenomenon. The temperature of the large air mass contained in the Balia Hall varies directly with the season and with changes in the weather. The air enclosed behind the counterwall is but little affected by such changes and remains at a virtually constant temperature. The two air masses are unequal in volume: the hall contains ca. 500 m^3, the cavity ca. 7 m^3 – a ratio of 71 to 1. The two walls enclosing the cavity are equally disproportionate: the master wall is 1.65 m thick on average, the counterwall, including plaster, is 7-8 cm thick; the ratio of the two masses is about 22 to 1. Therefore, the thermal inertia of the thin counterwall is minimal in respect to that of the massive master wall. Fresh air in the hall immediately influences the frescoed surface – heating it quickly in summer and cooling it just as quickly in winter – but the small amount of air enclosed in the cavity is slow to follow seasonal variations because its temperature is linked to the enormous thermal mass of the heavy wall behind it. In June-July, for instance, the frescoed surface of the counterwall can have a temperature of 23-24°C, while its internal surface, facing the cavity, may still be 15-16°C. Under these conditions, the RH of the Balia Hall need only oscillate around 60% (a frequent occurrence in summer) for the 8°C temperature differential between the two faces of the counterwall to cause condensation *on the frescoed*

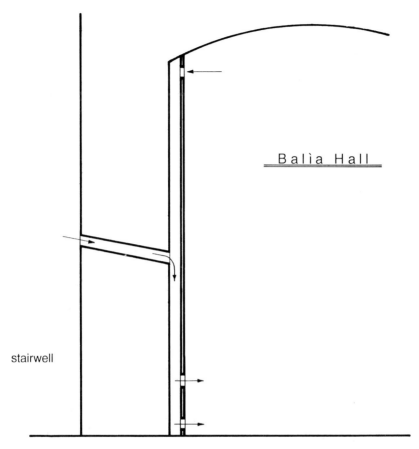

Balìa Hall

stairwell

Fig. 182.

The remedy used to eliminate condensation was to ventilate the air space in order to equalize the temperature on both sides of the counterwall.

side, which has become the 'cold wall' of the hall. The condensation will be abundant, and related to the tremendous volume of the Balia Hall.

RESTORATION MEASURES. The objective was to *equalize the temperature on the two faces of the counterwall.* In order for the small amount of air in the cavity to assume, winter and summer, the same temperature as the large air mass in the Balia Hall, it was necessary to put the cavity into as much communication as possible with the air in the hall. In 1960 this was done by opening a passage in the master wall and by placing air vents in the counterwall, as shown in figs. 182-183. The moisture content of the plaster dropped from the original measurement of 12-18%, as it was in 1960, to 4% in 1964. The restoration was quick and inexpensive.

Fig. 183.

The Spinello Aretino fresco with the air vents opened at the base of the wall. Within a few years, the moisture content of the intonaco decreased from 18% to 4%.

¶73. A church is abandoned because of humidity: Santa Maria della Rotonda in Albano Laziale, near Rome.

— In this case, humidity did not damage mural paintings or works of art, but threatened the health of the congregation and the priest himself to the extent that the religious authorities were forced to close the church. At the request of the Administration of Antiquities and Fine Arts, an examination of the church was begun in the winter of 1960.

The building is circular in plan, about 16 m in diameter, and covered by a dome; there are four large niches on the diagonals and the whole resembles a small Pantheon. It was originally a Roman thermal *nympheum*, and had been adapted since time immemorial, and through many vicissitudes and changes, to Christian worship. The church contained an ancient image of the Black Madonna, dear to the Albanese. For some time, the church had produced an unpleasant sensation of damp cold, which had caused the gradual desertion of the flock; religious services were consequently reduced until the church, as stated above, was finally closed.

There is a logic of appearances and a logic of substance. If one judges the causes

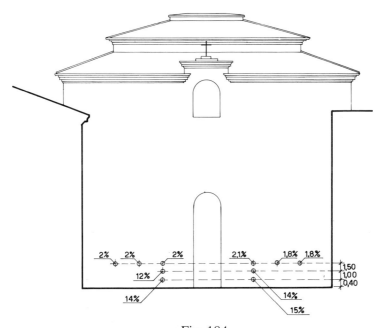

Fig. 184.

The 'common sense' diagnosis for the church of Santa Maria della Rotonda in Albano blamed the unhealthful conditions entirely on the rising damp which impregnated the outer wall up to a height of about 1.5 m.

of humidity on the basis of stains, mold, erosion, etc., one is following the logic of appearances. That is, one is applying what is called 'common sense' – a marvelous synthesis of intuition and rationality, valid in human relationships, but fallacious in the field of physical phenomena such as the humidity in a church. Here, understanding of the phenomenon requires that it be quantified and never judged offhand by common sense.

In the case of Santa Maria della Rotonda, the common-sense diagnosis seemed obvious, but was wrong. It had always been assumed that the problem was caused by evaporation from a visibly damp strip, about 1 m high, of ancient brick masonry in the ring wall (fig. 184, entrance to the church).

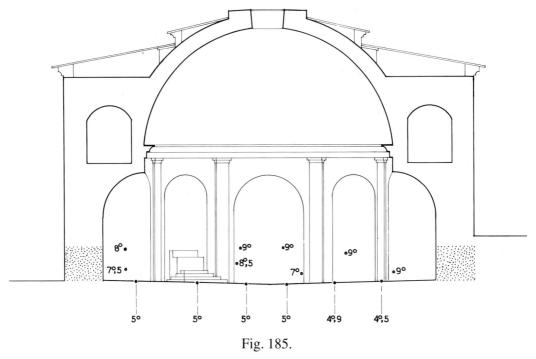

Fig. 185.

Measurement of surface temperatures inside the church revealed that the dry floor was much colder than the damp outer wall: a difference of 4°C.

THE DIAGNOSIS. The exact diagnosis was based on accurate measurements with instruments. It was found that two quite distinct factors combined to produce the high RH (87-95%) of the air: evaporation from the damp outer wall (evaporating surface: 75 m^2), and the condensation of water vapor due to the low temperature of the floor (condensing surface: 200 m^2). As can be seen in figure 185, the temperature of the floor (a compact, impermeable structure because in ancient times the bath water flowed across it to the central drain, which is still there) was on average 4°C lower in winter than the temperature of the outer wall: the floor was thus what physicists call the *cold wall*. Ample, rapid surface temperature measurements were possible thanks to an optical infrared thermometer, and allowed us to *quantify* the amount of damage caused by rising damp or by condensation. It was surprising to find that *condensation due to the cold floor was the more serious phenomenon.* The floor was cold and dry, while the encircling masonry was rather damp, but warm and not very damaging.

THE CENTRAL PROBLEM OF THE BATH FLOOR. Bearing in mind that the two entries to the church are both high, and that the church floor is thus in a 3 m declivity in relation to the surrounding street level, one sees how the floor's low temperature, by cooling the adjacent air layer, can create a vast stagnant area of damp, heavy air with no outlet whatsoever. The phenomenon is shown in figure 186: it is a condition similar to the last circle of Dante's Inferno. Like the damned, in winter the faithful sat with their feet nearly freezing at 5°C and their bodies immersed in saturated air. Here was the crux of the entire problem. Even if one managed to dry the damp masonry wall with suitable repairs, the principal cause of the church's unhealthy atmosphere would remain: the icy floor. Figure 187 shows the typical structure of the pavement, a perfect, heavy bath floor.

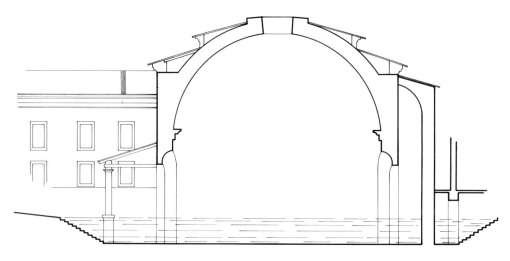

Fig. 186.

The floor's low temperature caused stagnation of damp, cold air which could not exit because the floor level was 3 m below street level.

RESTORATION WORK. This was aimed at modifying the floor structure to a depth of 60 cm, reducing its apparent specific gravity by half, considering the interposed air spaces (fig. 188). Heating coils were embedded to raise the temperature slightly. N.B. this was *not* a heating plant for the church because the heat supplied through the floor is only a third of that necessary for full heating. Still, it sufficed to eliminate the 'cold wall,' together with the stratification of damp, heavy air that had previously occurred. In fact, the dampness completely disappeared (1966) and the church is again comfortable and welcoming. This work can be regarded as a prototype for similar cases of ground-floor humidity in churches or large halls.

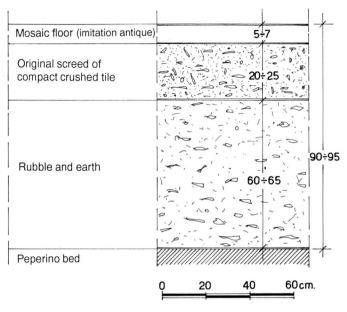

Fig. 187.

Section of the ancient bath floor in the church of Santa Maria della Rotonda. It is heavy and compact, favorable to condensation.

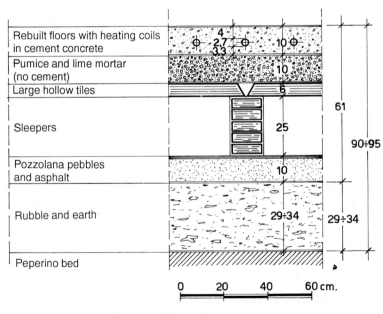

Fig. 188.

Section of the new, light floor with air space underneath. Embedded heating coils lightly heat the floor mass and impede the stratification of cold air.

Changes in the hygrometric situation inside the church can be represented by a chart of temperature and RH measurements taken six years apart on two similar winter days with outdoor RH at 70%:

		Before restoration Jan. 26, 1960	After restoration Feb. 23, 1966 (furnace off)
Surface temperature of masonry structures	outer wall floor	9°C 5°C	9°C 12°C
RH of closed indoor air	left side right side sacristy hall	95% 87% 100%	86% 86% 88%

As can be seen, the surface temperature of the damp outer wall remained the same: 9°C. The temperature of the rebuilt floor was completely changed: it rose from 5°C in 1960 to 12°C in 1966, although the heating plant had been off for three days. The RH, which had differed inexplicably between the left and right sides of the church, had become uniform and had dropped to a minimum of 86%. It is interesting to note that although the damp strip of the outer wall had the same temperature and moisture content as in 1960, this masonry humidity has become innocuous because the water vapor emitted is carried upwards by the column of warm air rising from the floor. Conditions favoring ventilation have been created where they were lacking before. In fact, one no longer feels any sensation of dampness inside, and the church is again open for worship.

¶74. Knapen siphons and the Palazzo of the Accademia di San Luca in Rome.

— We have already had occasion to speak of Knapen tubes and the many offspring that followed them on the construction market (see ¶33). The following is a summary of a case, which might be called instructive, of the total failure of an application in a well-controlled environment: the ancient and noble Accademia di San Luca. Since the beginning of this century, attempts had been made to use the magnificent vaulted rooms on the ground floor of the academy for exhibiting drawings, plans, and works of art. Yet, even good central heating was unable to eliminate mold and erosion in the damp plaster.

Around 1935, the academy had the building's external travertine plinth drilled and so-called *Knapen dehumidifying siphons* inserted in the wall (fig. 189). This messianic finding was in vogue at the time, being promoted by apparently rational, though pseudo-scientific, advertising. The siphons were used only on the outside because Knapen stoutly maintained that they would damage the interior with their discharge of extremely damp air. While the siphons were being installed, the project technicians also saw to the demolition of all the stained and ruined plaster on the inside and replastered the wall, using liberal amounts of hydrofuge cement. The rooms that had formerly been so unpleasant and disfigured were immediately spruced up, cleared of all trace of the old dampness and extremely pleasant in their fresh coats of paint. As was discovered later, the effect lasted three or four years, after which stains, efflorescence and erosion reappeared and everything was as before. A mere face lift had been done. In reality, the

Fig. 189.

The Palazzo of the Accademia of San Luca in Rome, seen from Vicolo Scavolino. Knapen dehumidifying siphons, applied in 1935, are visible in the plinth.

external dehumidifying pipes had not dehumidified anything, and the renewed internal plaster was simply a temporary cover-up of the damage, having the additional malice of crediting the tubes with the apparent initial improvement.

THIRTY YEARS LATER. The problem was the same as ever when a few architects in the academy raised the question of effective restoration once again. They felt, however, that a proper study should be made, rather than relying on some miracle cure. For the first time, common sense was overruled and measurements were taken of the moisture content of the walls in the unhealthy rooms. The investigation showed that, of the two parallel walls enclosing the damp premises (see plan fig. 190), the inner one on the porch side was dry, whereas the other wall along Vicolo Scavolino contained high quantities of water (up to 20% by weight, i.e., 30-32% by volume), distributed rather capriciously, as happens when the water supply is irregular.

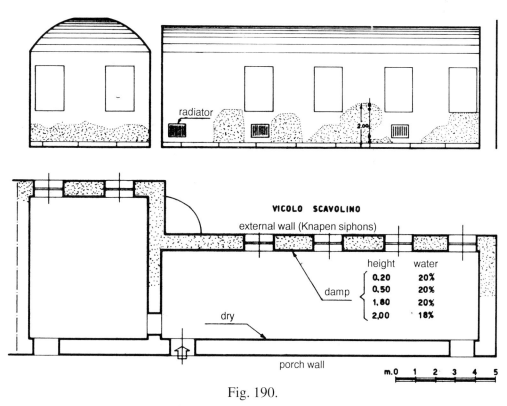

Fig. 190.

Only 30 years later were measurements taken of moisture content and distribution in the walls, and an exact diagnosis of the origin of the dampness was finally obtained.

DEDUCTION: The water supply could not have come from the groundwater table or from uniformly dispersed surface water at foundation level because both parallel walls would then have been equally soaked. Therefore, there must have been a specific, localized cause affecting only the wall along the street.

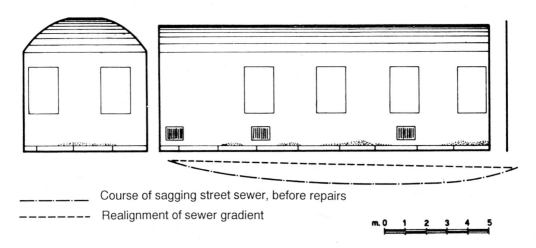

▬ ▬ ▬ ▬ ▬   Course of sagging street sewer, before repairs

▬ ▬ ▬ ▬ ▬   Realignment of sewer gradient

Fig. 191.

Simply realigning the gradient of a street sewer was enough to make the dampness disappear from the walls of the building.

THE TRUE CAUSE OF THE HUMIDITY. When, at the academy's request, the city technical services dug a hole to inspect the subsoil under Vicolo Scavolino, they found that the ancient brick sewer, used for both water and sewage, had subsided considerably along the entire front of the damp wall of the building, even though the street level had remained unchanged. The *sewer no longer flowed freely, but functioned under pressure* for many meters, irrigating the foundations of the building with the periodical loads of water that remained in the sagging portion. This flaw must have existed for more than half a century, but the sewer (even though occasionally under pressure) continued to work normally and city technicians had not noticed anything amiss. Once the subsidence was corrected and the sewer gradient realigned (fig. 191), the wall of the building slowly began to dry out. After three years (1965), the upper limit of the damp invasion, which was previously 2 m above floor level, had already sunk to 0.30 m and the restoration of the wall was assured.

The Knapen tubes are still there. Perhaps, 20 or 30 years hence, someone will claim that they restored the wall.

¶75.   The rescue of a Hellenistic painting in Bulgaria.

— In 1944, during the war, some soldiers digging an air-raid shelter discovered an ancient Thracian tomb in a mound not far from the city of Kazanlak (fig. 192). The tomb was perfectly conserved, although its furnishings had been stolen long ago. Apart from its archaeological importance, the find was of great artistic interest because of the mural painting that decorated the dome of the tomb chamber and the vault of the entryway. The painting was very well preserved, despite rivulets of dirty water, root penetration and, finally, scars from the many earthquakes suffered over 23 centuries. The painting was, in fact, dated around the turn of the third and fourth centuries B.C., about the time of

Alexander the Great, and is a rare example of Hellenistic wall painting that has survived to our day (fig. 193). The discovery was made in the midst of wartime tumult, and the fact that the Bulgarian people religiously protected the mural paintings is a sign of great cultural sensitivity on their part. Unfortunately, as soon as the tomb was opened, progressive deterioration of the paint layer began. This phenomenon is unhappily well known to the French, from experience with Paleolithic caves in the Pyrenees, and to the Italians, from experience with Etruscan tombs. Thus arose the knotty question of how to save the work of art. Between the conflicting opinions of experts and the impassioned suggestions of amateurs, the earth mass over the tomb was removed and the masonry structure laid bare. This action destroyed the thermo-hygrographic equilibrium that had conserved the mural paintings for 23 centuries. After various hasty and mostly ineffectual attempts at protection from the weather had been made, a sturdy shed was eventually built over the tomb, and is still there today. Its walls and roof are insulated (fig. 194) in order to create an environment that is protected, as much as possible, from climatic variations.

When H.J. Plenderleith (then director of ICCROM) visited the tomb in 1962, mold was already present, and the RH fluctuated between 95% and 100% despite the protective building. The mural paintings seemed doomed to disappear.

FIRST GUIDELINES FOR RESTORATION. In 1962, Plenderleith promptly suggested the following measures, which should be kept in mind for similar cases:

- A permanent air conditioning system must be installed to make the tomb independent of daily and seasonal changes in the climate.

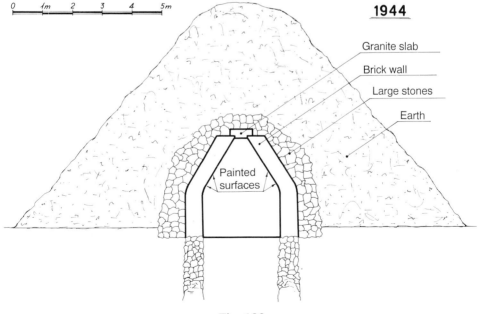

Fig. 192.

Vertical section of the Thracian tumulus tomb as it was when discovered in 1944.

- The RH of the inside air, which touches the painted surface, must be kept higher than the RH of the air at the back of the wall.
- Using the air conditioning, the RH should be gradually reduced from the original 95-100% limit to about 65-60%, but never below that limit.
- The reduction in RH must be brought about very slowly and under control, taking about three years.

These measures proved effective. The first was aimed at controlling alternate wet-dry cycles, a well-known cause of ruin for disinterred mural paintings. The second was intended to inhibit capillary water movement from the inside to the outside of the wall, so as to ward off efflorescence on the painting's surface. The last two guidelines were intended to restrain the overenthusiastic restorers by forbidding forced or hasty drying, which could cause crumbling of the intonaco or flaking and pulverization of the paint layer.

Fig. 193.

A detail of the Kazanlak mural painting, one of the rare Hellenistic paintings to have survived to our day.

In 1966, after the air-conditioning plant had been working for a few years, an international commission of experts, sent by Unesco at the invitation of the Bulgarian government, carefully examined the condition of the mural paintings.

MEASUREMENTS TAKEN IN 1966. Measurements of the temperature and moisture content of the air and masonry, entrusted to the author, gave the following results:

- The RH in the painted dome was still rather high: 76%. In the shed surrounding the back of the wall, it was 67%, i.e., notably lower, in compliance with Plenderleith's instructions.

- The painted wall was dry (less than 3% water) and thus already in excellent condition to ward off the development of mold.

- The original ancient floor of the tomb, consisting of a compact, colored mass, was extremely damp (moisture content above 20%). Thus the high RH was attributable to evaporation from the floor and not the wall.

The commission found that the development of mold had been blocked, that no new efflorescence had formed and that, on the whole, deterioration of the pigment layer seemed to have been arrested. Nevertheless, they were obliged to point out that the situation of hygrometric equilibrium in which the mural painting lived (and still lives) was a delicate one. It is also probable that the number of spores introduced from outside has been kept down by closing the tomb to tourists and insisting that only a few scholars be admitted after meticulous precautions for disinfection are taken. As it is, the presence of only two people profoundly alters the humidity and temperature of the 12 cubic meters of air in the tomb chamber. There has been a proposal, following H.J. Plenderleith's suggestion, that a periscope be installed on the floor of the tomb. The tomb would act somewhat like a camera oscura and the image of the mural painting would be transmitted to the outside. This technique might also be extended to similar cases; one is reminded of the Etruscan tombs in Italy.

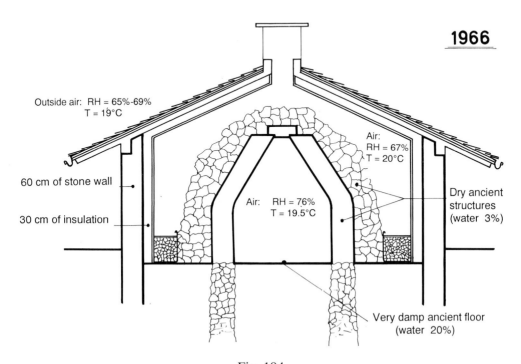

Fig. 194.

The tomb was enclosed in a study protective building, with constant temperature and RH.

¶76.   Modern utilization of historic buildings: the Palazzo del Te in Mantua.

— For Europeans, adaptive use of historic buildings is a vital intellectual, aesthetic and economic question. The legacy of the past – villas, castles and monasteries – must be saved from abandonment and given the vibrancy and warmth of life with a utilization that may be new, or perhaps even daring, yet must also be respectful, intelligent and acceptable to the community.

The Palazzo del Te in Mantua, Italy, is a grandiose suburban Renaissance villa that belonged to the Gonzaga family. It was splendidly decorated inside (1525-1535) by Giulio Romano, and has survived in good condition because it served as an army barracks after the fall of the Gonzaga (1707) and had always been properly maintained. Two technico-hygienic problems must be resolved in order to reinsert the building into the life of the community: elimination of dampness that invades the walls and disfigures the mural paintings; and loosening the icy grip of cold that forbids practical use of the building for

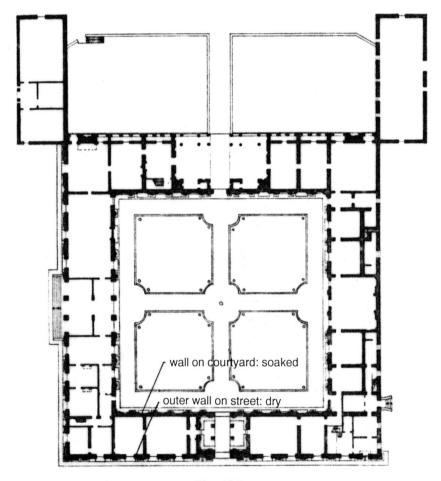

Fig. 195.

In the Palazzo del Te in Mantua, Italy, an enormous courtyard collected all the rainwater that flowed from the unguttered eaves.

several months of the year. An occasional fire in the monumental sixteenth-century fireplaces for some festive occasion will not suffice. The drawing rooms must be made welcoming and warm, enjoyable without a staged effort, and present-day technology is up to the task.

MEASUREMENT AND DISTRIBUTION OF HUMIDITY. The city of Mantua is built in the midst of swamps formed by the Mincio river, and the groundwater table is thus near the surface. The Palazzo del Te is raised only 78 cm above the local ground level and has no basements. It has a simple square plan with a single large interior courtyard, 45 meters on each side (fig. 195). The stains on the walls in the Sala dei Cavalli (Hall of the Horses) go up to 4 m high, and this phenomenon is visible all year round, independent of the season or of heat and cold: it is capillary rising damp. When the investigation was made in April 1966, the distribution of water in the masonry structures was as follows:

- The face of the outer wall, on the street, was unstained and dry (less than 3% water).
- The face of the internal perimeter wall (the courtyard wall, that is) was very damp to a height of 1.5 m.
- The transverse wall faces were all very damp (from 15 to 18% water) up to 1.5 m above the floor; they were relatively dry above that, though often stained up to a height of 4 m.

The two external walls (dry on the street and very damp on the courtyard) behaved quite differently. Why was this so?

INTERPRETATION OF THE MEASUREMENTS. DIAGNOSIS. It was clear that the stained walls, all built of brick *even in the part below ground,* were suffering from rising damp, as the staining was persistent and independent of the season. To discover whether the water supply came from the water table (in which case restoration is unlikely) or from dispersed surface water (in which case restoration is almost always possible), we dug two inspection holes next to the principal damp walls. The result of the inspection is shown in figure 196. Two facts relevant to our question stand out: first, there is a distance of 170 cm between the foundation level and the upper limit of the water table; second, the ground is composed of fine sand. The sand was probably brought in by a competent builder before the foundations were laid in order to prevent rising damp, which would otherwise have been a certainty in the clayey soil of the Mantua countryside. As may be remembered from figure 7, water rises very little by capillary action in sandy soil, but rises much more in clayey soil, and even ascends up to 8 m in pure clay. In the present case, the groundwater cannot climb 170 cm to the wall foundations because of the nature of the soil, for in *fine sand,* water rises little more than half a meter. Therefore, *the rising damp afflicting the walls of the Palazzo del Te originates from dispersed surface water* and is facilitated by the wall structure, which is of brick well down into the foundations. It is not difficult to deduce that the problem comes from rainwater accumulated in the courtyard itself. Situated higher than the outside grade, the courtyard acts as a gigantic, spongy reservoir into which liberal amounts of rainwater flow from the eaves. The sandy nature of the ground, which obstructs the capillary rise of groundwater, also favors the descent of rainwater to the wall footings. The walls then take up the water by capillarity and carry it upwards again to the frescoed rooms.

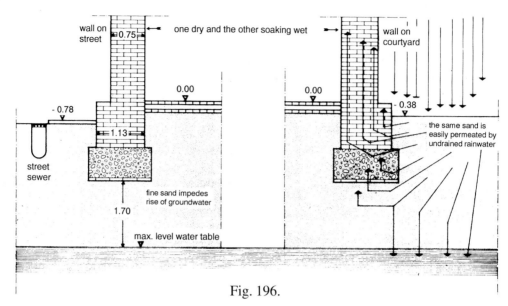

Fig. 196.

The outer wall of the Palazzo del Te (vertical section at left) is perfectly dry because the anti-capillary layer of sand interposed between the foundation and the groundwater table does not permit water to rise to the foundation. (Remember fig. 7.) The inner wall on the courtyard, however, is very damp because it absorbs the rainwater arriving laterally from the courtyard, which has no drainage (vertical section at right).

SUGGESTED REPAIRS. Only two measures were suggested:

- build a comprehensive drainage system with gutters, downspouts, and a network of pipes in the courtyard in order to carry off the rainwater; there may be aesthetic difficulties in adding downspouts to a Renaissance building, but this is the architect's challenge

- set up a functional heating system, perhaps divided into separate sectors in view of the vast size of the building and the difficulty of a single use. The most suitable type of heating in this case is radiant heating embedded in the floor, so that downward thermal dispersion is eliminated. This system is also the best answer for condensation because it heats the floor mass directly; it is also the least troublesome aesthetically because no radiators are seen

¶77. The mechanical breach cut in damp churches at Rome, Florence, Venice, Galatina. Safety precautions.

— The first experimental application of the Massari method (see ¶30) took place in the small eighteenth-century church of Santa Maria della Neve in Rome. The church had been closed to worship in 1965 because rising damp had made it unusable. Every conventional repair previously tried by the administration had failed: counterwalls, hydrofuge rendering, bituminized cardboard, transverse ventilation channels, aeration rosettes, etc. The case was desperate and the patient moribund. The National Research Council showed confidence and daring in financing and initiating the experiment, which meant facing the unknown factors involved in bringing research out of the laboratory to work on the living reality of a historic building.

The case was complex, both because of the height attained by the humidity and because the water came from two different sources: the ground and an embankment situated behind the sacristy and higher than the floor level of the church. In figure 197, which shows the dampest wall, the two proposed breach-cut lines are shown: a horizontal one to block the water rising from the subsoil and a vertical one to block lateral infiltration of water from the embankment. As explained in ¶30, a slot is progressively drilled and filled in short stretches with a fluid polyester resin-base mix (fig. 197). Epoxy resin can also be used but is much more expensive. The resin mix sets rapidly and has extremely high compressive strength, which guarantees the building's stability during and after the work. If the cut were filled with asphalt instead of resin, the building would crack from settlement because the loading is so total and immediate. Asphalt can be inserted in a wall base during the course of new construction because the loading is gradual in that case. In other words, loading produces elastic deformation in a resin mix, and plastic deformation in asphalt.

The experiment took three months to complete and was highly successful.[1]

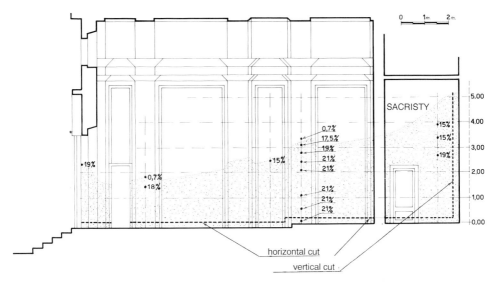

Fig. 197.

View of the dampest wall of the church of Santa Maria della Neve in Rome, with moisture content percentages and an indication of the two breach cuts executed: one horizontal, the other vertical.

1   Report of Chief Restorer Paolo Mora and Giovanni Massari to the International Congress on Museum Climatology in London, September 1967.

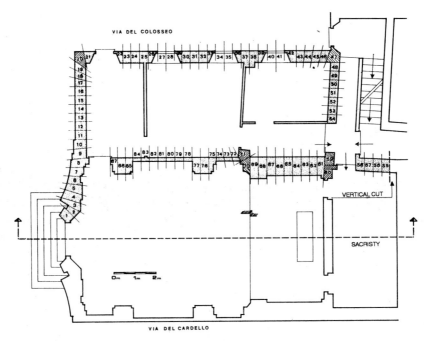

Fig. 198.

Plan of the church of Santa Maria della Neve in Rome, and of the equally damp annex rooms on Via del Colosseo. The 87 standard sections of the long horizontal cut are shown. Each section measures 42 cm across, as in fig. 53, p. 87. The church wall along Via del Cardello was not cut, as it was dry.

From subsequent applications of the method, we have learned that the risk in this new type of restoration is less of a static nature – i.e., inherent in the cutting – but more likely to arise from inattention during the preparation of the resin mix or lack of proper quality control of the resin received. One must acquire the same scientific attitude that is applied during reinforced concrete construction, when cubes of concrete are sent to a laboratory for compression tests.

Safety precautions

Just as poor-quality cement can compromise the stability of a reinforced concrete building, so poor-quality resin can compromise anti-humidity repairs and produce some cracking.

Before using a new batch of resin (or resin that has been stored for many months or poorly looked after), it is indispensable to make a test slab measuring 40 x 40 x 3.5 cm and check whether polymerization occurs in three, or at most four hours, depending on the season. The so-called 'chisel test' shown in figure 200 is a practical method. At least three hours should pass after casting before the test is made; it is positive if the chisel, dropped head first, bounces off the resin with a clear, metallic ring. This is the sign of good polymerization.

Fig. 199.

Facade of the church of Santa Maria della Neve during restoration (1966). At the lower left, the first four alternate breach cuts are ready to be filled with impermeable resin.

Fig. 200.

Just as building yards test the setting of each new batch of cement before use, so in repairs against rising damp one must check the quality of polyester resin before mixing. Three or four hours after setting, a test slab must be completely hardened and ring when a chisel is dropped on it.

Fig. 201.

When a single fresco must be protected from rising damp, a U-shaped cut is made around it. This was done in Florence for Perugino's Crucifixion in the Refectory of Santa Maria Maddalena dei Pazzi. (Dotted line = upper moisture limit; broken lines = path of damp-proof course.)

It is also necessary to check the compressive strength of the mix occasionally as the work goes forward. For instance, after every 20 m^2 of barrier completed, make two resin cubes, 16 cm per side, to be sent for compression tests no later than 24 hours after casting. This test, as for concrete, should be entrusted to the laboratory of the nearest engineering or architecture school. The breaking point should never drop below 800 kg/cm^2; it usually fluctuates between 1000 and 1300 kg/cm^2.

When the on-site chisel test and the laboratory compression test are both positive, one can be sure that the resin mix embedded in the wall functions not only as an absolutely waterproof barrier but also as a **load-distributing member** which makes a notable contribution to the wall's stability. If the building's static condition is rather unsatisfactory, the resin acts as an excellent consolidant. Even if, heaven forbid, the building's stability were threatened by an exceptional occurrence such as fire (in which case the works of art would be the first to suffer), the behavior of the embedded barrier layer would always be very helpful to the building's static resistance.

Fig. 202.

Beginning of mechanical breach cut with a core drill. The first two rows of cylindrical holes, separated by a stretch of solid wall, are visible in the lower part of the wall.

Mechanical breach-cutting and a fresco in Florence

From an economic standpoint, there is no reason why breach-cutting must be extended to all the walls in a building or to the entire perimeter of a church. In Florence, rising damp was beginning to attack an isolated Perugino fresco: the famous Crucifixion in the chapter room of the convent adjacent to the church of Santa Maria dei Pazzi. The new, thin breach-cut technique could resolve the problem inexpensively if the cut could be made in a U shape around the fresco alone. This is what was done, as illustrated in figure 201. The dotted line shows the upper limit of the rising damp, and the broken line shows where the breach cut was placed. The humidity was blocked just in time for, having surmounted the footings, it was about to invade the fresco itself.

Fig. 203.

General view of Perugino's Crucifixion in Florence during the work: on the lower right, three slots alternating with solid wall are visible. The slots are ready to receive the fluid resin mix.

The cutting was more difficult in Florence than in Rome, both because the wall was thicker and more uneven (between 80-85 cm) and because the wall had a motley structure, consisting of blocks of hard Fiesole sandstone and large calcareous river pebbles that the local foremen call 'Arno pills.' The first phase of the breach-cut operation is shown in figure 202, where the core drill has completed the first two rows of circular holes. In the next phase, the drill passes over each row again and clears out the masonry remaining between the holes, creating the clean, uniform horizontal slots that can be seen in the lower right-hand part of figure 203. In this figure, one can also see the entire grandiose fresco, which is 8.25 m across. All the restoration work, including a total of about 18 m^2 of cutting and the insertion of the resin layer, was completed in a month. The polymerization (i.e., setting and hardening) of the resin mix in each section of the cut took three hours on average. The average compression coefficient of the resin cubes after 24 hours was found to be 1050 kg/cm^2 by the laboratory of the Faculty of Architecture. This coefficient is higher than that of the best concrete used in reinforced structures.

Reclamation of the church of the Miracoli in Venice

In the church of Santa Maria dei Miracoli, a fifteenth-century masterpiece of Lombard architecture in Venice, the target of humidity was the polychrome facing of streaked and breccia marble. The church was completely faced, inside and out, with this marble, which was all deteriorating to some extent (fig. 204). The mechanism of the attack was not as simple as it had seemed at first, however, for the marble was compact and crystalline and had originally been polished. In brief, a stone of such high specific gravity either does not absorb water by capillary action at all, or else it absorbs ridiculously small amounts. Thus, the marble in the facing was not drawing up water from the lagoon; rather, it was the wall fabric, built of excellent brick as is customary in Venice, that was responsible for the dampness. The water in the wall core, kept from evaporating by the double marble facing, had continued to rise over the centuries as if in a capillary conduit until it reached a height of almost 6 m – a record that only a lagoon city could attain.

The water, however, did not cause so much damage in breaking height records as it did in keeping the entire wall temperature very low. The key point was this: the air layer in contact with the marble surface inside the church was cooled, giving rise to a pathological microclimate – the sort Harriet Ryd of the Swedish Building Research Institute calls a *climate envelope*[2]. If one bears in mind that the RH is always very high in Venice, one understands how the formation of condensation on the marble surfaces is facilitated by such cooling. The condensation water paves the way for the formation of acids (sulfuric especially) derived from the anhydrides of the Venetian smog, and for the attack of aerosols, such as those that transport sea salt, which are naturally abundant in the air of the lagoon. In fact, deterioration of the marble decoration inside the church of the Miracoli is found only on the visible side exposed to the air. The side against the brick core is intact, even though the bricks are soaking wet. Because of the marble facing, it was not possible to use the conventional manual breach cut, with hammer and chisel, which the Venetians have developed to a fine art. The facing would have been severely damaged because it is not held with cramps, but irreversibly attached with cement (a late nineteenth-century restoration).

The mechanical breach cut resolved this difficult problem to perfection. With the core drill, a row of horizontal slots was made across the thickest marble slabs (8 cm) *without dismantling any of the decoration,* as indicated in the vertical section shown in

---

2   Harriet Ryd, note in French edition of *Build International*, September 1969.

Fig. 204.

In the church of Santa Maria dei Miracoli in Venice, a damp-proof course was inserted around the entire perimeter without removing the marvellous marble facing.

figure 205. This was quite a feat. When the work was finished and the resin hardened, the visible horizontal strip of resin, which ran right across the marble about 35 cm above the floor, was masked by carving back the resin and marble surface (which was possible in the 8 cm thick strip) and refacing it with the same Verona marble that had been used before. The complexity of the restoration can be seen in figure 205.

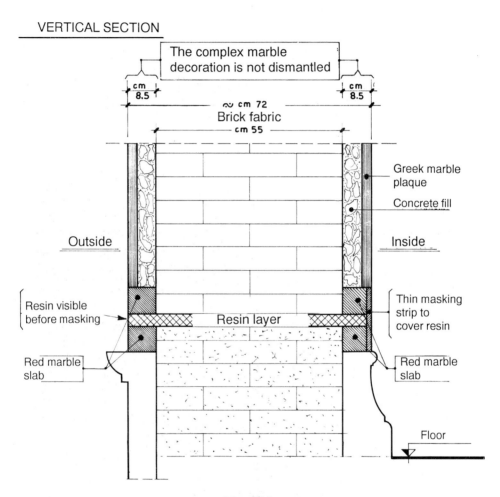

VERTICAL SECTION

The complex marble decoration is not dismantled

cm 8.5

cm 8.5

≈ cm 72
Brick fabric
cm 55

Greek marble plaque

Concrete fill

Outside

Inside

Resin visible before masking

Resin layer

Thin masking strip to cover resin

Red marble slab

Red marble slab

Floor

Fig. 205.

In Venice, interception of rising damp in the Lombardesque church of Santa Maria dei Miracoli was done around the entire perimeter to halt the ruin of the marble facing. With clever masking, a marble worker then hid the resin strip from view.

To summarize, the entire perimeter of the church and the transverse wall of the transept were cut for a total of about 100 linear meters of master wall, with over 80 m^2 of horizontal cutting. In Venice, it will take several years for the enormous mass of water still bottled inside the wall above the cut to evaporate. This problem is discussed in ¶78.

The breach cut in a large frescoed church at Galatina, Lecce

Rising damp in Venice is certainly understandable, but it seems strange for a large and beautiful church in arid Puglia to suffer from the same ailment. In Galatina di Lecce we encountered such a paradox. An imposing church, with walls on the order of 3 m thick, had risen in a dry environment, without fog and with an extremely low rainfall (between 500 and 750 mm of water annually). Yet its precious mural paintings had suffered extensive damage due to rising damp (fig. 206).

The masonry, which acted as a support for the various pictorial cycles, was literally soaking wet, with a moisture content between 10% and 14% by weight. At some points, the magnificent painted areas of the central nave of Santa Caterina seemed to be invaded by damp right up to the top of the wall. The structure is made of soft local stone, a sort of calcareous tufa used in regular blocks without rendering. The pictorial cycles are done on intonaco, of course. The specific gravity of the calcareous tufa blocks is very low:

Fig. 206.

In the grandiose church of Santa Caterina in Galatina (Lecce, Italy), the breach-cut pillars of the central nave are 3 m thick. In the photo, two workmen are pouring the fluid resin mix into the first cut. Note, above the cut, the advanced deterioration of the mural paintings affected by rising damp.

from a minimum of 1,340 mg/m^3 to a maximum of 1,680 kg/m^3. The moisture content of samples examined in the laboratory was extremely high: from 28.4% to 13.8% by weight. In compensation, the drying time of samples was found to be rather brief: in laboratory tests carried out at Rome, samples from Galatina took from 6 to 9 days to dry in the open air, as against 11 days for common Roman brick.

This important restoration work was carried out in about eight months, during 1972. The total extent of the cut was 282 m^2, which to date (1978) is the maximum area treated by the Massari method in rehabilitating an historic building from rising damp.

¶78.   Drying time after breach cutting.

— Do not expect a wall to dry out immediately after the breach cut has been made and a damp-proof course inserted. The load of water remaining above the barrier must exit by evaporation, a process that involves not a matter of months, but of years. If the premises are ventilated, however, signs of returning dryness can usually be seen on the wall *surface* by the first summer following the cut: marble facings become slightly opaque and frescos become lightly glazed. This dimming of fresco surfaces occurs simply because salts, which had been there all along, crystallize and *become visible*. It is well known that a clouded fresco can be brought to life momentarily by spraying it with water or passing a damp cloth over it, if its condition permits. After the damp-proof course has been inserted, the task of the restorer, a valuable co-worker, is to remove the veiling and fasten any flaking of the pigment layer. One should never think that moisture 'is good' for the conservation of a fresco, and that dampness should therefore not be controlled. If this were true, any restoration treatment would be illogical – even the *strappo*.

As to the wall fabric, evaporation will be more rapid in a dry climate, and slower, or even extremely sluggish, in a damp climate. As a follow-up to our first experiment in Rome, we kept track of the drying of the facade of Santa Maria della Neve (fig. 198), taking masonry samples at a depth of 20-25 cm and having the moisture content measured. We should specify that the masonry is 80 cm thick and is a mixture of brick and tuff, with tuff predominating. The facade is well insolated, with a SE exposure. Given the amount of tuff present, we hold that a similar wall could be considered no longer a cause of damage and, therefore, restored when its moisture content by weight is reduced to 5%.

The change in moisture content, about three years after the cutting, was as follows:

Moisture content % at depth					Avg. content in first 2 m above the floor
Height (m)	+0.30	+0.80	+1.30	+1.80	
When cut, 20/XII/66	15.03%	10.10%	8.50%	8.73%	10.60%
Almost 3 yrs later, 20/X/69	8.70%	5.20%	6.00%	5.50%	6.35%
Water evaporated in ca. 3 yrs			in % by weight in liters/m^2 of wall		4.25% 58 lt

As can be seen, the facade wall was almost completely restored after three years. To arrive at 5%, which, as stated above, no longer causes damage, a further evaporation of 1.35% was necessary equivalent to another 18 liters per m^2 of wall.

Conditions in Venice are quite different. As Venetian walls are usually made of brick, their residual water must drop to at least 3% by weight to be tolerable, i.e., no longer a cause of damage. Moreover, the RH of the air is much higher than in Rome. In 1967, in the church of San Sebastiano, we were able to measure (using the more precise weight method) the water remaining in the *interior* wall, between the church and the sacristy hallway, 3 years after the wall had been cut. The Superintendence of Monuments had supervised the work, which was done with the laborious traditional technique of hand chiselling followed by insertion of a lead sheet. Analysis of the wall samples, taken above and below the lead strip, demonstrated that a notable amount of drying had occurred, for the moisture content had been halved, dropping from 20% to 10%. Yet, even optimistically expecting the water to continue evaporating at the same rate, it would take at least 9 years to reduce the moisture content to 3% (fig. 207).

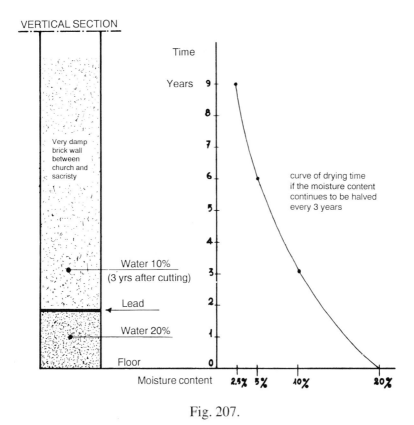

Fig. 207.

Drying of breach-cut walls in Venice is extremely slow because of the high RH. At least 9 years are calculated as necessary for full drying of an interior wall in the church of San Sebastiano, restored years ago with the traditional lead-sheet technique.

General measures to accelerate the drying process in a breach-cut wall must be aimed at reducing the RH of the inside air, for example, by opening the windows frequently. Heating is another possibility: on this subject, see the *windshield effect* technique in ¶63. If the floor is damp because it is laid directly on the ground, as in the Florentine refectory which houses Perugino's fresco, it should be rebuilt with a good *subfloor with air spaces* so that it ceases to add moisture to the environment.

When one is rebuilding a ground floor pavement with a subfloor, another useful innovation is to insert a light, insulating layer, 10 cm thick, mixed with pumice, expanded clay or vermiculite. This lightweight bed should be placed directly beneath the flooring material. This precaution will ensure that condensation does not form on the floor in damp rooms, and is also helpful in shortening the drying time of the breach-cut wall.

BIBLIOGRAPHY

PHYSICS AND HYGIENE

JAMIN, M.J. *Cours de physique de l'école polytechnique*. Paris: Gauthier-Villars, 1871.

TURSINI, A. "L'umidità nelle case di Napoli e nuovo metodo per determinarla." *Rivista d'Igiene* (1891).

De BLASI and CASTIGLIA, "Richerche fisico-igieniche sui materiali da costruzione comunemente usati in Palermo." *Rivista d'Igiene e sanità pubblica* (1891).

BIANCHINI, R. "Intorno all'umidità di tipi differenti di muri." *Rivista d'igiene e sanità pubblica* (1906) 74.

MAJONE, P. "Metodo semplice per misurare il potere di assorbimento capillare nei materiali da costruzioni." *Annali d'igiene* (1909) 123.

PAGLIANI, L. *Trattato d'igiene e sanità pubblica*. Milan: Vallardi, 1913.

BONASSE, H. *Capillarité: phénomènes superficiels*. Paris, 1924.

ISSOGLIO, G. *Nuova enciclopedia di Chimica*, vol. 13, pt 1, p. 561. Turin: Utet, 1925.

SCALA, A. *Applicazioni di fisica e chimica all'igiene*. Turin: Utet, 1926.

DEPT. SCI. AND INDUS. RESEARCH, *Report Building Research Board*. London, 1928, 1929.

PERUCCA, E. *Fisica generale e sperimentale*. Turin: Utet, 1932.

FIORANI GALLOTTA, P.L. *L'igiene della casa*. Padua: Cedam, 1932.

OTTOLENGHI, D. *Trattato d'igiene*. Vallardi, 1933.

DE FERMO, V. and R. TECCE, "L'umidità delle abitazioni." *Annali d'Igiene* (1935) 389.

ABBA, F. *Manuale pratico d'igiene*. Turin: Utet, 1936.

KRISCHER, O. and P. GÖRLING, *Versuche über die Trocknung poriger Stoffe und ihre Deutung* [Experimental drying tests of porous materials and their explanation]. Verfahrenstechnik, supplement of V.D.I. Zeitscrift, 1938.

SCHÜLE, W. "Wärmetechnische und wirtschaftliche Fragen im Wohnungsbau [Technico-thermal and economic issues in the construction of homes – Surveys of moisture content in exterior walls of inhabited buildings]." *Gesundheits-Ingenieur* (November 1939) 639.

———, "Warmedurchlasszahl von Aussenmauern [Coefficient of heat passage in exterior walls]." *Gesundheits-Ingenieur* (1939) 641.

VINACCIA, G. *Il corso del sole in urbanistica ed edilizia*. Milan: Hoepli, 1939.

MISSENARD, A. *L'uomo e il clima*. Milan: Bompiani, 1940.

SCHUBERT, H. "Wohnungsfeuchte und Gesundheit [Humidity of homes and health]." *Wärme-und-Kältetecnik*, no. 8 (1941) 121.

MASSARI, G. and M. TALENTI, *Nuovi criteri per giudicare lo stato di umidità delle vecchie murature*. Atti dell'Accademia d'Italia, series 7, vol. 5 (July-October 1943).

GIOVANARDI, A. and G. BONCI-CASUCCINI, *Ventilazione e microclima degli ambienti confinati*. Atti della R. Accademia dei Fisiocratici in Siena e Studi della Facoltà Medica Senese, 1938, 163.

PUNTONI, V. *Trattato d'Igiene*. Rome: Tumminelli, 1948.

TALENTI, M. and G. MASSARI, "L'accertamento e la misura dello stato di umidità degli ambienti confinati." *Nuovi Annali d"Igiene e Microbiologia* (1951).

TIZZANO, A. "Su alcuni esigenze igieniche delle abitazioni." *Documenti di architettura e industria edilizia*, no. 6 (1951).

BEHAVIOR OF MATERIALS

SESTINI, F. *Studio sui tufi della campagna romana*. Annali della R. Stazione Chimico-Agraria sperimentale di Roma, series I (1872-74) 54-62.

SALMOIRAGHI, F. *Materiali naturali da costruzione*. Milan: Hoepli, 1892.

ARTINI, E. *Lezioni di mineralogia e materiali da costruzione*. Milan: Lib. Edl. Politecnica, 1922.

PALMER, A. "Water Penetration through Brick-Mortar Assemblages." *Rock Products,* no. 24 (1931) 34.

DE ANGELIS D'OSSAT, G. *Materiali da costruzione in Roma e nel Lazio*. Rome, 1932.

THEIN, W. "Baustoff und Regendurchlässigkeit [Materials and their permeability to rainwater]." *Tonindustrie* (1933) 748.

PHILADELPHEUS, A. "La conservation de marbres antiques." *Mouseion* (1933) 138.

GRIFFINI, E.A. *Dizionario nuovi materiali per edilizia*. Milan: Hoepli, 1934.

HUEBNER, P.H. "Les maladies du papier et leur traitement." *Mouseion* (1934) 242.

ERIKSON, H.A. "Condizionamento dell'aria ed essiccamento delle cartiere." *L'Ingegnere* (1939) 42.

TOMMASI, G. and V. MORANI, *Studio chimico-agrario dei terreni del Lazio*. Annali della R. Stazione Chimico-Agraria sperimentale di Roma, series 2, vol. 16 (1939).

U.S. DEPARTMENT OF COMMERCE, *Technical News Bulletin of the National Bureau of Standards*. (January 1939) 5.

VAN GELDER, E.M. "La putredine del legno nelle costruzioni civili." *L'Ingegnere* (1939) 951.

VINACCIA, G. *Gli agglomerati di sughero nell'edilizia moderna*. Rome: Usila, 1940.

CAMMERER, J.S. Über die kapillaren Eigenschaften der Baustoffe im Hinblick auf den Kühlhausbau [On the capillary properties of building materials for refrigerating cells]." *Gesundheits-Ingenieur* (1942) 386.

SAVIRON CARAVANTES, "Un agente aggressivo del conglomerato cementizio." *Stele* 2 (1942) 209.

GEIGER, F. "Contributo alla determinazione della dipendenza dall'umidità della resistenza a compressione dell'abete." *Stele* 5 (1943) p. 78.

LLEWELLYN, H.M. and H.J. ELDRIGE, "Painting new plaster and cement." *National Building Studies Bulletin* 2 (1948). London.

WEBB, T.L. and J.H.P. VAN AARDT, "Breve studio delle proprietà della vermiculite e dei suoi usi nell'edilizia." *Documenti di architettura e industria edilizia*, no. 4 (1950); also published in *National Building Research Institute, Bulletin* 3 (September 1949). Pretoria.

GALLO, A. *Patologia e terapia del libro*. Lazio, 1951.

SCHÜLE, W. and H. SCHÄCKE, Untersuchungen über den praktischen Feuchtigkeitsgehalt von Aussenwänden aus Bimsbaustoffen [Studies of the practical moisture content of exterior walls built with pumice]." *Gesundheits-Ingenieur* (1951) 33.

CADIERGUES, R. and J. GENEVAY, "La conducibilité thermique des materiaux." *Chauffage, Ventilation, Conditionnement*, no. 10 (December 1953).

HALLER, P. "Questioni di cui si deve tener conto nello studio dei mattoni de grande formato in terracotta." *L'industrie céramique* (February, 1954).

DESLEX, R. "Problèmes techniques qui se posent dans la fabrication et l'emploi des briques de grand format." *L'industrie céramique*, no. 450 (1954).

CROISET, M. *L'emploi des maçonneries légeres en consideration de leurs caracteristiques thermiques utiles*. Cahiers du Centre scientifique et technique du bâtiment, no. 28. Paris, 1958.

PROTECTION AND REHABILITATION

D'ARMAILHACQ, M. GR. S*aint Louis des Français à Rome*. Rome: Cuggiani, 1894.

CHOISY, A. *Vitruve*. Paris: Lahure, 1909. Table 7, figs. 1, 2, 3.

PAPINI, R. *Il deperimento delle pitture murali nel Camposanto di Pisa*. Rome: Calzone, 1909.

MUÑOZ, A. *Questioni tecniche relative al restauro degli antichi affreschi*. Rome: Loescher, 1914.

KNAPEN, M.A. "Méthodes d'assainissement des constructions et des logements insalubres." *Revue d'hygiène*, no. 1 (1924). Paris.

———, "Le problème de la conservation des matériaux des habitations et des monuments." *Revue des Entrepreneurs de Maçonnerie Ciments et Beton armé* (April-December 1925). Paris.

KETTENACKER, L. "Über die Feuchtigkeit von Mauern [Humidity in walls]." *Gesundheits-Ingenieur* (November 1930) 721.

"Anweisung für richtige Klinkermauerung [Rules for proper construction of cinder-block walls]." *Tonindustrie* (1931) 356.

RICCI, C. "Les agents atmosphériques et la conservation des oeuvres d'art." *Mouseion* (1931) 8.

SCHMIDT, G. "Die chemische Untersuchung von feuchten Ziegelmauerwerk [chemical analysis of brick walls]." *Chemikerzeitung* (1931) 558.

CELLERIER, I.F. "La désagrégation des pierres naturelles et les moyens de préservation." *Mouseion* (1932) 65.

KIESLINGER, A. *Zerstörungen an Steinbauten* [Deterioration of stone constructions]. Vienna, 1932.

POHL, K. "Emploi de la silicatisation pour la construction dans les terrains meubles." *Le Génie civil* (January 1932).

"Vergleichende Untersuchungen über die Wirksamkeit von Dichtungsmitteln [Comparative analysis of effectiveness of waterproofing]." *Tonindustrie-Zeitung* (1933) 295.

VITRUVIUS, *Dell'Architettura*. U. Fleres edition. See Book 6, chap. 4. Rome, 1933.

BASILE, F. *Tetti piani*. Messina, 1935.

DE SIMONE, D. "Procedimenti di impermeabilizzazione e di consolidamento chimico dei terreni." *Annali dei LL. PP.* (1935) 443.

"Etanchéité des terrasses." *L'architecture d'aujourd'hui* (December 1935) 64.

STRADELLI, A. *Il condizionamento dell'aria*. Milan: Hoepli, 1935.

RINAUDO, M. *Ventilazione degli ambienti*. Florence: Bemporad, 1936.

CAMMERER, J.S. "Über die Feuchtigkeitsänderung in den Wänden von Wohnräumen und Ställen [Humidity movement in occupied rooms and stables]." *Gesundheits-Ingenieur* (June 1939) 306.

SALAZ, O.P. *L'umidità delle case: come prevenirla, come reprimerla*. Bologna: E.T.U, 1939.

SCHÜLE, W. Wärmetechnische und wirtschaftliche Fragen im Wohnungsbau [Technico-thermal and economic issues in the construction of homes – Influence of exterior walls, windows and fixtures on heating economy]." *Gesundheits-Ingenieur* (1939) 653.

CORMIO. "I costruttori edili e l'impiego del legno nei solai e nei soffitti." *L'Ingegnere* (November 1941) 1005.

GALLO, A. *Termoigrografi*. Circ. no. 46, R. Rome: Istituto di Patologia del libro, 1941.

COMMISSIONE PER IL RESTAURO DELLA CHIESA SUPERIORE DI ASSISI, "Report." *Le Arti* (1941-42) 217.

IMHOLZ, F. "Per la buona conservazione dell'armatura dei tetti." *Stele* 3 (1942) 285.

PALUMBO, E. "Efflorescenza sui materiali da costruzione." *L'Ingegnere* (1942) 146.

STOIS, A. and G. CLAUS, "Sui mezzi di protezione delle pietre." *Stele* 2 (1942) 86.

GOIDANICH, G. *Sulle cause dei cedimenti nella pavimentazione del palazzo Corsini sede dell'Accademia Naz. dei Lincei*. Atti dell'Accademia dei Lincei, series 8, 1946, p. 872 of Rendiconti.

MASSARI, G. "Un capolavoro malato: diagnosi e cura del Cenacolo di Laonardo." *Sapere*, nos. 293-4 (1947).

SCHÄFER, J. "Pappe und metallfreie Bautenisolierungen [Insulation of buildings without cardboard and metal]." *Asph. u. Teer.*, no. 5 (1942) 87.

MASSARI, G. and M. TALENTI, "Soleggiamento ed umidità dei muri." *Annali d'Igiene* (January-February 1946).

CAMMERER, J.S. "Die Verdunstungsfähigkelt verschiedener Putze mit Rücksicht auf die Mauerfeuchtigkeit im Wohn, Stall und Kühlbausbau [Evaporation capacity of different plasters in relation to humidity in walls of homes, stables and refrigeration storerooms]." *Gesundheits-Ingenieur* (1944) 31.

GALLO, G. *Sulle cause di deperimento degli affreschi di Benozzo Gozzoli nel Camposanto Monumentale di Pisa*. Extract of Report 20 December 1942 to Ministero. Ed. Naz. Pisa, 1945.

PIROTTE and TROMMELMANS. "La perméabilité et les efflorescences en maçonnerie." *Techn. Travaux*, nos. 1-2 (1948) 38.

BILLINGTON, N.S. and G.R. BONNEL. *Pattern Staining in Building*. National Building Studies Special Report, no. 6. London, 1949.

"Condensation Problems in Building." *Building Research Station Digest* 23 (October 1950). London.

EGNER, K. *Feuchtigkeitsdurchgang und Wasserdampfkondensation in Bauten* [Humidity passage and water vapor condensation in buildings]. Stuttgart, 1950.

EGERTON, A.C. *Heating and Ventilation of Dwellings*. Post-war Building Studies 19. London, 1945. (Subsequently reprinted.)

BECKER, P. *Okonomisk varmeisolering*. Staten Byggeforskingsintitut Rapport 1. Copenhagen, 1950.

ISAR, A. *Termotecnica*, 2nd ed. Milan, 1951.

MASSARI, G., TALENTI, M. and TIZZANO, A. "Relazione al Convegno del progresso edile in Roma." *Agere*, Proceedings 1953.

CADIERGUES, R. *Isolation et protection des bâtiments*. Paris: Eyrolles, 1954.

VON KNODEL, H. "Ein Wandschimmeltest zur Beurteilung der Feuchtigkeitseigenschaften von Wänden [A mold sample from the wall to judge humidity characteristics]." *Gesundheits-Ingenieur*, no. 273 (September 1954) 308.

MASSARI, G. "Equilibrio fra protezione termica muraria ed impianto di riscaldamento." *L'installatore Italiano*, no. 10 (October 1954).

LEVY, J.P. *Les bétons légers*. Paris: Eyrolles, 1955.

LIBERTI, S. Consolidamento dei materiali da costruzione di monumenti antichi. *Bollettino dell'Istituto Centrale del Restauro*, nos. 21-22 (1955).

VON SCHÄCHE, H. "Untersuchungen über die Feuchtigkeitsverhältnisse in Stall-Aussenwänden aus vershiedenen Baustroffen [Study of relationship of humidity in exterior stable walls constructed with different materials]." *Gesundheits-Ingenieur*, nos. 15-16 (August 1956).

GUIDI, G. "Le murature nei regolamenti edilizi." Report to the IV Congresso Nazionale Edilizia e Abitazione. *Industria Italiana dei Laterizi*, no. 2 (1956).

BALZANO, M. "Le impermeabilizzazioni nell'edilizia moderna con particolare reguardo ai materiali asfaltici." *Ingegneri-Architetti* (August-September 1956). Rome.

FOURNOL, A. and M. CRIOSET. *L'eau dans les murs*. Cahiers du Centre scientifique et technique du bâtiment, no. 28, Paris, 1958.

CROISET, M. *L'humidité dans les toitures plates et a faible pente*. Cahiers du Centre scientifique et technique du bâtiment, no. 31, Paris, 1958.

MASSARI, G., TIZZANO, A. and M. TALENTI. "Impiego del campo d'alta frequenza per il dosaggio dell'acqua in campioni di muratura umida." *La ricerca scientifica*, no. 7 (July 1959).

CROISET, M. and R. DELAHYE. *La résistence des murs à la pénétration de l'eau de pluie*. Cahiers du C.S.T.B. no. 39, Paris, August 1959.

COLOMBO, G. "Esperienze sul prosciugamento elettrosmotico delle murature umide." *La Ricerca Scientifica* 33 (II A) (1963). Rome.

MATVEEV, B.V. "Electroosmotische Methode zur Trocknung von Wänden." *Bauzeitung*, no. 4 (1963). Berlin. [Electroosmotic method for drying walls.]

VARLAN, G.E. *L'étanchéité dans la construction*. Paris: Eyrolles, 1964.

ISTITUTO D'IGIENE DELL'UNIVERSITA' DI NAPOLI. CAMPANILE, E., ORTOLANI, G. and D. CIULLO. "L'umidità rilevata con metodi elettrici." *L'Igiene moderna*, nos. 5-6 (1965) 271. Parma.

COMMISSIONE DI STUDIO PER L'UMIDITA DELLE MURATURE. CONSIGLIO NAZIONALE DELLE RICHERCHE, "Attività svolta nell'anno 1963-1964." *La Ricerca Scientifica* 4, no. 2 (May 1965) 83-6. Rome.

MASSARI, G. "Sette anni di osservazioni sulle case umide." *La Ricerca Scientifica* 35 (II A) (July-August 1965) 881-93. Rome.

LACY, R.E. "Driving-rain maps, and the onslaught of rain on buildings." *Proceedings of the RILEM Symposium on Problems of Humidity in Buildings, Helsinki, August 1965.*

KORSGAARD, V. and M. BYBERG. "Driving rain test with cavity filled hollow brick walls." *Proceedings of the RILEM Symposium, Helsinki, August 1965.*

LIPCSEY, M. "Installation for drying and damp-proofing hydrophilic structural portions of buildings, particularly brickwork." *Proceedings of the RILEM Symposium, Helsinki, August 1965.*

WATSON, A. "Measurement of moisture content in some structures and materials by microwave absorption." *Proceedings of the RILEM Symposium, Helsinki, August 1965.*

PACQUET, J. "Application des méthodes electriques à la mesure de la teneur en eau des matériaux. *Proceedings of the RILEM Symposium, Helsinki, August 1965.*

TORRACA, G. and P. MORA, "Fissativi per pitture murali." *Bollettino dell'Istituto Centrale del Restauro* (1965). Rome.

PHILIPPOT, P. and P. MORA. *Technique et conservation des peintures murales.* Mixed meeting at Washington and New York, 17-25 September 1965.

URBANI, G., TORRACA, G. and P. MORA, "Nuovi supporti per affreschi staccati." *Bollettino dell'Istituto Centrale del Restauro* (1965). Rome.

GIACOPINI, C., and R. LACERNA, "Problemi di microbiologia nel settore degli affreschi." *Bollettino dell'Istituto Centrale del Restauro* (1965). Rome.

LIBERTI, S., ROSSI, G.A. and M. SANTINI. "Un nuovo metodo elettrofisico per la disincrostazione di superfici pittoriche affrescate." *Bollettino dell'Istituto Centrale del Restauro* (1965). Rome.

MAMILLAN, M. *Le mouvement de l'eau dans les murs.* Annales de l'Institut technique du bâtiment et des travaux publics, no. 217. Paris, January 1966. 132.

PLENDERLEITH, H.J. *La conservation des antiquités et des oeuvres d'art.* Translated by P. Philippot. Paris: Eyrolles, 1966.

INTERNATIONAL COMMISSION ESTABLISHED BY UNESCO UNDER THE CHAIRMANSHIP OF HAROLD J. PLENDERLEITH, *Conservation of the Thracian Tomb with Murals at Kazanluk in Bulgaria.* Rome, 1966.

THE INTERNATIONAL INSTITUTE FOR CONSERVATION OF HISTORIC AND ARTISTIC WORKS, 1967 *Conference on Museum Climatology.* Ed. Garry Thomson. London: IIC, 1967.

ICOMOS – International Council on Monuments and Sites, Paris, *Actes du Congrès international sur l'humidité des monuments. Rome, 1967.*

CROISET, M. *L'hygrothermique dans les bâtiments.* Paris: Eyrolles, 1968.

MORARU, D. and E. DIMITRIU-VALCEA. *Umezeala in constructii si combaterea ei.* Bucharest: Editura Tehnicâ, 1969.

GRATWICK, R.T. *L'humidité dans le bâtiment.* Trans. from English. Paris: Eyrolles, 1970.

FEDOROV, V.I. "Sur quelques procédés de protection des monuments contre l'humidité ascendante." *Monumentum* 7 (1971) p. 35.

MORA, P., MORA, L. and P. PHILIPPOT. *La conservation des peintures murales.* Bologna: ICCROM, 1977.

PINNA, M. *L'atmosfera ed il clima.* Turin: Utet, 1978.

[Although this bibliography does not cover more recent publications, it has been included because it provides an interesting historical perspective on seminal research in this field.]

Index